OCR
gateway

GCSE
physics

Authors

Graham Bone

Jim Newall

Contents

How to use this book

Welcome to your Gateway Physics course. This book has been specially written by experienced teachers and examiners to match the 2011 specification.

On these two pages you can see the types of pages you will find in this book, and the features on them. Everything in the book is designed to provide you with the support you need to help you prepare for your examinations and achieve your best.

Module openers

Specification matching grid: This shows you how the pages in the module match to the exam specification for GCSE Physics, so you can track your progress through the module as you learn.

Why study this module: Here you can read about the reasons why the science you're about to learn is relevant to your everyday life.

You should remember: This list is a summary of the things you've already learnt that will come up again in this module. Check through them in advance and see if there is anything that you need to recap on before you get started.

Opener image: Every module starts with a picture and information on a new or interesting piece of science that relates to what you're about to learn.

Main pages

Learning objectives: You can use these objectives to understand what you need to learn to prepare for your exams. Higher Tier only objectives appear in pink text.

Key words: These are the terms you need to understand for your exams. You can look for these words in the text in bold or check the glossary to see what they mean.

Questions: Use the questions on each spread to test yourself on what you've just read.

Higher Tier content: Anything marked in pink is for students taking the Higher Tier paper only. As you go through you can look at this material and attempt it to help you understand what is expected for the Higher Tier.

Worked examples: These help you understand how to use an equation or to work through a calculation. You can check back whenever you use the calculation in your work.

4

Summary and exam-style questions

Every summary question at the end of a spread includes an indication of how hard it is. You can track your own progress by seeing which of the questions you can answer easily, and which you have difficulty with.

When you reach the end of a module you can use the exam-style questions to test how well you know what you've just learnt. Each question has a level next to it, so you can see what you need to do for the level you are aiming for.

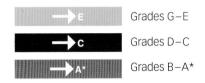

Grades G–E

Grades D–C

Grades B–A*

Revision checklist: This is a summary of the main ideas in the module. You can use it as a starting point for revision, to check that you know about the big ideas covered.

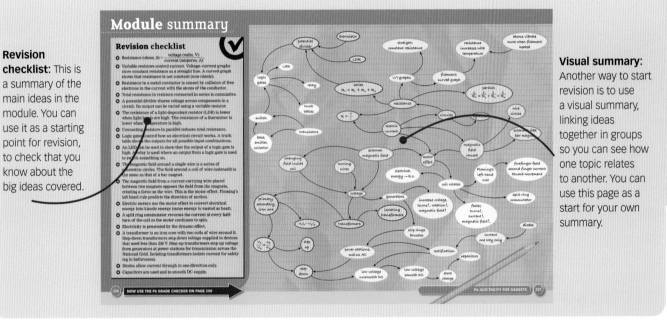

Visual summary: Another way to start revision is to use a visual summary, linking ideas together in groups so you can see how one topic relates to another. You can use this page as a start for your own summary.

Upgrade: Upgrade takes you through an exam question in a step-by-step way, showing you why different answers get different grades. Using the tips on the page you can make sure you achieve your best by understanding what each question needs.

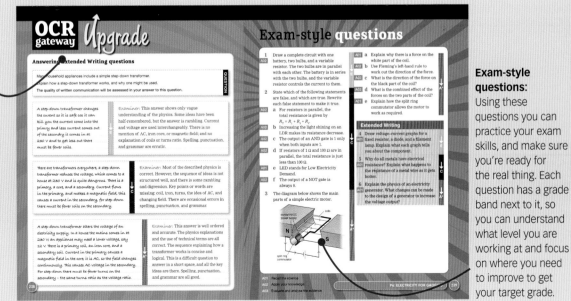

Exam-style questions: Using these questions you can practice your exam skills, and make sure you're ready for the real thing. Each question has a grade band next to it, so you can understand what level you are working at and focus on where you need to improve to get your target grade.

Routes and assessment

Matching your course

The modules in this book have been written to match the specification for **OCR GCSE Gateway Science Physics B**.

In the diagram below you can see that the modules can be used to study either for **GCSE Physics** or as part of **GCSE Science** and **GCSE Additional Science** courses.

	GCSE Biology	GCSE Chemistry	GCSE Physics
GCSE Science	B1	C1	P1
	B2	C2	P2
GCSE Additional Science	B3	C3	P3
	B4	C4	P4
	B5	C5	P5
	B6	C6	P6

GCSE Physics assessment

The content in the modules of this book match the different exam papers you will sit as part of your course. The diagram below shows you which modules are included in each exam paper. It also shows you how much of your final mark you will be working towards in each paper.

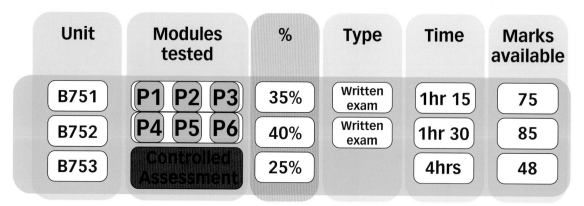

Unit	Modules tested	%	Type	Time	Marks available
B751	P1 P2 P3	35%	Written exam	1hr 15	75
B752	P4 P5 P6	40%	Written exam	1hr 30	85
B753	Controlled Assessment	25%		4hrs	48

Understanding exam questions

The list below explains some of the common words you will see used in exam questions.

Calculate
Work out a number. You can use your calculator to help you. You may need to use an equation. The question will say if your working must be shown. (Hint: don't confuse with 'Estimate' or 'Predict')

Compare
Write about the similarities and differences between two things.

Describe
Write a detailed answer that covers what happens, when it happens, and where it happens. Talk about facts and characteristics. (Hint: don't confuse with 'Explain')

Discuss
Write about the issues related to a topic. You may need to talk about the opposing sides of a debate, and you may need to show the difference between ideas, opinions, and facts.

Estimate
Suggest an approximate (rough) value, without performing a full calculation or an accurate measurement. Don't just guess – use your knowledge of science to suggest a realistic value. (Hint: don't confuse with 'Calculate' and 'Predict')

Explain
Write a detailed answer that covers how and why a thing happens. Talk about mechanisms and reasons. (Hint: don't confuse with 'Describe')

Evaluate
You will be given some facts, data or other information. Write about the data or facts and provide your own conclusion or opinion on them.

Justify
Give some evidence or write down an explanation to tell the examiner why you gave an answer.

Outline
Give only the key facts of the topic. You may need to set out the steps of a procedure or process – make sure you write down the steps in the correct order.

Predict
Look at some data and suggest a realistic value or outcome. You may use a calculation to help. Don't guess – look at trends in the data and use your knowledge of science. (Hint: don't confuse with 'Calculate' or 'Estimate')

Show
Write down the details, steps or calculations needed to prove an answer that you have been given.

Suggest
Think about what you've learnt and apply it to a new situation or a context. You may not know the answer. Use what you have learnt to suggest sensible answers to the question.

Write down
Give a short answer, without a supporting argument.

Top tips
Always read exam questions carefully, even if you recognise the word used. Look at the information in the question and the number of answer lines to see how much detail the examiner is looking for.

You can use bullet points or a diagram if it helps your answer.

If a number needs units you should include them, unless the units are already given on the answer line.

As part of the assessment for your GCSE Physics B course you will undertake a Controlled Assessment task. This section of the book includes information designed to help you understand what Controlled Assessment is, how to prepare for it, and how it will contribute towards your final mark.

Understanding Controlled Assessment

What is Controlled Assessment?

Controlled Assessment has taken the place of coursework for the new 2011 GCSE Sciences specifications. The main difference between coursework and Controlled Assessment is that you will be supervised by your teacher when you carry out some parts of your Controlled Assessment task.

What will I have to do during my Controlled Assessment?

The Controlled Assessment task is designed to see how well you can:

- develop hypotheses
- plan practical ways to test hypotheses
- assess and manage risks during practical work
- collect, process, analyse, and interpret your own data using appropriate technology
- research, process, analyse, and interpret data collected by other people using appropriate technology
- draw conclusions based on evidence
- review your method to see how well it worked
- review the quality of the data.

How do I prepare for my Controlled Assessment?

Throughout your course you will learn how to carry out investigations in a scientific way, and how to analyse and compare data properly. These skills will be covered in all the activities you work on during the course.

In addition, the scientific knowledge and understanding that you develop throughout the course will help you as you analyse information and draw your own conclusions.

How will my Controlled Assessment be structured?

Your Controlled Assessment is a task divided into three parts. You will be introduced to each part of the task by your teacher before you start.

What are the three parts of the Controlled Assessment?

Your Controlled Assessment task will be made up of three parts. These three parts make up an investigation, with each part looking at a different part of the scientific process.

	What skills will be covered in each part?
Part 1	Research and collecting secondary data
Part 2	Planning and collecting primary data
Part 3	Analysis and evaluation

Do I get marks for the way I write?

Yes. In two of the three parts of the Controlled Assessment you will see a pencil symbol (✏). This symbol is also found on your exam papers in questions where marks are given for the way you write.

These marks are awarded for quality of written communication. When your work is marked you will be assessed on:

- how easy your work is to read
- how accurate your spelling, punctuation, and grammar are
- how clear your meaning is
- whether you have presented information in a way that suits the task
- whether you have used a suitable structure and style of writing.

Part 1 – Research and collecting secondary data

At the beginning of your task your teacher will introduce Part 1. They will tell you:

- how much time you have – for Part 1 this should be about 2 hours, either in class or during your homework time
- what the task is about
- about the material you will use in Part 1 of the task
- the conditions you will work under
- your deadline.

The first part of your Controlled Assessment is all about research. You should use the stimulus material for Part 1 to learn about the topic of the task and then start your own research. Whatever you find during your research can be used during later parts of the Controlled Assessment.

Sources, references, and plagiarism

For your research you can use a variety of sources including fieldwork, the Internet, resources from the library, audio, video, and others. Your teacher will be able to give you advice on whether a particular type of source is suitable or not.

For every piece of material you find during your research you must make sure you keep a record of where you found it, and who produced it originally. This is called referencing, and without it you might be accused of trying to pass other people's work off as your own. This is known as plagiarism.

Writing up your research

At the end of Part 1 of the Controlled Assessment you will need to write up your own individual explanation of the method you have used. This should include information on how you carried out your own research and collected your research data.

This write up will be collected in by your teacher and kept. You will get it back when it is time for you to take Part 3.

Part 2 – Planning and collecting primary data

Following Part 1 of your Controlled Assessment task your teacher will introduce Part 2. They will tell you:

- how much time you have – for Part 2 this should be about 2 hours for planning and 1 hour for an experiment
- what the task is about
- about the material you will use in Part 2 of the task
- the conditions you will work under
- your deadline.

Part 2 of the Controlled Assessment is all about planning and carrying out an experiment. You will need to develop your own hypothesis and plan and carry out your experiment in order to test it.

Risk assessment

Part of your planning will need to include a risk assessment for your experiment. To get the maximum number of marks, you will need to make sure you have:

- evaluated all significant risks
- made reasoned judgements to come up with appropriate responses to reduce the risks you identified

- manage all of the risks during the task, making sure that you don't have any accidents and that there is no need for your teacher to come and help you.

Working in groups and writing up alone

You will be allowed to work in groups of no more than three people to develop your plan and carry out the experiment. Even though this work will be done in groups, you need to make sure you have your own individual records of your hypothesis, plan, and results.

This write up will be collected in by your teacher and kept. You will get it back when it is time for you to take Part 3.

Part 3 – Analysis and evaluation

Following Part 2 of your Controlled Assessment task your teacher will introduce Part 3. They will tell you:
- how much time you have – for Part 3 this should be about 2 hours
- what the task is about
- about the answer booklet you will use in Part 3
- the conditions you will work under.

Part 3 of the Controlled Assessment is all about analysing and evaluating the work you carried out in Parts 1 and 2. Your teacher will give you access to the work you produced and handed in for Parts 1 and 2.

For Part 3 you will work under controlled conditions, in a similar way to an exam. It is important that for this part of the task you work alone, without any help from anyone else and without using anyone else's work from Parts 1 and 2.

The Part 3 answer booklet

For Part 3 you will do your work in an answer booklet provided for you. The questions provided for you to respond to in the answer booklet are designed to guide you through this final part of the Controlled Assessment. Using the questions you will need to:
- evaluate your data
- evaluate the methods you used to collect your data
- take any opportunities you have for using mathematical skills and producing useful graphs
- draw a conclusion
- justify your conclusion.

P1

Energy for the home

Why study this module?

You use energy in your home in many different forms. Energy is used to heat homes and for cooking. You also use energy to communicate using mobile phones, to access the Internet on computers, and to watch TV. All of these depend on the transfer of energy in one form or another.

In this module you will look at the different ways that energy can be transferred by conduction, convection, and radiation, and how these transfers are minimised in homes to save energy. You will learn about how you use microwaves and infrared for cooking, and how the same waves, along with radio waves and light, are used for communication.

You will also find out how the energy produced by earthquakes is transferred by waves, and how ultraviolet radiation can be harmful.

You should remember

1. The difference between heat and temperature.
2. Energy can be transferred by different methods.
3. The properties of light.
4. There are three states of matter – solids, liquids, and gases.

This house in Kent is so well insulated that it does not need any central heating. The house uses energy from the Sun and stores it for when the weather is cold. The house uses less than 10% of the energy that a conventional three-bedroom house uses for heating rooms and water. Most of the energy used by this house is for heating hot water. The house has a ventilation system which takes in fresh air from outside and transfers energy to it from the stale air that is about to be pumped outside.

Learning objectives

After studying this topic, you should be able to:

- understand the difference between heat and temperature
- recognise that energy flows from a hotter body to a cooler one
- understand how the temperature difference affects the rate of energy transfer

A What are the units of:
   (a) temperature
   (b) energy?

▲ A thermogram of a man holding a hot drink

B What happens to the temperature of an object that is cooler than its surroundings?

Heat and temperature

The **temperature** of an object tells us how hot it is and is measured in degrees Celsius (°C), but it does not tell us how much heat it contains. **Heat** is a form of energy and is measured in joules (J).

However, the hotter something is, the more heat energy it has.

The hot drink in the picture stores energy in the form of heat. The hot drink will cool down because energy is transferred from it to its surroundings. Energy is transferred until the temperature of the drink is the same as its surroundings.

▲ This hot drink will cool down as energy is transferred to its surroundings

The difference in temperature between an object and its surroundings affects the rate at which energy is transferred. When the temperature difference is greater, the rate of energy transfer is higher.

If an object is warmer than its surroundings, then energy flows from the object to its surroundings and the object cools down. If an object is cooler than its surroundings, it gains energy from its surroundings and warms up.

A **thermogram** can be used to show how hot an object is (its temperature). You take a picture using a special camera. Different temperatures are shown by different colours. The photo on the left shows a thermogram of a hot drink.

Colours in a thermogram

In a thermogram, the hottest areas are white. The colours then go through red, yellow, green, and light blue to dark blue for the coldest areas.

Temperature

Temperature is a measure of the average kinetic energy of the particles in a substance. We construct temperature scales by choosing reference points that are easy to observe. For instance, the Celsius temperature scale has zero at the freezing point of pure water. At 0 °C, the particles in ice are still vibrating. If you could keep cooling the particles down until they stopped vibrating, this would happen at absolute zero or −273.16 °C.

Heat

Heat is a measure of energy on an absolute scale. Unlike temperature, it is not related to reference points.

▲ African elephants use their large ears to help control their body temperature

Questions

1 Look at the picture of the cold drink. Describe what happens in terms of the temperature of the drink and the flow of heat energy.

▶ What will happen to this cold drink?

↓ E

2 What is the difference between heat and temperature?

3 Which will cool down quicker – a kettle of water at 100 °C or a kettle of water at 70 °C? Explain your answer.

↓ C

4 Which stores more energy – a kettle full of water at 60 °C or a tank of hot water at 60 °C?

5 What can you say about the rate of heat energy transfer in an object that is at the same temperature as its surroundings?

↓ A*

Did you know...?

African elephants live in a hot climate and need to cool down. An elephant has large ears to help it control its body temperature. The ears have a large surface area and so more energy can be transferred to the elephant's surroundings.

Exam tip   OCR

✓ Remember that, overall, energy flows from a warmer place to a cooler place.

Key words

temperature, heat, thermogram

Learning objectives

After studying this topic, you should be able to:

✔ understand what the specific heat capacity of a material is

✔ use the equation for specific heat capacity

Key words

specific heat capacity

A What is specific heat capacity?

▲ A kettle

B How much energy is required to heat a 500 g aluminium pan containing 1 kg of cooking oil from 20 °C to 180 °C?

C The amount of energy you calculated in B is less than what is actually needed. Explain why.

Storing energy

You have seen that when an object gets more energy it gets hotter. When it cools down it is losing energy. However, different materials will hold different amounts of energy. For example, it takes much more energy to raise the temperature of 1 kg of water than it does to raise the temperature of 1 kg of aluminium. We say that water has a much higher **specific heat capacity**.

The specific heat capacity of a material is defined as the amount of energy in joules needed to raise the temperature of 1 kg of the material by 1 °C. Its units are joules per kilogram per °C, or J/kg °C. Some specific heat capacities are given in the table.

Material	Specific heat capacity (J/kg°C)
water	4200
aluminium	880
copper	380
cooking oil	1200 (about)

Calculating the amount of heat transferred

You can calculate the amount of energy required to heat an object using this equation:

$$\frac{\text{energy}}{\text{J}} = \frac{\text{mass}}{\text{kg}} \times \frac{\text{specific heat}}{\text{capacity}} \times \frac{\text{temperature}}{\text{change}}$$
$$\text{J/kg °C} \qquad \text{°C}$$

Worked example

A kettle contains 1.5 kg of water at a temperature of 18 °C. How much energy is needed to bring the water to the boil?

$$\text{energy needed} = \text{mass} \times \frac{\text{specific heat capacity}}{\text{of water}} \times \frac{\text{temperature}}{\text{change}}$$

$$= 1.5 \text{ kg} \times 4200 \text{ J/kg °C} \times (100 - 18) \text{ °C}$$

$$= 1.5 \times 4200 \times 82 \text{ J}$$

$$= 516\,600 \text{ J} = 516.6 \text{ kJ}$$

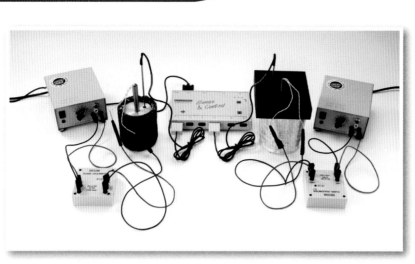

You can use this apparatus to find the specific heat capacity of a material

How much energy is required to heat the oil to fry food?

Using specific heat capacity

Water has a very high specific heat capacity and needs a lot of energy to raise its temperature. This is why water is used in central heating systems to transfer thermal energy from the boiler to the radiators. It can store much larger amounts of thermal energy than a liquid with a lower specific heat capacity. This also means that the water does not need to be pumped very quickly around the central heating circuit.

Finding specific heat capacity

You can work out the specific heat capacity if you know the amount of heat transferred, the mass of the object and the temperature rise. Rearrange the equation on the left to make the specific heat capacity the subject.

Questions

1 What are the units of specific heat capacity?

2 Explain why water is used to cool car engines.

3 Which one of the following will require more energy? Heating 5 kg of copper to 150 °C from 20 °C or heating 250 g of water from 20 °C to 50 °C?

4 50 kJ of energy is transferred to a material with a mass of 5 kg. The temperature increases from 20 °C to 60 °C.

What is the specific heat capacity of the material?

E

↓ C

↓ A*

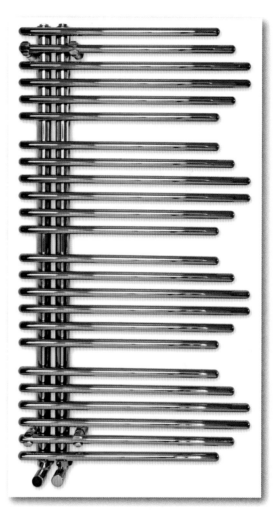

This radiator contains water which transfers thermal energy from the boiler

Exam tip   OCR

✓ Don't forget to work out the temperature difference to substitute into the equation.

▲ The temperature of this ice cube stays the same while it melts

Did you know...?

The word 'latent' means 'hidden'. When we melt ice we know that we are giving energy to it but its temperature does not rise. It is as though the energy is concealed.

Exam tip   OCR

✔ Remember that the melting point and freezing point of a substance are at the same temperature.

Key words

change of state, specific latent heat, fusion, vaporisation, intermolecular bond

Changes of state

When something melts it takes in energy just to change from solid to liquid. For example, when you heat ice it melts to form water. While the ice is melting, its temperature stays constant, even though it is gaining energy. In the same way, when something boils it needs energy just to change from a liquid to a gas. These are both **changes of state**.

When you heat a solid, its temperature rises at a steady rate until the temperature reaches the melting point. The temperature then stays constant while the solid is melting.

Once the solid has melted, if you carry on heating it, the temperature rises at a steady rate again until the liquid boils. The rate of temperature rise for the liquid will not be the same as it was for the solid.

When the liquid is boiling, the temperature will stay constant as it turns into a gas.

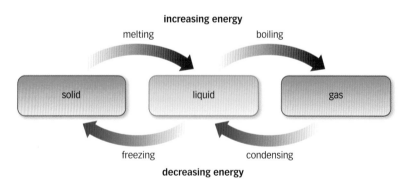

▲ Graph of temperature against time for ice being heated at a constant rate

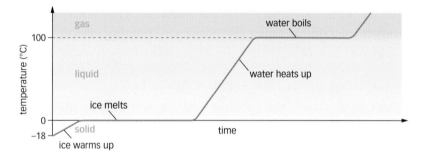

▲ Changes of state

A What needs to happen for something to change state from solid to liquid?

Specific latent heat

The amount of energy (in joules) needed to change the state of 1 kilogram of a substance is called its **specific latent heat**.

You can calculate the amount of energy needed using the equation:

$$\frac{\text{energy}}{\text{J}} = \frac{\text{specific latent heat}}{\text{J/kg}} \times \frac{\text{mass}}{\text{kg}}$$

The units are joules per kilogram (J/kg). Often the energy is measured in kilojoules (1 kJ = 1000 J). Then the specific latent heat is given in kilojoules per kilogram (kJ/kg).

The specific latent heat of **fusion** (for melting a substance) is not the same value as the specific latent heat of **vaporisation** (for boiling and evaporating a substance).

Material	Specific latent heat of fusion (J/kg)	Specific latent heat of vaporisation (J/kg)
water	334 000	2 260 000
lead	24 500	871 000
ethanol	108 000	855 000

▲ Specific latent heats of some materials

Intermolecular bonds

The latent heat of fusion is the energy needed to break the **intermolecular bonds** between the particles in the solid so that they can move around. When a liquid boils and evaporates, energy is used to break the bonds between the particles in the liquid to change their state to a gas.

As energy is needed to break the intermolecular bonds, the temperature of a substance does not change while it is being heated and these bonds are being broken.

You can use the equation above to calculate the mass of a substance when you know the amount of energy needed to change its state.

Worked example

How much energy is required to melt 2 kg of ice?

$$\text{energy needed} = \frac{\text{specific latent}}{\text{heat of fusion}} \times \frac{\text{mass}}{\text{of ice}}$$
$$= 334 \text{ kJ/kg} \times 2 \text{ kg}$$
$$= 668 \text{ kJ}$$

B How much energy is required to evaporate 0.25 kg of water?

Questions

1. What is specific latent heat?

2. What is the difference between latent heat of fusion and latent heat of vaporisation?

3. How much energy is needed to:
   (a) evaporate 0.5 kg lead?
   (b) evaporate 6 kg of ethanol?

4. The amount of energy needed to melt a lump of lead was 4.9 kJ. What was the mass of the lead?

5. Why is the latent heat of vaporisation of a substance higher than its latent heat of fusion?

6. What mass of lead could you melt with the amount of energy you would need to melt 2 kg of ice?

Exam tip OCR

✔ Remember:
- a good heat insulator is a poor heat conductor
- a poor heat insulator is a good heat conductor.

▲ Loft insulation traps air, preventing convection, and it is also a poor conductor of heat

Conducting energy

Energy is transferred through solid materials by **conduction**. The particles in a solid are always vibrating, even though they are fixed in position by forces between them. When the particles are hotter, they have more energy and so vibrate more.

When you heat one end of an object, the particles start vibrating more. The particles collide with other particles. Kinetic energy is transferred from one particle to its neighbours, in the same way that energy is transferred from the cue ball when it collides with another ball on a snooker table. Energy can be conducted through the solid by the particles colliding with each other.

heat

▲ Conducting heat in a metal

Conductors and insulators

Some materials such as metals are good **thermal conductors**. Energy is conducted through them easily. Their particles are close together in a regular pattern and so the vibrations are passed on easily. This is why radiators are made of metal.

Some materials do not conduct heat very well – they are called **thermal insulators**. Materials such as wood and plastics are insulators and they transfer heat slowly. The particles are close together, but the pattern is not as regular as in a metal. This means that energy only passes slowly from one particle to another.

Liquids and gases are poor thermal conductors. The particles in a liquid are not in any regular arrangement, so it is much more difficult for the energy to be passed on by conduction. In a gas, the particles are far apart so gases are very poor conductors. Double glazing works using a layer of gas between the panes of glass.

Energy transfer by free electrons

There is another way of transferring energy in metals, Metals have many electrons that are free to move through the metal. Metals are also good conductors of electricity because of these electrons. The **free electrons** gain more kinetic energy from collisions as the metal is heated. They transfer the energy very quickly as they travel through the metal.

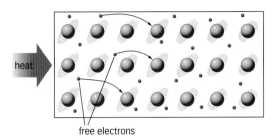

heat

free electrons

▲ Free electrons move through the metal, transferring the energy more quickly

Heat energy transfer in liquids and gases

Fluids (liquids and gases) are poor conductors of heat. They can still transfer heat, because the particles are free to move. When moving particles carry energy from one place to another this is called **convection**. For instance, hot air rises and is replaced by cold air.

For example, when particles of air gain more energy, they move faster and that part of the air expands. The density of this region of air decreases because there is the same number of particles, but in a larger space.

The cooler fluid nearby is denser than the heated fluid. The denser cooler fluid falls to the bottom, and the less dense hotter fluid rises. This movement is called a **convection current**. Cavity wall insulation prevents convection currents and loss of heat.

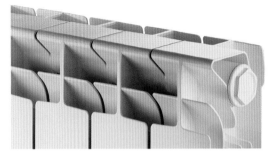

▲ Radiators are designed to maximise energy transfer through convection, by having openings in the top to allow hot air to rise as cooler air is brought into the bottom

The convection current moves through the room. By the time the air reaches here it will have lost some of its heat energy and cooled down slightly.

The air particles gain energy from the radiator. The air becomes less dense than the surrounding air and rises.

the cooler more dense air falls

some energy will be absorbed by the walls and objects in the room

▲ Convection currents can heat a room

A Why can convection currents occur in liquids?

Questions

1 Give an example of a good thermal conductor.

2 Draw a diagram and label it to show how convection currents transfer energy through the water in a saucepan that is being gently heated.
↓ E

3 Harry is sitting in the chair in a room like the one in the diagram when the heating is switched off on a cold day. Why does he feel cold?

4 Why is the handle of a kettle made of plastic?
↓ C

5 Why are liquids and gases poor thermal conductors?

6 Explain how free electrons transfer energy in a metal.
↓ A*

Learning objectives

After studying this topic, you should be able to:

- ✔ understand that all bodies both emit and absorb infrared radiation
- ✔ investigate what surfaces are good and bad at absorbing infrared radiation

> **A** How is energy transferred via radiation?

▲ A thermogram of a hot drink

> **B** Can you tell if an object is emitting infrared radiation just by looking at it? Explain your answer.

Infrared radiation

When you put your hands on a cup that contains a hot drink, energy is transferred to your hands by conduction. If you take your hands off the cup, but keep them close to it, you can still feel energy being transferred from the cup.

This energy is being transferred by radiation. It is known as **infrared radiation** (IR) and is the transfer of energy by electromagnetic waves.

All bodies **emit** and absorb infrared radiation.

When something hot is glowing then it is also emitting light radiation. The electric cooker ring in the photo is glowing red – it is emitting light as well as infrared radiation.

▲ This cooker ring is emitting infrared radiation and also red light

Sometimes you can feel infrared radiation from something hot but no light radiation is being emitted. For example, you can feel the heat being radiated by a dish that has just come out of the oven, but the dish does not glow.

A **thermogram** is a picture taken using a special camera which is sensitive to infrared radiation but not visible light.

The hotter something is, the more energy it will radiate in a certain time. If two objects are similar but one of them is hotter, the hotter object will emit more infrared radiation.

Objects can absorb radiation from the Sun. For example, if you put an object in sunlight, it will absorb infrared radiation from the Sun and its temperature will increase.

The surface of the object affects how much energy it absorbs. A dark matt surface is good at absorbing infrared radiation. A light-coloured or shiny surface is bad at absorbing infrared radiation. This is why people sometimes place reflective foil behind radiators.

A dark matt surface is also a good emitter of infrared radiation and a light or shiny surface is a poor emitter of infrared radiation.

light shiny surface   matt black surface

▲ How infrared radiation is absorbed or reflected by different surfaces

▲ These buildings are designed to stay cool in the summer as they reflect infrared radiation

Energy transfer by infrared

Infrared radiation is an electromagnetic wave, like light. It can travel through a vacuum, like light does. It does not need a **medium** to travel through. This is why although cavity wall insulation can prevent heat loss by conduction and convection, it cannot prevent energy loss by radiation.

Questions

1 Draw up a table to summarise which surfaces are the best and worst at absorbing and emitting infrared radiation. ↓E

2 Why does an electric fire usually have a shiny panel behind the heating element?

3 Look at the picture of the houses. What features help them to stay cool in the summer? ↓C

4 Why does your house still lose heat even when it is well insulated? ↓A*

Exam tip   OCR

✓ Remember that the hotter an object is, the more infrared radiation it emits.

Learning objectives

After studying this topic, you should be able to:

- ✔ describe methods of reducing energy transfer in buildings
- ✔ calculate payback time
- ✔ evaluate the effectiveness of different types of material used for insulation

Key words

heat source, sink, payback time, cost-effective

▲ This thermogram shows the areas transferring the most energy in red (warmest), then yellow, green and blue

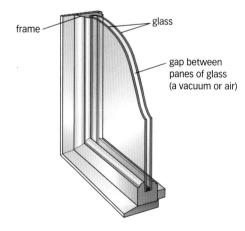

▲ Cross section of a double-glazed window

Insulating houses

Houses transfer energy to their surroundings. Energy flows from the hotter region to the colder one, from the **heat source** (the house) to the cold **sink** (the surroundings). This cools the house and warms the surroundings. It costs money to heat a house, so home owners try to reduce the cost of heating by insulating them better. When you insulate a house you reduce energy losses through conduction, convection, and radiation.

The diagram shows a cross-section of a well insulated cavity wall. The outside walls of houses are actually not one wall but two walls with a cavity between them. Air is a good thermal insulator and a poor thermal conductor. However, if there is nothing in the wall cavity but air, the air can move around and transfer heat from the inner wall to the outer wall through convection. The cavity is filled with an insulating material. This is usually something with small pockets of trapped air. This makes use of air as a good insulator, but prevents loss of heat through convection as the air cannot form a convective current.

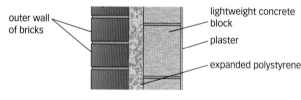

Cross-section of a cavity wall

This principle is also used in insulation of lofts using fibreglass, mineral wool, or rock wool.

A How could you reduce the energy transfers from a house to its surroundings?

Payback time

You can cut your energy bills by reducing the amount of energy that you use. Some ways do not cost money. For example, you could turn the thermostat on your central heating down by 1 °C.

Other methods do cost money. To decide whether they are worth doing, you need to calculate how long it will take to recover the amount of money you spend. This is the **payback time**. The method with the shortest payback time is the most **cost-effective**.

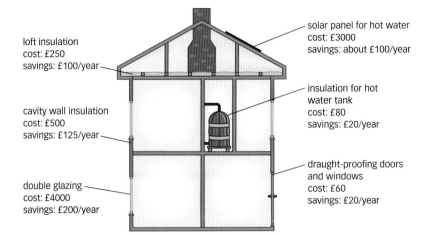

loft insulation
cost: £250
savings: £100/year

cavity wall insulation
cost: £500
savings: £125/year

double glazing
cost: £4000
savings: £200/year

solar panel for hot water
cost: £3000
savings: about £100/year

insulation for hot
water tank
cost: £80
savings: £20/year

draught-proofing doors
and windows
cost: £60
savings: £20/year

▲ Different methods of reducing your energy consumption

Worked example

Jack currently has 50 mm of insulation in his loft. It will cost £250 to increase the thickness of the insulation to the recommended 270 mm. His heating bill would decrease by £100 per year. What is the payback time for adding the extra insulation?

$$\text{payback time} = \frac{\text{cost}}{\text{savings per year}} = \frac{£250}{£100 \text{ per year}} = 2.5 \text{ years}$$

Questions

1 Describe how double glazing reduces energy transfer.

2 In the house shown in the diagram, which method of reducing energy consumption is:
   (a) most cost-effective?
   (b) least cost-effective?

3 Sometimes grants are available to help with the cost of insulation. For the house shown in the diagram, work out the payback time for:
   (a) solar panels, when there is a grant of £500
   (b) loft insulation, when there is a grant of £200.

4 Compare the houses in the thermogram on the previous page and comment on the forms of insulation used.

5 Give two ways in which a radiator is designed to maximise energy transfer to the air in a room.

Energy transfers in your home

In homes, some appliances and features are designed to maximise energy transfer through conduction, convection and radiation. For example, a boiler is specially designed to have a heating element at the bottom. Convection currents heat all the water in the boiler. A radiator is designed to maximise the energy transfer from the water in the central heating system into a room by having a large surface area.

Other appliances and features are designed to minimise energy transfers. For example, double glazing and cavity walls reduce the energy transferred outside the house. They do this by reducing energy transfers through conduction and convection. However, energy is still transferred through radiation.

B What is payback time?

Exam tip

✓ You do not need to remember any particular values. In exam questions, you will be given the data and asked to calculate the payback time to evaluate which methods of insulation are the most cost-effective.

Learning objectives

After studying this topic, you should be able to:

- ✔ understand the difference between useful and wasted energy
- ✔ understand what the efficiency of an appliance is
- ✔ calculate the efficiency of an appliance

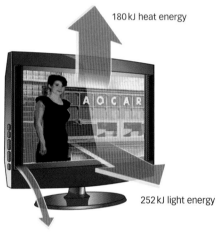

180 kJ heat energy

252 kJ light energy

18 kJ sound energy

▲ Energy transfers for a television

Key words

Sankey diagram, efficiency

Exam tip OCR

- ✔ Remember that efficiency can never be greater than 100%. If your calculations produce an efficiency of greater than 100%, go back and check them – you will have done something wrong!
- ✔ If you express efficiency as a ratio, it can never be greater than 1.

Useful and wasted energy

In our homes we are always using appliances that transform energy from one form to another. For example a central heating boiler transforms chemical energy into heat, and the television transforms electrical energy into light, heat and sound. However, not all the transformed energy is useful. The heat energy from the television is wasted, for instance.

> **A** Which energy transfers in the TV are useful?

A light bulb produces heat as well as light. Light is useful energy, but the heat is wasted energy. You can show the energy transfers made by an appliance in a **Sankey diagram**.

▲ A range of standard and energy-efficient light bulbs. The bulb on the top left transfers more useful energy than the others.

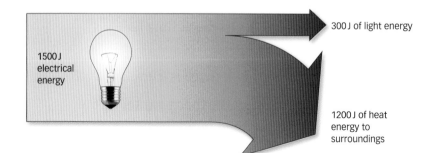

300 J of light energy

1500 J electrical energy

1200 J of heat energy to surroundings

▲ Sankey diagram for a light bulb. Energy must be conserved and the total energy in must equal the total energy out.

Efficiency

If you know how much energy is supplied to a light bulb, how much of the electrical energy is transformed into light energy, and how much to heat energy, you can work out how efficient the light bulb is.

$$\text{efficiency} = \frac{\text{useful energy output}}{\text{total energy input}} \times 100\%$$

Remember that the units for energy transferred and energy supplied should be the same – they should both be in joules or both in kilojoules.

You can give the efficiency as a percentage by multiplying the answer by 100% as above, or you can leave it as a ratio.

Efficiency calculations

When you know the efficiency of an appliance, you can use the efficiency equation to calculate the useful energy output if you know the total energy input. Or you can calculate the total energy input if you know the useful energy output. Knowing these values, you can work out the wasted energy. Rearrange the efficiency equation to show total energy input on the left. To do this, divide both sides by 'efficiency' and multiply both sides by 'total energy input':

$$\frac{\cancel{\text{efficiency}} \times \text{total energy input}}{\cancel{\text{efficiency}}}$$

$$= \frac{\text{useful energy output} \times \cancel{\text{total energy input}}}{\cancel{\text{total energy input}} \times \text{efficiency}} \times 100\%$$

Cancelling out gives:

$$\text{total energy input} = \frac{\text{useful energy output}}{\text{efficiency}} \times 100\%$$

Worked example 2

A television with efficiency of 60% converts electrical energy into 252 kJ of light energy and 18 kJ of sound energy. Calculate the wasted energy.

$$\text{total energy input} = \frac{252\ \text{kJ} + 18\ \text{kJ}}{60\%} \times 100\%$$

$$= \frac{270\ \text{kJ}}{60} \times 100 = 450\ \text{kJ}$$

$$\text{energy wasted} = \text{total energy input} - \text{useful energy output}$$

$$= 450\ \text{kJ} - 270\ \text{kJ} = 180\ \text{kJ}$$

Worked example 1

What is the efficiency of the light bulb shown in the diagram?

useful energy transferred = 300 J

total energy supplied = 1500 J

$$\text{efficiency} = \frac{300}{1500} = 0.2 \times 100\% \text{ or } 20\%$$

B How much energy is wasted in the light bulb?

Questions

1 What does a Sankey diagram show?

2 A kettle is supplied with 500 kJ of electrical energy. It transfers 99 kJ to the kettle itself and its surroundings as heat energy, and 1 kJ is transferred into sound energy. The rest of the energy is transferred to the water as heat energy.
   (a) What is the efficiency of the kettle?
   (b) How could you make the kettle more efficient?

3 A halogen light bulb has an efficiency of 12%. It transfers 30 J into light energy.
   (a) What is the total energy input?
   (b) How much energy is wasted?
   (c) Draw a Sankey diagram for this light bulb.

Learning objectives

After studying this topic, you should be able to:

✔ describe the main features of waves

✔ use the wave equation, $v = f\lambda$

Key words

crest, trough, oscillation, transverse wave, amplitude, wavelength, frequency, wave equation

---

A Give examples of two different types of wave.

B Draw a wave with an amplitude of 3 cm and a wavelength of 8 cm.

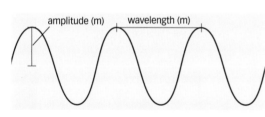

▲ Key features of a wave

Did you know...?

Some waves can have very high frequencies measured in kHz (kilohertz; 1 kHz = 1000 Hz) and MHz (megahertz; 1 MHz = 1 000 000 Hz). An FM radio station might transmit waves with a frequency of 97.7 MHz – that's 97.7 million waves every second!

What are waves?

Waves are around us all of the time. We see water waves on the surface of the sea, sound waves allow us to listen to our music – and just think what the world would be like without light. Waves, like ripples on a pond, contain a series of **crests** and **troughs.**

▲ Surfing some water waves

There are many different kinds of waves. They all transfer energy from one place to another. Waves are made up of a series of **oscillations** or vibrations travelling through space. In a **transverse wave** the oscillations are always at right angles to the direction of wave motion.

All waves have the key features shown in the table.

Amplitude in metres (m)	Maximum height of the wave measured from the middle
Wavelength in metres (m)	Shortest distance between one point and the same point on the next wave. For example the distance from one crest to the next crest.
Frequency in hertz (Hz)	The number of waves passing a point per second (or the number of oscillations each second). A frequency of 6 Hz would mean six waves pass a point every second (or six oscillations every second).

The wave equation

The speed of a wave depends on its frequency and its wavelength. They are related by the **wave equation**.

wave speed = frequency × wavelength
(metres/second, m/s)　　(hertz, Hz)　　(metres, m)

If the wave speed is called v, the frequency f and the wavelength λ (a Greek letter, pronounced lam-da), then $v = f\lambda$.

▲ Energy is transferred from the speaker to your ears

Worked example 1

Dylan is standing on the end of a pier. He measures the water waves going past him. The wavelength of each wave is 1.3 m. He counts 2 waves every second. Find the wave speed.

wave speed = frequency × wavelength or $v = f\lambda$

f = 2 Hz (as there are 2 waves every second) and λ = 1.3 m

$v = 2 \times 1.3$

$v = 2.6$ m/s

Exam tip　**OCR**

✔ Remember to look carefully at the units when using the wave equation. Pay particular attention to wavelength. This must be measured in m.

Rearranging the wave equation

At times we may already know the wave speed and wave length, but need to know the wave frequency. To find this, we need to rearrange the wave equation.

Worked example 2

A flute produces a note with a wavelength of 75 cm. The speed of sound is 330 m/s. Find the frequency of the note.

wave speed = frequency × wavelength

$\text{frequency} = \dfrac{\text{wave speed}}{\text{wavelength}}$ or $f = \dfrac{v}{\lambda}$

$f = \dfrac{330}{0.75}$

$f = 440$ Hz

Questions

1　Define the terms wavelength, frequency and amplitude. **↓E**

2　Find the speed of a wave with a wavelength of 30 m and a frequency of 120 Hz. **↓C**

3　A speaker produces a sound at a frequency of 6.6 kHz. The wavelength of the sound wave is 5.0 cm. Use these values to show the speed of sound is 330 m/s.

4　A radio station transmits waves with a frequency of 120 MHz. The radio waves travel at 3×10^8 m/s. Find the wavelength of the radio wave. **↓A***

Learning objectives

After studying this topic, you should be able to:

✔ describe some properties of electromagnetic waves

✔ know the order of the electromagnetic spectrum

✔ describe the reflection, refraction and diffraction of waves

✔ describe how diffraction is affected by the size of the gap

✔ know some of the problems caused by diffraction

Key words

electromagnetic wave, vacuum, reflection, law of reflection, refraction, diffraction

Did you know...?

As electromagnetic waves travel so fast, they are very useful for communications. Along with sending music to your car radio, radio waves are used to transmit signals around the world. Mobile phones transmit your voice by means of microwaves, a TV remote uses infrared, and high speed broadband uses pulses of visible light. The size of the receiver or aerial used to pick up these signals depends on the wavelength. The longer the wavelength, the longer the aerial needed to pick up the signal.

Electromagnetic waves

Light, microwaves and X-rays are examples of **electromagnetic waves**. Unlike other waves, they do not need a medium like air or water to travel through. Electromagnetic (EM) waves can travel through a **vacuum**, like space. This is how light and infrared waves reach the Earth from the Sun. If electromagnetic waves could not travel through a vacuum, then there would be no way to receive energy from the Sun. Life on Earth would not even exist.

The different electromagnetic waves form a family called the electromagnetic spectrum. This ranges from long wavelengths to very, very short ones.

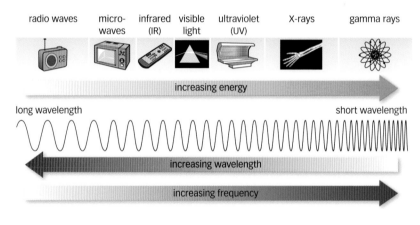

▲ Electromagnetic spectrum

> **A** What makes electromagnetic waves special compared with other waves?
>
> **B** List the electromagnetic waves from longest wavelength to shortest.

All electromagnetic waves travel in straight lines. Despite having different frequencies, energies and wavelengths, they all travel through space at the same speed. This is the speed of light, or 300,000,000 m/s (3×10^8 m/s).

Wave experiments

Every time you look in a mirror, you see your reflection. All waves can be **reflected**, not just light waves. We can draw simple ray diagrams to show reflection. Whenever we draw ray diagrams we must include a normal line. This is a line at 90° to the surface. We always measure angles to the normal.

The **law of reflection** states that the angle of incidence is always equal to the angle of reflection. Even if the surface is really rough, the two angles are always the same.

As with reflection, all waves can also be refracted. **Refraction** can lead to strange effects, like straight pencils looking bent when placed in water. When waves go from one medium to another they can be refracted. As they enter a different medium their speed changes and this causes them to change their direction. If the wave slows down it bends towards the normal, if it speeds up it bends away from the normal.

Whenever the waves pass through a gap or move around an obstacle, they spread out. This is called **diffraction**. You might have noticed the effect with sound. If you have your door open and someone is talking outside, even though you can't see them, you can hear their voice. The sound waves diffract when they go through your open doorway, spreading out and filling the room. It might sound as though the sound wave actually comes from the doorway itself.

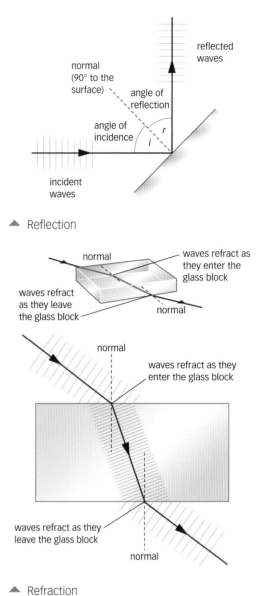

▲ Reflection

▲ Refraction

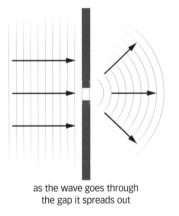

as the wave goes through the gap it spreads out

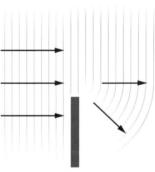

the same thing happens if it goes around an obstacle

▲ Diffraction

The size of the gap relative to the wavelength of the wave affects how much diffraction takes place. In general, the longer the wavelength or the smaller the gap, the greater the diffraction. The strongest diffraction occurs when the gap is the same size as the wavelength.

Diffraction causes problems when using optical instruments like microscopes and telescopes. When light enters the instrument, it passes through a small gap and diffracts a little. This can lead to a blurry image or a loss of detail.

Questions

1 Draw a diagram to show the law of reflection.

2 Which part of the electromagnetic spectrum travels the fastest? Explain your answer.

3 Draw a diagram to show how light is refracted when it travels from water to air.

4 Describe some of the problems caused by diffraction.

A What is the name given to the process where all the light is reflected internally inside a medium?

Total Internal Reflection

You may remember that when light travels from one medium to another it refracts. However, there is also a small amount of internal reflection. For example, if light travels from glass to air, it bends away as it leaves the glass but a small amount is reflected back into the glass.

If the light hits the boundary between the glass and air at a big enough angle of incidence, all of the light stays within the glass; it is all reflected internally. This is called **Total Internal Reflection** (TIR). It happens if the angle is above the **critical angle** for the material.

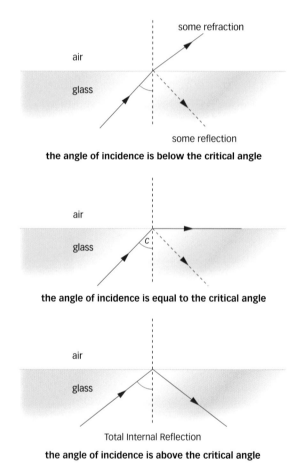

some refraction

air

glass

some reflection

the angle of incidence is below the critical angle

air

glass

c

the angle of incidence is equal to the critical angle

air

glass

Total Internal Reflection

the angle of incidence is above the critical angle

▲ Total Internal Reflection

This effect can be seen whenever light travels from a dense material to a less dense one (for example, water to air, glass to air, or Perspex to air). Total Internal Reflection only happens if both these requirements are met:

- The angle of the light is greater than the critical angle.
- The light is travelling in the denser of the two materials.

Fibre optics

Optical fibres are very fine glass cables. They can be used to transmit large amounts of information or to help doctors peer inside the body without cutting their patient open.

Waves travel along optical fibres by Total Internal Reflection. They enter the fibre and hit the edge at an angle greater than the critical angle. They reflect off the inside of the glass fibre until they reach the other end.

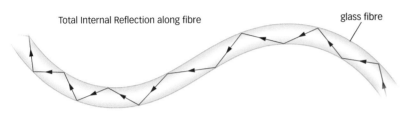

Total Internal Reflection along fibre   glass fibre

▲ Light is totally internally reflected along an optical fibre

With fibre optic broadband, pulses of visible light or infrared are sent down optical fibres. This allows large amounts of data to be sent very quickly. Fibre optic broadband is generally much faster than using normal phone lines.

Optical fibres are not just limited to communication. An **endoscope** is a medical instrument that can produce an image of the inside of the body through a tiny key-hole incision rather than cutting the patient open.

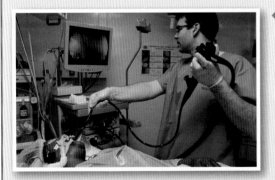

◀ An endoscope is a kind of probe using fibre optics to produce an image of the inside of the body

Inside the endoscope there are several bundles of optic fibres. The endoscope is inserted into the body and visible light is sent down one of the bundles of cables. The light illuminates the inside of the body and is then reflected back down a separate bundle of fibres. The doctor either looks along the fibre or the image is sent to a TV screen, providing a clear picture of the patient's insides.

B What material are most optical fibres made from?

▲ Fibre optic cable

Questions

1 What is the name given to the angle above which Total Internal Reflection occurs? ↓ E

2 State the two requirements for Total Internal Reflection.

3 Draw a diagram to show the path of light travelling from glass to air at the critical angle. ↓ C

4 Draw a diagram to show how light is totally internally reflected along an optical fibre.

5 Describe two uses of optical fibres. ↓ A*

11: Using light

Learning objectives

After studying this topic, you should be able to:

- ✔ describe how light has been used historically as a means of communication
- ✔ describe the key properties of laser light
- ✔ state some uses of lasers
- ✔ explain how laser light is used in a CD player

▲ Flashing lights are still used to communicate between ships

Key words

Morse code, laser, phase, monochromatic

Communicating using light

Before email and social networking revolutionised how we communicate, sending a message from one part of the country to the other would take hours, even days if you go back further, before the postal service.

Light, however, has been used for centuries to send messages at high speed across long distances. Native American Indians used smoke signals, and ships at sea in Napoleonic times would often communicate with each other by flashing a light.

Although light travels very fast, any message has to be sent in code. One of the most famous is **Morse code**. A series of flashes is used to represent different letters. These flashes could be relayed from one station to another and so cover many miles very quickly. Morse code can be thought of as an early type of digital signal as it consists of a series of on and off pulses or flashes of light.

> **A** Give one example of using light to communicate.

Lasers

A **laser** is a more modern use of light. Lasers are different from light sources such as light bulbs because lasers produce a narrow beam of light. This beam of light does not spread out very much as it travels. You may have seen the effects at a laser light show or from a laser pointer. The beams remain very narrow, even over long distances.

▲ Lasers have many uses

Another difference is that the light from any particular laser is just one colour. Usually this is red, but you can get green and even blue or purple lasers.

Lasers have a wide range of applications, including:
- surgery and dental treatments
- guiding weapons
- CD, DVD, and Blu-ray players
- cutting materials such as steel plates.

Nature of laser light

The waves emitted from a laser light all have the same frequency and they are in sync with each other. All the crests and troughs line up. We say that the light is in **phase**. Because of these features, lasers are described as a source of coherent **monochromatic** light. The laser light beam does not spread out very much. It is described as having a low divergence.

These two properties make laser light very useful for reading the information stored on CDs and other optical discs such as DVDs. On a CD the information on the disc is stored on the shiny side as a series of pits.

There are billions of pits on the average CD. This digital information is read by the laser. As the disc spins, a laser reflects from its surface. When the light enters a pit there is no reflection, and so the detector reads a series of light pulses. This is a bit like a more advanced version of Morse code. This digital code is then converted into sounds or images by computer chips in the CD player.

Questions

1 Give three examples of uses for a laser.

2 Describe how Morse code could be used to quickly send a message across the country.

3 Describe the properties of laser light.

4 Describe how Morse code can be thought of as a type of digital signal.

5 Explain how a laser is used to read data from a CD or DVD.

B Describe how laser light is different from light emitted by a light bulb.

▲ CDs, DVDs, and Blu-ray discs all have small pits that are read with a laser

Learning objectives

After studying this topic, you should be able to:

- ✔ describe the properties of microwaves and how they are used in microwave ovens
- ✔ describe the properties of infrared radiation and how it is used to cook food
- ✔ explain how both microwaves and infrared waves transfer energy to materials

Key words

microwave

A Does a hotter object emit more or less radiation than a cooler one?

B What happens to the surface of an object if it absorbs infrared radiation?

▲ The element glows red because it emits visible red light as well as infrared waves

Cooking with infrared

If you've ever made toast or grilled some bacon you've cooked with electromagnetic waves, specifically infrared radiation.

▲ The Sun emits a great deal of infrared radiation as well as light, as its surface is so hot

We've met infrared radiation as part of the heat topic. Infrared radiation is emitted by warm objects. The warmer an object is, the more infrared it emits. If an object absorbs infrared radiation its surface gets hotter. This is the heat you feel from an open flame. These two effects make infrared useful for cooking.

As the toaster in the photograph gets hotter, it emits more and more infrared. In fact it gets so hot, it also emits some red light. The infrared waves from the toaster are then absorbed by the food. This heats up the surface of the food and so it gets cooked. Most grills and toasters have a shiny surface on the bottom. This helps reflect the infrared back towards the food so that it gets cooked even more quickly.

Microwave ovens

The **microwaves** used in microwave ovens are another kind of electromagnetic wave. These are similar to infrared radiation, but have a much longer wavelength and cook food in a very different way.

A microwave oven produces a steady stream of microwaves. Instead of just heating the surface of the food being cooked, they travel about 1 cm into the food. The microwaves are absorbed by fat and water inside the food. This causes the food to heat up. Inside the oven there are shiny metal surfaces. These surfaces reflect the microwaves so that all parts of the food are heated. This helps to make sure the food is fully cooked.

Microwave ovens use microwaves to transfer energy to water or fat molecules in the food

> **C** Explain why microwave ovens have shiny metal surfaces on the inside.

Microwaves can cause burns to humans, as they are absorbed by body tissue just as they are absorbed by food in the microwave oven. Microwaves can pass through glass and plastics, and so to prevent the microwaves from microwave ovens causing damage, a metal mesh is placed inside the oven door.

Exam tip **OCR**

✔ Remember the colour and texture of an object affects emission and absorption of IR. Darker, rougher surfaces are better emitters and absorbers – shiny, smooth surfaces are much poorer (however, they are good reflectors).

How the energy is transferred

In both infrared and microwave cooking, energy is transferred from the electromagnetic wave to the molecules inside or on the food. This energy is then transferred to the rest of the food through conduction and convection. In microwave ovens, the fat and water molecules inside the outer layers of the food gain kinetic energy as they absorb the microwaves. In the case of infrared, only the particles on the surface of the food gain kinetic energy as they absorb the infrared waves.

The energy associated with both infrared waves and microwaves depends on how many waves there are per second. This is called the frequency of the wave. Higher frequency means more waves every second. Higher frequency waves have more energy. This makes them potentially more dangerous.

Questions

1 Give an example of an appliance which cooks food using infrared.

2 Why do grills and toasters often have shiny surfaces inside them?

3 Describe how microwave ovens can be used to cook food.

4 Explain why the sides of a microwave oven don't get hot.

5 Explain how energy from electromagnetic waves is transferred throughout the food that is being cooked.

↓ E

↓ C

↓ A*

Learning objectives

After studying this topic, you should be able to:

- ✔ describe how different waves can be used for communicating
- ✔ describe some of the concerns about the use of mobile phones
- ✔ describe how there can be a loss in signal when some waves are transmitted

Key words

line of sight

A What property of electromagnetic waves makes them useful for communication?

▲ Mobile phones use microwaves for communication

Using electromagnetic waves to communicate

Electromagnetic waves travel very, very fast. This makes them extremely useful for communications. Whenever you listen to a radio station, watch television or talk to a friend on your mobile phone you are using electromagnetic waves to communicate.

Mobile phones

All types of mobile phone send and receive microwaves. When you talk your phone converts the sound into a microwave signal which it sends to the nearest phone mast.

Microwaves can be transmitted over very large distances. However, there needs to be a **line of sight** between the phone (or other transmitter) and receiver (the phone mast). Microwaves travel in straight lines, but in some areas hills and buildings get in the way too much and the signals cannot get through. Microwaves are also affected by poor weather conditions and large surfaces of water. Over very long distances there can be no line of sight between the transmitter and receiver because the curvature of the Earth gets in the way.

▲ Mobile phone communication needs to be 'line of sight'

B What type of electromagnetic waves do mobile phones use to send and receive information?

Signal loss

There are several causes of signal loss when communicating with microwaves. Weather conditions like heavy rain and large surfaces of water, scatter the signal, making it more difficult to receive. Radio waves spread out, or diffract, whenever they pass through a gap, for example between buildings, or when they pass over an obstacle such a large hill. However, when microwaves travel through the air they don't spread out as much as radio waves. This makes line of sight even more important.

Another reason for signal loss is that other types of electromagnetic waves can interfere with the microwave transmission. To reduce both of these effects, microwave transmitters are usually placed close together to ensure the signal received remains strong. They are also placed high on hills to avoid other obstructions.

Will mobile phones fry your brain?

Some people are concerned about the dangers of using mobile phones, particularly if you use one regularly. Scientists are not sure whether using mobiles from a young age is safe, or whether this will cause any long term damage. Different studies have produced different results and reached different conclusions about the potential dangers of mobile phone use. These results are checked by other scientists, but there is no clear evidence either way.

Some research has shown that microwaves can cause a small heating effect in the brain. The current advice from the NHS is that mobiles should not be used regularly by younger children.

As there is no clear evidence, people need to make their own decisions when it comes to using a mobile phone. They must balance the known benefits of using a mobile phone against any potential risk. A similar decision must be made by town planners deciding on the location of a new phone mast.

▲ Placing mobile phone masts in towns and cities can lead to protests by concerned residents, despite the lack of evidence of any increased risk

Questions

1 State one of the concerns a parent might have about their child using a mobile phone.

2 Give two examples of features in the landscape that may affect the quality of a mobile phone signal.

3 Explain the meaning of the term line of sight.

4 Explain why you may be able to receive a radio signal in a valley, but not a signal for your mobile phone.

5 Describe some of the benefits and risks associated with using a mobile phone.

A What are the two different types of signal used to transmit data?

B What are the two possible states of a digital signal?

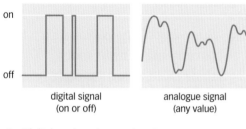

▲ Digital and analogue signals

Analogue versus digital

There are two different ways to transmit data signals: **analogue** and **digital**.

Recently parts of the UK have switched over to using a digital television signal. The stations are the same but there are some key differences in comparison with the previous analogue system.

Digital signals can only have two values. The signal is either on or off; it is a series of pulses. This is rather like turning a light switch on and off very quickly. The light is either on or off, just like the digital signal. These two states are often represented by numbers: on is 1 and off is 0. A TV remote sends a digital signal to your television when you change channel. Inside the remote there is a small infrared light, this rapidly flashes on and off.

An analogue signal is one which continuously changes its values. It is more like a dimmer switch, where adjusting the switch changes the brightness of the bulb through a range of different values. An analogue signal is always changing through different values.

Advantages of digital signals

Any interference (or **noise**) affecting the signal can be easily removed, giving excellent picture or sound quality.

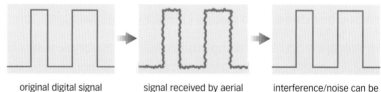

original digital signal   signal received by aerial   interference/noise can be removed, returning the signal to its original quality

▲ 'Noise' can be removed from a digital signal

As the digital signal can only be 1 or 0 it is still clear what state the signal is in. This means the noise can be removed and the signal returned to its original, perfect, state.

Another advantage is that many different digital signals can be sent at once, through a process called **multiplexing**. So more information can be sent at any given time. This is why you get more channels on digital television.

DAB radio

In some parts of the world, FM radio is being challenged by the introduction of digital audio broadcasting radio (or **DAB radio** for short).

There are arguments for and against the use of DAB radio, as shown in the table below.

Advantages	Disadvantages
More stations available	Not all areas of the UK are covered
Less chance of interference with other stations, so a clearer signal	Sometimes the sound quality is not as good as FM. This is because the sound is compressed, like an mp3 file.

Using infrared

Infrared waves can be used to communicate, but only over much shorter distances. Most remote controls use infrared to send a signal from the remote to the TV. There is a small infrared light at the end of the remote. This flashes on and off and this signal is detected by special sensors in the TV. A similar technique can be used to send data to and from some laptops or mobile phones. Both are examples of digital signals.

Infrared sensors can also be used to detect body heat. This can make them very useful for burglar alarms and automatic security lighting.

The digital signal sent from the remote is in the form of a coded series of flashes. A special sequence will cause the TV to change channel, a different sequence increases the volume. Only certain codes work with certain devices. This is why your TV remote has no effect on your stereo.

▲ DAB radios are becoming popular

▲ Remote controls send pulses of infrared to your television

Questions

1 Give an advantage and a disadvantage of using DAB radio.

2 Draw and describe a typical analogue and a typical digital signal.

3 Describe the differences between an analogue and a digital signal.

4 Explain the advantages of transmitting a digital television signal rather than an analogue one.

5 Describe how infrared radiation is used in remote controls.

E

C

A*

Learning objectives

After studying this topic, you should be able to:

- ✔ describe how radio waves can be used as part of wireless communication
- ✔ state some advantages of wireless communication
- ✔ explain how the quality of radio signal can be affected
- ✔ describe wireless communication over very long distances

▲ Wireless technologies now let you connect to the Internet from almost anywhere

▲ Drivers must use hands-free wireless appliances such as Bluetooth headsets if they want to talk and drive at the same time

Wireless technologies

Communicating via electromagnetic waves is often described as **wireless communication** as there is no need for a direct wired connection. You probably own several appliances that can communicate without wires:

- Televisions and radios use radio waves.
- Mobile phones use microwaves.
- Laptop computers use radio waves (Bluetooth and WiFi use radio waves, for example).
- Smart phones often use both radio waves and microwaves to communicate.

> **A** Give three examples of appliances that use wireless technologies to communicate.

Any appliance which communicates without wires needs an **aerial** to receive the wireless signal. Despite that extra complexity, this kind of communication has important advantages:

- No wired connection is needed. You don't need a telephone line to be able to make a phone call or connect to the Internet.
- Wireless technology is portable and convenient.
- You can use wireless technology whilst on the move, for example in a car or on a train.

> **B** State two advantages of using wireless technologies.

Whenever a wireless signal travels through the air it can be reflected and refracted by buildings or by layers in the atmosphere. This can allow a signal to be received that would otherwise be blocked by buildings and hills in the way. However, this can also lead to a drop in quality. The signal can lose too much energy and become too weak. Too many reflections can also cause a drop in quality because the wireless appliance receives more than one signal at once. You might have noticed a similar effect with some radio stations. If stations transmit on similar frequencies, the signal can get garbled and there is a great deal of static interference.

Long-distance communication

Technologies like WiFi and Bluetooth are excellent for short-range communication. If we want to send a wireless signal over a much greater distance, for example to America, then we need to use a different technique.

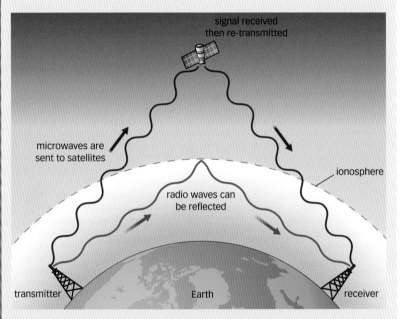

🔺 Two ways in which waves are sent over very long distances

You can't send a signal in a straight line to a receiver if it is too far away. The Earth's curvature gets in the way, like a giant wall of water between the transmitter and the aerial. Signals can be refracted by different layers in the atmosphere, allowing them to travel further. It is even possible to reflect radio waves from a special layer in the atmosphere called the **ionosphere**. This is like the Total Internal Reflection (TIR) described on spread P1.10. Alternatively, microwaves can be used to send a signal to satellites. These receive the signal, and then re-transmit it to a different receiver.

There are other problems which can lead to signal losses. Whenever the waves are transmitted from dishes, some of the signal spreads out (diffracts) rather than travelling in a perfectly straight line. As mentioned, waves bend or refract as they pass through different layers in the atmosphere. Both of these effects make it difficult to send the signal where you want to, and result in a drop in quality.

Key words

wireless communication, **aerial**, **ionosphere**

Did you know…?

Why do we still need wires? Wired communications, like fibre optics, can send rapid amounts of data very quickly. The pulses of light can be multiplexed, which allows several signals to be sent at once.

Perhaps the biggest advantage of wired communication is the lack of interference in the final signal. This means the signal is always high quality, allowing huge amounts of data to be transmitted at high speed.

Questions

1 What type of electromagnetic wave is used to transmit a TV signal? ↓ E

2 Describe how signal quality can be affected by reflections and refractions. ↓ C

3 Give two examples of techniques used to send signals over long distances.

4 Describe some of the problems encountered when you try to send a signal over a very long distance. ↓ A*

5 Describe some of the advantages of using wired connections, like fibre optics, over wireless ones.

Fault lines

Anyone who has ever experienced an earthquake will tell you it is a frightening experience.

The surface of the Earth is made of several plates of rock. These plates have faults between them, a bit like cracks in the shell of a hard-boiled egg. These plates are always drifting, but they can push or grind against one another. The pressure builds up in the plates, and then unpredictably there is an abrupt slip along the fault lines and the plates move. This is an earthquake.

Learning objectives

After studying this topic, you should be able to:

✔ describe how earthquakes produce shock waves

✔ name the two types of seismic waves and describe their differences

✔ explain how seismic waves may help in studying the structure of the Earth

Key words

seismic waves, P-wave, S-wave, seismometer

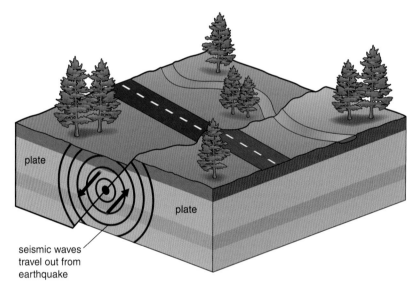

plate

plate

seismic waves travel out from earthquake

▲ An earthquake happens when the plates suddenly slip past each other

The earthquakes send out a series of shock waves, called **seismic waves**, through the Earth. These can cause serious damage when they reach the surface of the Earth as they make buildings shake. If the earthquake happens under the sea it may even cause a tsunami.

> A What is the name for the shock waves caused by earthquakes?

▲ Seismic waves from earthquakes can cause significant damage

Seismic waves and the structure of the Earth

Earthquakes produce two types of seismic wave:

- **P-waves**. These can travel through the solid and liquid parts of the Earth. They travel very fast. The vibrations take place in the same direction that the wave is moving in. This makes them an example of a longitudinal wave.
- **S-waves**. These still travel very fast but are slower than P-waves. They are only able to travel through the solid parts of the Earth; they cannot travel through any liquid regions. The vibrations in S-waves are at right angles to the direction the wave is moving in. This makes them an example of a transverse wave.

Both types of wave are detected on **seismometers** placed around the Earth. The data is recorded on seismographs.

Evidence about the structure of the Earth

Using carefully recorded data from seismographs, scientists are able to use seismic waves for evidence about the structure of the Earth.

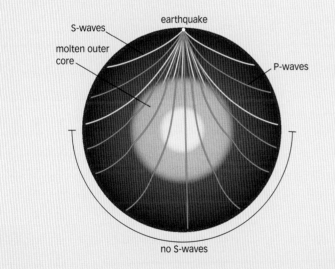

▲ Seismic waves can tell us a lot about the structure of the Earth

After an earthquake, S-waves are only detected in certain parts of the Earth. Scientists believe this is because the Earth has a molten iron outer core. S-waves cannot travel through liquids and so they are stopped by the outer core.

B Name the two types of wave produced by earthquakes.

C What is the name of the device that detects seismic waves?

Questions

1 Explain how earthquakes can damage buildings on the surface of the Earth. ↓ E

2 Describe what happens during an earthquake.

3 State the similarities and differences between P-waves and S-waves. ↓ C

4 Explain how observing seismic waves has led scientists to believe that the Earth's outer core is made of molten iron. ↓ A*

Learning objectives

After studying this topic, you should be able to:

- ✔ understand the effects of being exposed to ultraviolet radiation and explain how darker skins have a lower cancer risk
- ✔ describe how the ozone layer protects the Earth from ultraviolet radiation

▲ Sunscreen absorbs ultraviolet radiation and protects the skin underneath

▲ People with darker skin have more natural resistance to the effects of ultraviolet

Getting a suntan

Ultraviolet (UV) radiation is another type of electromagnetic wave. It has a short wavelength and a high frequency. This means ultraviolet radiation has a lot of energy. When your skin is exposed to a small amount of ultraviolet it gives you a suntan. Too much exposure leads to sunburn, premature skin ageing and even skin cancer.

Sunscreen can reduce the damage caused by ultraviolet radiation. The sunscreen absorbs the ultraviolet and protects the skin underneath. When you apply sunscreen you can stay in the Sun longer without burning. Different sunscreens offer different **sun protection factors** (SPFs). The higher the factor used, the greater the amount of ultraviolet radiation absorbed and the greater the protection for the skin underneath. In general, an SPF of 30 means you can spend 30 times as long in the Sun without burning.

> **A** What type of electromagnetic radiation gives you a suntan?
>
> **B** A sunscreen may have an SPF of 15. Explain the meaning of SPF 15.

The darker your skin, the more ultraviolet is absorbed at the surface. This protects the sensitive cells underneath. The Government spends millions of pounds each year on informing people about the risks of too much ultraviolet. In spite of this, the number of people with skin cancer is currently rising. Overuse of sun beds has been suggested as a possible reason for this increase.

▲ Sunbeds emit ultraviolet, giving you a tan, but they can be hazardous

The ozone layer

Our atmosphere contains several different layers, each with different properties. The **ozone layer** is a very important layer in our atmosphere. It is a thick layer of gas around the entire Earth, protecting us from the highest energy ultraviolet radiation. It acts like a shield, preventing the ultraviolet radiation from reaching the surface.

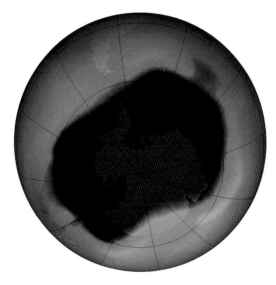

▲ Use of chemicals such as CFCs has led to the formation of a hole in the ozone layer

In the 1980s, scientists were shocked to find a huge 'hole' in the ozone layer. Above Antarctica, the layer was much, much thinner than it should have been. Some scientists didn't believe it, so more experiments were carried out in order to verify the findings. Different scientists repeated the experiments using new equipment. They found the measurements to be correct - the ozone layer was thinning.

Further research found that chemicals released into the atmosphere, like CFCs (chloroflourocarbons), have broken down parts of the ozone layer. This allows more ultraviolet radiation to reach the surface of the Earth, which is potentially very dangerous.

Several countries have worked together to address this problem. This international collaboration has led to new laws. Use of CFCs was banned under the terms of the 1987 Montreal Protocol, and the hole in the ozone layer is gradually reducing in size.

Key words

ultraviolet, sun protection factor, ozone layer

Did you know...?

Exposure to too much ultraviolet radiation can also cause cataracts, a condition where the lens inside your eye becomes cloudy. This makes it difficult to see. Treatment involves using high frequency sound waves to break up the lens before it is removed and replaced with a plastic one.

Questions

1 Describe how sunscreen protects the skin from the effects of ultraviolet radiation. ↓E

2 Explain the effect of using a sunscreen with a higher Sun protection factor.

3 When the hole in the ozone layer was first discovered, describe what scientists did to confirm the measurements. ↓C

4 Describe how the ozone layer protects us from ultraviolet radiation and how the ozone layer was depleted. ↓A*

Module summary

Revision checklist

- Heat is a form of energy. Temperature is a measure of the kinetic energy of particles in a substance.
- Objects transfer energy to their surroundings quicker if the temperature difference between the object and surroundings is greater.
- Specific heat capacity measures the thermal energy stored.
- Specific latent heat measures the amount of energy needed to change the state of a substance.
- Houses lose energy by conduction and convection, reduced by good insulation.
- Energy is transferred from one type to another by appliances at home. Calculating energy efficiency helps reduce wasted energy.
- Solids transfer energy when their closely packed particles vibrate. This is called conduction. Liquids and gases have particles free to move and transfer energy by convection.
- All objects emit and absorb infrared radiation as electromagnetic waves. Dark, matt objects are good infrared radiation emitters and light, shiny objects are not.
- Electromagnetic waves travel at the speed of light. Infrared waves and microwaves are used for cooking food.
- Electromagnetic waves are used to communicate: infrared (remote control); radio waves (radio and TV); microwaves (mobile phones).
- Analogue signals have varied values and are susceptible to interference or noise. Digital signals are either 1 or 0 so the signal can still be interpreted correctly.
- Fibre optic cables transfer information using light. Light travels through the denser of two materials and its angle is greater than the critical angle of the two mediums. Total Internal Reflection (TIR) occurs.
- Waves travel at various speeds and have characteristic peaks and troughs.
- Light can be used to send messages using Morse code. Lasers use a monochromatic light beam.
- Seismic waves are of two main types – longitudinal P-waves and transverse S-waves.
- Ozone in the atmosphere blocks UV radiation. UV light causes tanning and can cause cancer.

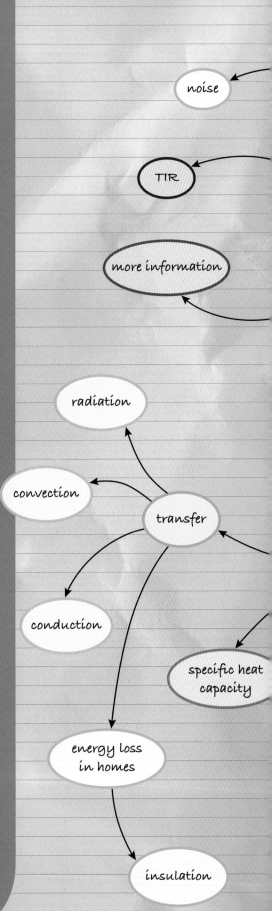

NOW USE THE P1 GRADE CHECKER ON PAGE 240

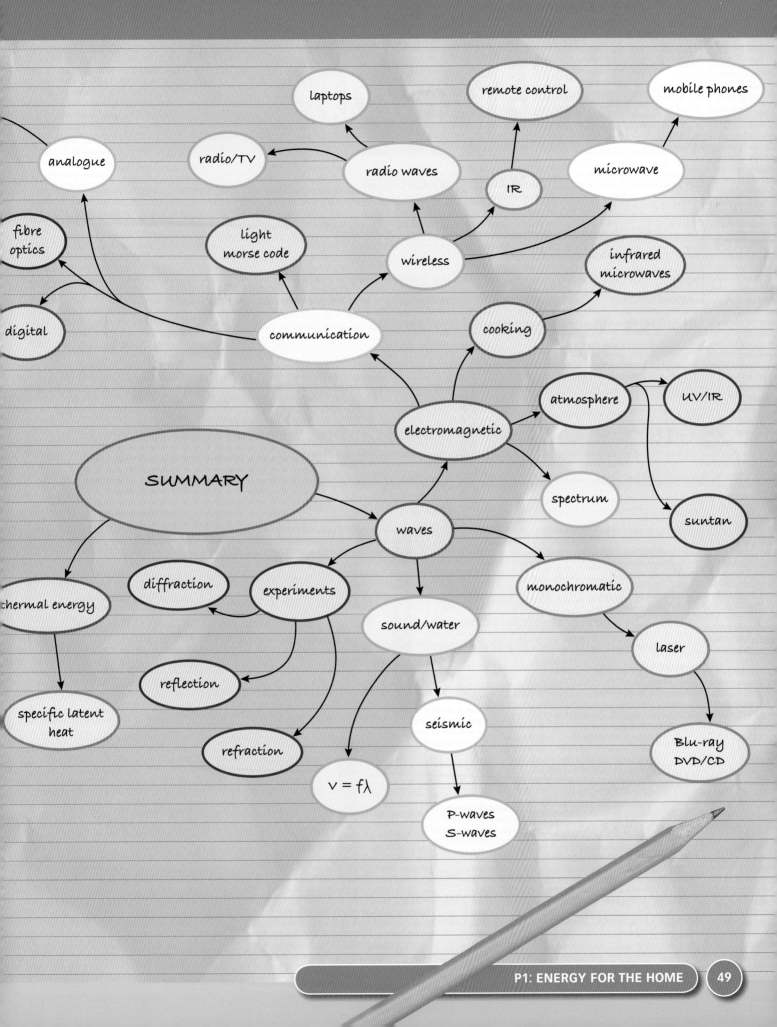

laptops

remote control

mobile phones

analogue

radio/TV

radio waves

IR

microwave

fibre optics

light morse code

wireless

infrared microwaves

digital

communication

cooking

electromagnetic

atmosphere

UV/IR

SUMMARY

spectrum

suntan

waves

thermal energy

diffraction

experiments

monochromatic

reflection

sound/water

laser

specific latent heat

refraction

seismic

Blu-ray DVD/CD

$v = f\lambda$

P-waves
S-waves

OCR gateway *Upgrade*

Answering Extended Writing questions

QUESTION

Dave wants to insulate his loft. He has a choice of three possible insulation materials – fibreglass, sheep wool, and a material made from recycled plastic bottles.

Explain, in terms of energy transfer, how the insulation materials will help to keep Dave's home warm. Then suggest the factors Dave might consider in choosing between the three insulation materials.

The quality of written communication will be assessed in your answer to this question.

Dave needs to no the cost of the insulators, and how long it will be befor he get his money back! you need to wear gloves with fibreglass because it has sharp bits in it.

↓ E

Examiner: This answer correctly mentions economic considerations, but also needs to mention that Dave needs to estimate the annual savings in his heating bills. The candidate has not answered the first part of the question at all. There are several errors of spelling, punctuation and grammar.

All three materails contain trapped air, so they do not conduct heat out of the roof very well. The recycled plastic bottle materail is good because otherwise the plastic bottles might go into landfill. The sheep wool is good because if you leave wool on sheep too long the sheep get diseesis.

↓ C

Examiner: The candidate has made a good point in the first sentence, and explained it clearly. It would be good to mention convection here, too. The points about the plastic material and wool are relevant. It is a shame the candidate did not mention economic factors, such as payback time. There are spelling errors.

The insulation materials contain trapped air. Trapped air is a very good insulator, because it does not transfer heat well by either conduction or convection. Dave should compare the costs of buying and putting in the three materials. Then he should find out how much cheeper his heating bills would be every year for each material. Then he can work out the payback times, and choose the shortest.

↓ A*

Examiner: This answer covers the main scientific and economic points, and includes scientific vocabulary used correctly. The answer is logically organised, and there is just one spelling mistake. The answer would be even better if the candidate had also considered the environmental impacts of producing the three materials.

Exam-style questions

1 Microwaves are used for mobile phone communications, but because all electromagnetic waves have the same property of reflection it is impossible for one satellite to send your message to all parts of the world. Draw a circle to represent the Earth and use a pencil and ruler to show how you can communicate with all parts of the planet.

A01

2 Lisa has recorded the temperature rise and fall inside two empty sealed aluminium drinks cans. One was painted matt black, the other was painted gloss white. She heated the cans by placing a 100 W lamp between them.

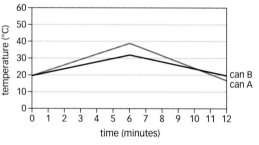

a At what time did Lisa turn off the lamp?

A01

b Which aluminium can heated up the quickest and cooled the quickest?

A02

c What does this tell you about the absorption and emission of infrared radiation for both cans?

A03

3 The graph below represents the results from an experiment when a student was melting 0.05 kg solid stearic acid.

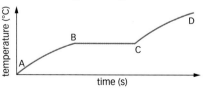

a What is happening between A and B?

A01

b What is happening between B and C?

A02

c What is happening between C and D?

A01

d 9.95 kJ of heat energy was needed to melt the stearic acid. What is its specific latent heat of fusion?

A03

Extended Writing

4 Mountaineers and mountain rescue teams often use shiny aluminium blankets to protect themselves and others from the effects of the cold. Explain how this helps.

A01

5 Geologists studying the seismic activity of our planet are detecting P- and S-waves from various places around the world. The Earth is made of solid crust, molten magma and a core which is semi-solid in nature.
If an earthquake were to happen on the other side of the Earth from the geologists, which type of wave would they detect first? Explain your answer.

A03

6 The town of Punta Arenas in southern Chile, South America has a population of 120 000. In the 1990s, it was discovered that the ozone layer almost totally disappeared over this part of the world during different times of the year. There are regular warnings announced when low ozone levels are detected. Despite this, the levels of UV-related skin disorders remain very low.
Explain what may account for this.

A03

A01 Recall the science

A02 Apply your knowledge

A03 Evaluate and analyse the evidence

P2

Living for the future

Why study this module?

Human activity is leading to changes in climates and we are rapidly using up our natural resources. Scientists are working on solutions to these problems. We consume vast amounts of electricity every day, to power our TVs, mobiles and computers. In the future, how will we generate enough to meet our needs? In this module you will learn about how electricity is generated, and the advantages and disadvantages of the different technologies, from large coal-fired power stations to small solar cells on calculators.

Our planet is in a delicate balance. In this module you will be introduced to the science behind global warming and the impact of humans on the environment. You will learn about Earth's place in the Universe, where it fits into the Solar System, how humans have explored space, and about the threats posed by asteroid impact. Finally, you will study scientific ideas about the origin of the Universe, how these ideas have changed over time, and how our Sun will eventually expand and incinerate the Earth.

You should remember

1 All human activity has an impact on the environment.

2 The law of conservation of energy states that energy cannot be created or destroyed.

3 Electricity may be generated in different types of power station.

4 The Earth is one of a number of planets in our Solar System, all in orbit of the Sun.

The world's largest power station is the Three Gorges Dam on the Yangtze River in China. The project has been in development since 1994. When it reaches full capacity it will be able to produce as much as 22 500 000 000 watts of power (22.5 gigawatts, GW). That's enough electricity for every person in the UK and Australia to watch their own large plasma TV at the same time.

The world's smallest 'power station' is a phytoplankton – a single-celled aquatic organism that converts sunlight into chemical energy to create living biomass.

Energy from the Sun

The Sun is a stable source of energy. It transfers energy to the Earth as light and infrared radiation.

Energy from the Sun can be used to generate electricity directly. **Photocells** absorb light energy and transform it into electrical energy. They produce **direct current** (DC). A direct current is in the same direction all the time. Cells (batteries) produce direct current.

The amount of current that a photocell produces depends on the area of solar cell that has light shining on it.

> A What is direct current?
>
> B What energy transfer takes place in a photocell?

Solar cells do not need much maintenance and there is no need for a fuel. They have a long life and do not produce any waste. They are a **renewable** energy resource.

There is no need for power cables and so they can be used in remote locations, to provide electricity for mobile phone masts, lights and phone boxes. They are even used in space, for example on satellites orbiting the Earth. You can also use them to recharge mobile phones and mp3 players.

▲ Photocells provide the electrical energy for the light on this speed warning sign

▲ Photocells can be used to recharge electronic appliances

On the other hand, you would need a very large area of photocells to generate the amount of electricity that is used by a small town. Photocells only work when the Sun is shining, and not at night or in bad weather.

▲ A photocell power station

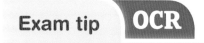

▲ The Hubble Space Telescope uses photocells to transform light energy from the Sun into electrical energy

Exam tip **OCR**

✓ Remember a photocell cannot produce electricity at night.

How a photocell transforms light into electrical energy

When light shines on a photocell, energy is absorbed by silicon atoms in the photocell. Electrons are knocked out of the silicon atoms. These electrons are then free to flow, creating the direct current.

To increase the output from a photocell:

- Increase the light intensity (make the light brighter)
- Increase the surface area of the photocell
- Reduce the distance between the light source and photocell

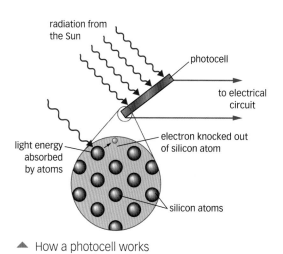

▲ How a photocell works

Questions

1 What is a photocell?

2 Draw up a table to summarise the advantages and disadvantages of photocells.

3 Why are photocells used to provide a source of electrical energy for the Hubble Space Telescope?

4 Describe how a photocell works.

5 Photocells are used to provide electricity to garden lights. What is needed so that the lights can work at night?

Learning objectives

After studying this topic, you should be able to:

✔ understand what passive solar heating is

✔ describe how curved mirrors can be used to reflect light energy from the Sun into one place

✔ explain how energy from the Sun produces wind and can be used to generate electricity

Key words

passive solar heating, focus, solar stove, wind turbine

A What is passive solar heating?

▲ Light from the Sun is reflected on to the cooking pot using curved mirrors

Passive solar heating

Some buildings use **passive solar heating**. They have large windows on the south side. Light energy passes through the windows and is absorbed by surfaces inside the building, heating them up.

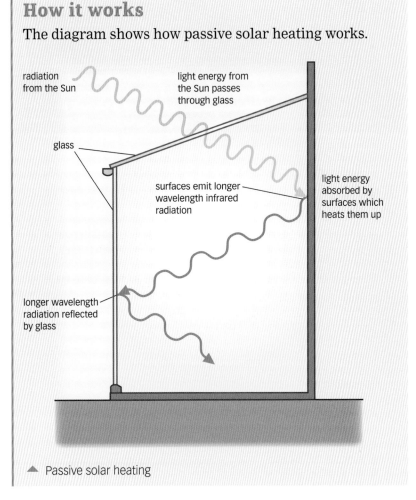

How it works

The diagram shows how passive solar heating works.

radiation from the Sun

light energy from the Sun passes through glass

glass

surfaces emit longer wavelength infrared radiation

light energy absorbed by surfaces which heats them up

longer wavelength radiation reflected by glass

▲ Passive solar heating

Reflecting energy from the Sun

Another way of using energy from the Sun is to reflect the light from the Sun using a curved mirror. The curved mirror **focuses** the light energy onto one place. As a great deal of energy is focused there, this place can get very hot.

This principle is used in a **solar stove**. Light energy from a larger area is reflected by curved mirrors on to a cooking pot.

A large number of mirrors can be used to reflect light from the Sun into one spot at the top of a solar thermal tower. The temperature there can reach 500 °C. The energy is used to heat water into steam.

Tracking the Sun

The mirrors or solar collectors have motors so that they can track the position of the Sun during the day and keep reflecting the light energy onto the same place.

Energy from the wind

Winds are convection currents set up in the Earth's atmosphere by energy from the Sun. The kinetic energy of the wind can be used to drive **wind turbines** directly.

Advantages and disadvantages of wind turbines

Wind turbines are a renewable energy resource. They do not produce any waste, but many people think that they spoil the landscape. The wind speed has to be high enough. They must also be built where they are not sheltered from the wind. A wind farm that could generate as much electricity as a normal power station would take up a large area.

▲ Mirrors reflecting radiation (heat and light) from the Sun towards a solar thermal tower

B Explain how a solar stove works.

C What energy transfer takes place in a wind turbine?

Questions

1 How does the Sun cause winds?

2 Which method of using energy from the Sun happens in a glasshouse?

3 Which of the ways of using energy from the Sun shown on this spread can be used at night? Explain your answer.

4 Give the advantages and disadvantages of using wind turbines.

5 Explain how passive solar heating works.

6 A person sets up a solar stove as shown in the photo on the left. One hour later the stove is not working. Explain why.

▲ Wind turbines

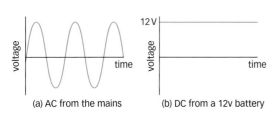

▲ How voltage changes with time for alternating current (AC) and direct current (DC)

(a) AC from the mains (b) DC from a 12v battery

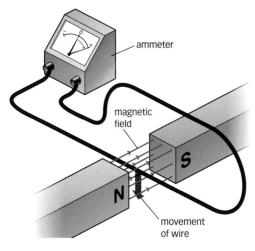

▲ A simple demonstration of the dynamo effect

A Give three examples of appliances that use AC and three that use DC.

B Describe the dynamo effect and list three ways to increase the size of the current it produces.

AC vs DC

There are two different types of electricity:
- direct current (DC)
- alternating current (AC).

You probably use both every day. When you use a mobile phone, laptop or mp3 player you are using direct current. Direct current is usually produced by batteries. The voltage from the battery remains the same and so the current through the device is in one direction only.

The electricity from the mains is described as AC. The **alternating current** happens because the voltage switches smoothly between positive and negative values. This means the current reverses direction very rapidly. The mains voltage in the UK is 230 V AC. The current changes direction 50 times every second.

Frequency of alternating current

One cycle of alternating current is completed when the current changes direction and then changes back again. The number of complete cycles per second is called the frequency. Frequency is measured in hertz (Hz). In the UK the frequency of the mains supply is 50 Hz – that is, 50 cycles per second.

The dynamo effect

One way to generate electricity is to move a piece of wire between the poles of a magnet. This creates, or **induces**, a voltage. An electric current then passes through the wire, giving a reading on a sensitive ammeter.

This is called the **dynamo effect**. As the wire passes through the magnetic field between the poles of the magnet, a voltage is induced. You get the same effect by moving a wire near the poles of a magnet or by moving a magnet close to a piece of wire. The wire or magnet must be moving for a voltage to be induced. If you keep the wire still, no voltage is induced, and so there is no current.

The size of the current is increased if
- stronger magnets are used
- there are more turns of wire (making a coil)
- you move the wire faster.

A simple AC generator

The simple generator below will supply a small alternating current (DC can be generated using a slightly different design). To induce a voltage, the coil of wire rotates inside a magnetic field instead of moving through it.

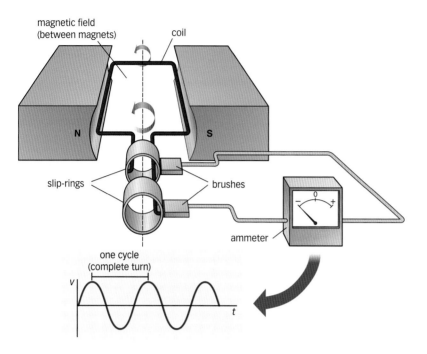

▲ An AC generator and its output

Generators in power stations produce an AC output. This is essential when transformers are going to be used. These generators spin at 3000 rpm (that's 50 rotations every second) and provide an output of 11 kV. That is nearly 50 times the output from your plug socket at home.

Key words

alternating current, induce, dynamo effect

Exam tip — OCR

✔ Don't be tempted to say using larger magnets will generate more current. It is not the size of the magnet which is important, it is its strength. Some small magnets can be much stronger than larger ones.

◀ When the pedal is rotated, a microgenerator lights it up

Did you know...?

You can buy lots of different types of mini-generators. These include mini wind turbines which can be attached to your bike and are used to power or recharge various devices. On microgenerator pedals the current produced powers lights on the pedal whenever the pedal rotates.

Questions

1 Which type of electric current is produced by a battery?

2 Describe how an AC generator works.

3 State three ways to increase the size of the voltage output from a generator.

4 Sketch a graph of voltage against time to show the output from an AC generator.

Learning objectives

After studying this topic, you should be able to:

- ✔ explain that in some power stations, fuel is used to heat water to produce steam
- ✔ describe how steam drives a **turbine** connected to a **generator**
- ✔ calculate the efficiency of a power station

▲ A turbine in a power station being repaired. The turbine is about 5 m across.

A **What does the turbine do?**

B **What does the generator do?**

C **How much energy is wasted in the power station shown in the Sankey diagram?**

Generating electricity

Electricity is generated using sources of energy. A great deal of the electricity in the UK is generated by using an energy source to heat water. The energy source can be fossil fuels, nuclear or biomass. This type of power station is called a **thermal power station**.

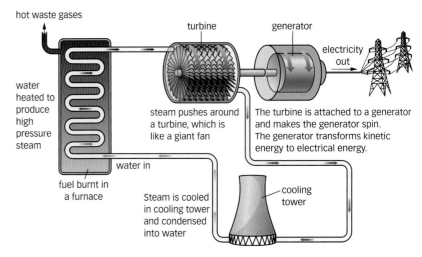

▲ A conventional power station where an energy source is used to heat water

Efficiency of a power station

In a power station, not all of the heat energy is transformed into electrical energy. A significant amount of heat energy is transferred to the environment and is wasted.

You can work out the efficiency of a power station using the equation:

$$\text{efficiency} = \frac{\text{useful energy output}}{\text{total energy input}} \ (\times 100\%)$$

Efficiency can be given as a ratio or a percentage.

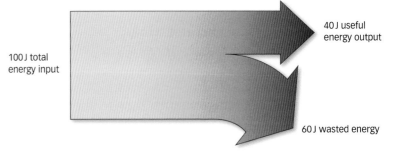

▲ Sankey diagram for a coal-fired power station showing that every 100 joules (J) of energy input there is an output of 40 J of useful energy

Distributing electricity

When electricity has been generated it needs to be distributed to consumers. These include homes, factories, offices, and farms. The electricity you use is transmitted around the country by the **National Grid**. This is the **mains supply** that is available whenever you switch on an appliance at home.

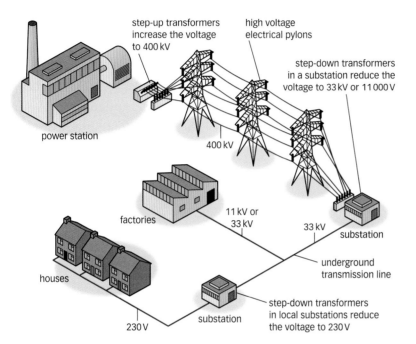

step-up transformers increase the voltage to 400 kV

high voltage electrical pylons

step-down transformers in a substation reduce the voltage to 33 kV or 11 000 V

power station

400 kV

factories

11 kV or 33 kV

33 kV

substation

houses

underground transmission line

230 V

substation

step-down transformers in local substations reduce the voltage to 230 V

▲ The National Grid

Questions

1. What is a thermal power station? **E**

2. A gas-fired power station produces 48 J of useful energy output for every 100 J of energy input. What is its efficiency:
   (a) as a ratio?
   (b) as a percentage?
   (c) How much energy is wasted by the power station for every 100 J of energy input? **C**

3. Draw a flow diagram to show all of the energy transfers taking place in the power station shown in the diagram.

4. The efficiency of a power station is 44% and the total energy input is 150 kJ. Calculate the useful energy output and the wasted energy. **A***

D What is the National Grid?

Did you know...?

The shape of cooling towers at a power station helps to set up a natural convection current. The cool air is drawn in at the base and flows over radiators. Energy from the steam is transferred to the air.

Key words

thermal power station, turbine, generator, National Grid, mains supply

Exam tip

✔ Remember that electricity is not a source of energy, but is a form of energy.

✔ When calculating efficiency, both the useful energy output and total energy input must be in the same units, eg joules.

Key words

greenhouse effect, greenhouse gas, climate change, evidence

A What would happen to the temperature of our planet if there were no atmosphere?

B Give two examples of greenhouse gases.

Did you know...?

Dust from cities can also reflect radiation back to the surface of the Earth, causing warming. In the past, huge clouds of volcanic ash have led to the cooling of the planet. If the ash is thick enough, it can reflect the radiation from the Sun before it reaches the Earth. Some scientists believe that large volcanic eruptions in the past have led to ice ages.

What is global warming?

The atmosphere around our planet is essential for life. Not only does it contain the essential oxygen for all living things, we've already learnt how it protects us from high energy ultraviolet radiation from the Sun.

Our atmosphere also performs another important role. Most electromagnetic waves are able to pass through it. However, some wavelengths are absorbed. Some gases within our atmosphere absorb infrared radiation and prevent this heat from radiating into space. This process is called the **greenhouse effect**. Without this effect, our planet would simply freeze.

▲ Our atmosphere forms a thin blue line around our planet

Gases that absorb infrared radiation are called **greenhouse gases**. There are a number of natural and man-made sources of these gases:

Greenhouse gas	% of atmosphere	Natural source	Man-made source
water vapour	0.4	The water cycle	None of significance
methane	0.0002	Animal waste	Intensive farming Extraction and burning of fossil fuels
carbon dioxide	0.039	Volcanic eruptions Waste product from all living things	Extraction and burning of fossil fuels Transport (aircraft, etc)

The greenhouse effect is a three-step process, as shown in the diagram on the right.

Water vapour accounts for the largest percentage of the greenhouse effect (around 50%).

On a molecule-for-molecule basis, methane is about 80 times stronger than carbon dioxide as a greenhouse gas, but it is present in the atmosphere in much smaller amounts. Carbon dioxide accounts for around 20%, and methane around 8%.

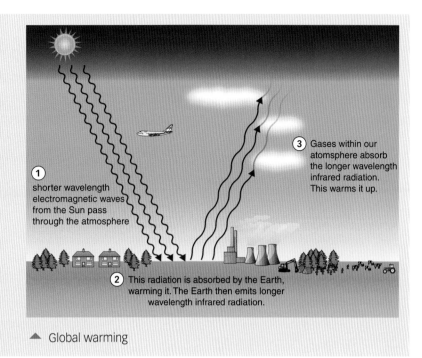

1 shorter wavelength electromagnetic waves from the Sun pass through the atmosphere

2 This radiation is absorbed by the Earth, warming it. The Earth then emits longer wavelength infrared radiation.

3 Gases within our atomsphere absorb the longer wavelength infrared radiation. This warms it up.

▲ Global warming

Is climate change man-made?

Scientists agree that we are in a period of global warming. The greenhouse effect is warming our planet at an increasing rate, leading to **climate change**. However, it is not clear if this is entirely man-made.

Climate change is a very complex process, taking place over hundreds of years. There are climate variations every year, which makes global warming difficult to measure. Scientists use **evidence** to support their ideas, rather than relying on opinions. It is important that scientists share their data.

A small number of scientists do not believe that global warming is man-made, believing instead that it is part of a regular cycle of warming and cooling. There is some historical evidence to support this idea. The planet has been both cooler and warmer in the past.

Most scientists believe that humans are having an effect on global warming. As we demand more and more energy to power our lives we produce more of the greenhouse gas carbon dioxide. Together with deforestation, this has led to an increase in the amount of carbon dioxide in the atmosphere. There is good evidence that this increase is causing our planet to warm up. As more and more carbon dioxide is released, the process of global warming appears to be accelerating.

Questions

1 What is the name given to the process where some gases absorb infrared radiation and prevent the Earth from cooling too much? ↓ E

2 Outline the evidence that supports the idea of man-made global warming. ↓ C

3 Describe the greenhouse effect in detail. Include a diagram showing the stages of the process.

4 Explain why it is possible for scientists to agree about the greenhouse effect, but disagree about whether or not human activity is affecting global warming. ↓ A*

Learning objectives

After studying this topic, you should be able to:

✔ calculate the power rating of an appliance

✔ calculate the amount of energy transferred from the mains supply by an appliance

✔ calculate the cost of energy transferred from the mains supply

✔ explain how transformers are used in the National Grid

✔ describe the advantages and disadvantages (for consumers and producers) of using off-peak electricity in the home

Key words

power rating, kilowatt hour, unit, step-up transformer, voltage, substation, step-down transformer

---

A A light bulb uses 0.2 kW and is switched on for 10 hours. How much energy does it use? Give your answer in kWh.

Exam tip    OCR

✔ If power is given in watts, don't forget to convert it to kilowatts by dividing by 1000 when you substitute it into the equation.

Power rating

Every electrical appliance has a **power rating**. Sometimes this is given on the appliance. Sometimes you have to work it out using the equation:

$$\text{power (watts, W)} = \text{voltage (volts, V)} \times \text{current (amps, A)}$$

Energy transferred

The amount of energy used by an electrical appliance is measured in **kilowatt hours** or **units**. The amount of energy used depends on the power of the appliance and the length of time it is switched on for.

The amount of energy used is given by the equation:

$$\text{energy transferred (kilowatt hours, kWh)} = \text{power (kilowatts, kW)} \times \text{time (hours, h)}$$

Worked example 1

The mains supply is 230 V and the current used by a television is 0.75 A. What is the power of the TV?

power = voltage × current

= 230 V × 0.75 A

= 172.5 W

Worked example 2

A computer uses 0.25 kilowatts and is switched on for five hours. How much energy does it transfer?

Energy transferred = power × time

= 0.25 kW × 5 hours

= 1.25 kWh

Cost of energy supplied

The amount of electricity you use at home is recorded by an electricity meter. Electricity is charged by the unit, or kilowatt hour. You can work out the cost of the electricity that a device uses if you know how much energy it transfers.

The cost of electricity used is given by the equation:

$$\text{cost} = \text{energy transferred (kilowatt hour, kWh)} \times \text{cost per unit (pence per kWh)}$$

Worked example 3

A kettle uses 3.5 kWh of energy. A unit of electricity costs 10.2p.
What is the cost of the energy transferred by the kettle?

cost of electricity = energy transferred × cost per unit

= 3.5 kWh × 10.2p/kWh

= 35.7p

Transformers

The electricity goes from the power station to a **step-up transformer** where the **voltage** is increased. Electricity is transferred from the transformer by high-voltage transmission lines to an electricity **substation**. Here, the electricity goes through a **step-down transformer** to reduce the voltage to a safer level for use by consumers.

The power transferred is given by the equation

$$\underset{\text{(watts, W)}}{\text{power}} = \underset{\text{(volts, V)}}{\text{voltage}} \times \underset{\text{(amps, A)}}{\text{current}}$$

When electrical energy is transmitted at a high voltage, energy losses in the power lines are reduced.

Why the National Grid uses high-voltage transmission

When a current flows through a wire, there is a heating effect and this dissipates some energy. The larger the current, the more heat is produced, and the more energy is wasted. Using the equation you can see that for a given power, if you increase the voltage, the current decreases. This reduces the amount of energy wasted in the power lines.

Some power lines are overhead, but others are buried underground. When power lines are buried underground, it reduces their visual impact and reduces the risk of tall objects colliding with them. However, it is much more expensive to bury power lines underground. They have to be insulated and waterproofed. Also, if something goes wrong, the ground has to be dug up.

Off-peak electricity

Electricity can be cheaper at night if you have off-peak electricity (or Economy 7). Some people take advantage of this cheaper electricity and heat their homes and water using off-peak electricity. Some people also set their washing machines to run when off-peak electricity is available.

Questions

1   A toaster uses the mains supply at 230 V and a current of 5 A. What is the power of the toaster? ↓E

2   What is a kilowatt hour?

3   An electric heater has two settings. The first setting uses 0.5 kW and the second 1.5 kW. Work out the cost of using the fire for:

(a) five hours at the 0.5 kW setting

(b) two hours at the 1.5 kW setting.

A unit of electricity costs 10.2p. ↓C

4   What are the advantages and disadvantages of using off-peak electricity at home?

5   An electric fire is turned on for 2 hours and uses 3 kWh. What is its power? ↓A*

▲ Coal is a fossil fuel

Did you know...?

Fuels are a concentrated store of chemical energy. One kilogram of coal contains a lot more energy than one kilogram of wood. So when these fuels are burned in a power plant, they can generate very large amounts of electricity. In Yorkshire, the coal-fired power station at Drax produces 7% of the UK's power needs, supplying power to over 2 million homes. You would need around 4000 of the largest wind turbines to generate the same amount of electricity. (There are only around 3000 turbines currently in use in the UK.)

Different fossil fuels

Coal, crude oil and natural gas are examples of **non-renewable** energy resources. All three are formed in similar ways. They are the remains of living organisms which died millions of years ago; this is why they are called **fossil fuels**. It takes a long time for a fossil fuel to form, and we are using them up far more quickly than they are being replaced. They will eventually run out.

In 2009, around 77% of the UK's electricity came from fossil fuels (mainly coal and natural gas). In every fossil fuel power station, fuel is burnt and the heat produced turns water to steam. This steam turns a turbine. The turbine spins a generator to produce electricity.

> **A** Give two examples of fossil fuels used to generate electricity.

There are a number of disadvantages of using fossil fuels. Burning the fuel releases a number of pollutants into the atmosphere. One of the gases released is carbon dioxide, which contributes to global warming. All three fossil fuels (coal, crude oil, and gas) have to be mined and transported, which can have negative impacts on the environment. However, fossil fuels offer a number of advantages over some other methods of generating electricity. Fossil fuel power plants are an established, reliable technology, producing large amounts of electricity.

▲ Burning any fossil fuel releases carbon dioxide into the atmosphere

Biomass

Biomass is a **renewable** energy resource. There are lots of different types, but all forms of biomass involve material produced from living organisms. Biomass used for burning is called a **biofuel**. These are similar to fossil fuels, but with fossil fuels the living organisms died millions of years ago.

Electricity is generated in a similar way as in other thermal power stations (water is heated to form steam, and so on).

Biofuels can be solids, liquids or gases. Some examples include:

- Wood, woodchips, and straw from specially grown trees or crops (new trees are planted when old ones are cut down).
- Alcohol fuels (such as ethanol), produced by fermenting sugar cane crops.
- Methane gas, given off by animal waste (manure) in storage tanks called sludge digesters, and also from other rotting waste (for example food waste from homes).

In the UK, biomass is used to generate more electricity than any other form of renewable energy. Over 40% of the electricity from renewable sources comes from biomass.

The table below shows the advantages and disadvantages of burning biomass compared with other methods of generating electricity.

Advantages	Disadvantages
Uses products which might otherwise be wasted, so the fuel costs are very low.	Releases atmospheric pollutants.
Power stations can also supply hot water to local industry/houses.	In developing countries, land which could be used for food is now used to grow crops for biofuels, leading to food shortages.
Carbon neutral: burning biomass releases carbon dioxide into the atmosphere. However unlike fossil fuels, there is no overall increase in carbon dioxide as the amount released is the same as the plant absorbed while it was alive.	Power plants can be ugly to look at (visual pollution).

▲ This biomass fuel is ready for burning

B Give three examples of different biofuels.

Key words

non-renewable, fossil fuels, biomass, renewable, biofuel, carbon neutral

Questions

1 Explain why fossil fuels are a non-renewable energy resource.

2 What percentage of the UK's electricity that is generated from renewable resources comes from biomass?

3 Describe how fossil fuels are used to generate electricity. List some of the disadvantages of generating electricity in this way.

4 State two advantages and two disadvantages of using biofuels to generate electricity.

Learning objectives

After studying this topic, you should be able to:

- ✔ describe how electricity is generated by a nuclear reactor
- ✔ describe some ways of disposing of radioactive waste
- ✔ outline the disadvantages of using nuclear power to generate electricity

Key words

nuclear reactor, nuclear fission, radioactive waste, decommissioning

Did you know...?

To produce the same amount of electricity you get from 1 kg of uranium you would need over 15 000 kg of coal!

Nuclear power is a controversial method of generating electricity. Currently around 13% of the electricity generated in the UK comes from nuclear power. There are plans to build several more nuclear reactors.

▲ Uranium is made into pellets that are inserted into a nuclear reactor

Inside a nuclear reactor

Nuclear power can be used to generate electricity. Inside a **nuclear reactor,** atoms of uranium or plutonium undergo **nuclear fission**. This releases a great amount of energy in the form of heat. The heat is used to turn water to steam, as in other thermal power plants. The steam drives turbines. No burning is involved, so there is no release of carbon dioxide.

The uranium fuel used in most reactors is a non-renewable resource. We have enough to last thousands of years, but we will eventually run out of it.

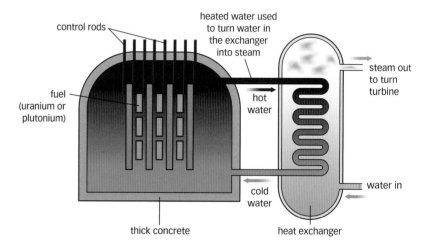

▲ Controlled nuclear fission inside the nuclear reactor releases a huge amount of energy

> **A** Name the fuel used inside most nuclear reactors.
>
> **B** At present, how much of the UK's electricity supply is generated by nuclear power?

Radioactive waste

As nuclear reactors do not produce carbon dioxide, they do not contribute to global warming. However, nuclear reactors produce **radioactive waste**. This type of waste can be very dangerous to living things.

> **C** Explain why using nuclear power does not lead to global warming.

The low level waste from nuclear reactors can go into landfill sites. However, reactors also produce some very radioactive waste (high-level waste). The radiation from this waste decreases over time, but the waste remains dangerous for millions of years. To store it safely it is usually encased in glass and buried deep underground, away from any water sources.

Radioactive waste can be reprocessed. Unused uranium can be extracted and put back into reactors. One of the waste products from this process is plutonium, which can be used to make nuclear weapons.

Arguments for and against nuclear power

Despite the risks and dangers associated with radioactive waste, nuclear power has some benefits when compared with other methods of generating electricity:

- Large amounts of electricity can be generated for each kilogram of fuel used.
- The fuel is readily available and, unlike fossil fuels, it won't run out for thousands of years.
- No polluting gases such as carbon dioxide are produced, so there is no contribution to global warming or acid rain.

As well as the production of radioactive waste, nuclear power has other disadvantages:

- The cost of building the plant and taking it down when it has finished (called **decommissioning**) can be quite high. This means the electricity generated can be relatively expensive.
- Nuclear fuel has to be processed before it can be used.
- Nuclear reactors have a very slow start up time. It takes a long time to increase or decrease the amount of electricity they are generating.
- It can be very expensive to process radioactive waste, and the stored waste may be a future terrorist target.
- There is always the risk of an accident that could release radioactive waste into the environment.

▲ Highly radioactive waste is stored in a pond until it can be processed

Exam tip OCR

✔ Remember, one advantage of nuclear power is that a large amount of electricity can be generated per kilogram of fuel. It is not enough to say a lot of electricity can be generated, as that is also true for fossil fuels.

Questions

1. State the energy changes inside a nuclear power plant (ending with electrical energy from the generator). ↓E
2. Describe how nuclear reactors can be used to generate electricity.
3. Describe some ways of disposing of radioactive waste. ↓C
4. Is nuclear power a renewable or non-renewable energy resource? Explain your answer.
5. List the advantages and disadvantages of using nuclear power. ↓A*

Learning objectives

After studying this topic, you should be able to:

✔ describe the penetrating powers of the three types of nuclear radiation

✔ describe the harmful effects of radiation on the body

✔ describe techniques used to handle radioactive sources safely

Key words

radioactive decay, ionising radiation, ion

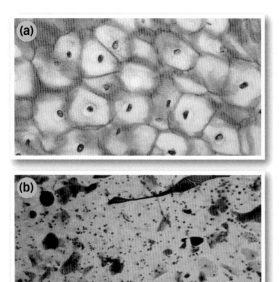

▲ (a) Healthy cells and (b) cells exposed to a high dose of ionising radiation

A State the three types of radiation and give examples of materials which stop them.

B What effect does ionising radiation have on human cells?

Radioactive decay

Nuclear radiation is around us all of the time; it occurs naturally. The nuclei of some atoms are unstable, and **radioactive decay** occurs when a nucleus from one of these atoms breaks down and emits radiation. The radioactive (or nuclear) waste from nuclear reactors is dangerous because it contains a very high concentration of radioactive atoms.

There are three types of radiation:
- alpha particles (sometimes shown using the Greek letter 'α')
- beta particles ('β')
- gamma rays ('γ').

Nuclear radiation can be detected by a Geiger–Muller (GM) tube. All forms of radiation travel through some materials, but the different types of radiation have very different penetrating abilities.

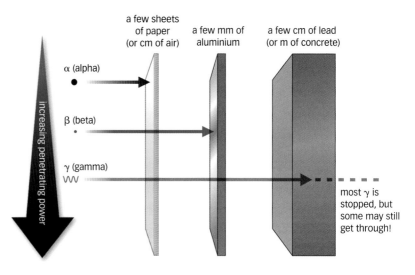

▲ The different penetration of the three types of radiation

A GM tube and a set of absorbers can be used to determine what type of radiation is emitted from different substances. For example, if the radiation passes through paper but is stopped by a few mm of aluminium, it must be beta.

All three types of nuclear radiation are called **ionising radiation**. This means the radiation causes electrons to be added or removed from atoms, forming charged **ions**. When electrons are removed, the atom becomes a positive ion. When electrons are added, the ion is negative.

Alpha particles are the most ionising, and gamma rays are the least ionising.

If atoms within human cells are ionised, the cells may be damaged or even killed.

> When the DNA inside the cell is ionised, it changes the interactions inside the cell. The ionised parts repel or attract each other, so the cell does not behave as it should. Ionisation can also initiate chemical reactions that would not normally take place. Severe damage to the DNA may lead to cancer and cell death.

Handling radioactive substances safely

We have already looked at how high level radioactive waste from nuclear reactors is encased in glass and buried underground. All radioactive sources are potentially dangerous, but different sources of radiation have a number of important uses. It is very important that they are used safely, minimising the risks to those using them and to the surrounding environment.

Radioactive sources must be handled very carefully. It is very important that their storage boxes are labelled, providing a clear warning to anyone using them. Different precautions are needed, depending on the type of radiation and the strength of the radioactive source.

Precaution	Action
Shielding	This can be as simple as wearing gloves before handling the source. If the source emits more penetrating radiation, denser shielding such as lead, lead crystal glass or special radiation suits might be needed.
Time	It is important that you reduce the time for which you are exposed to the radiation. The sources should only be taken out of their lead box when they are being used, and should be returned to safe storage when they are finished with.
Distance	The further away you are from the source, the lower your exposure. Using tongs when handling the sources keeps them at a safer distance.

◀ This clothing is worn to protect against radioactive sources

Questions

1 List the three types of radiation in order of their penetrating power. **E**

2 Describe why some of the waste from nuclear reactors is dangerous.

3 Explain what is meant by the term ionising radiation and describe how positive and negative ions are formed. **C**

4 Using a GM tube and an assortment of different absorbers, describe an experiment you could do to determine the types of radiation emitted from a radioactive source. **A***

5 Explain how ionisation damages living cells.

Smoke alarms and alpha particles

Alpha particles do not travel very far, but they are very ionising. This makes them ideal for smoke alarms. Smoke alarms contain a weak source of alpha radiation. This ionises air inside the alarm and creates a very small electric current (just like in the GM tube). When smoke enters the alarm, this current drops, setting off the alarm. If there is no smoke, there is no change in current and so the alarm stays quiet.

> **A** Suggest why gamma radiation would not be suitable for use in a smoke alarm.

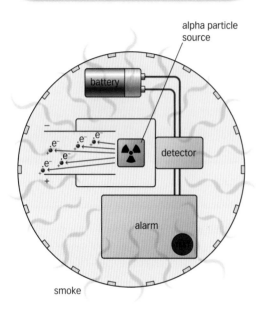

▲ Alpha particles are used in smoke alarms

Beta particles and paper mills

Compared with alpha particles, beta particles are more penetrating and less ionising. Most of them are able to travel through several sheets of paper. In paper mills, sheets of paper pass between a beta source and a detector which counts them. Some beta particles don't get through the paper. The thicker the paper, the fewer get through and so the counts recorded by the counter go down. If the counts fall too low, this shows that the paper is too thick and so the rollers squeeze together.

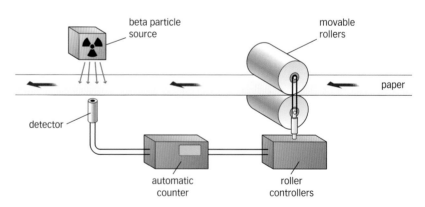

▲ In a paper mill, beta particles may be used to automatically monitor the thickness of paper as it is being made

> **B** Describe what would happen if the paper was too thin.

Medical uses of gamma rays

Gamma rays are very penetrating, but not very ionising. They have many medical uses and can be used to kill cancerous cells within the body. A special machine called a **gamma knife** contains a movable source of gamma rays. The gamma rays are fired into the body and focused on the tumour. The source is moved around in order to reduce the exposure of the healthy tissue but provide a high enough dose to kill the cells inside the tumour.

Other uses of gamma rays include:

* Medical tracers. A weak source of gamma rays is either swallowed by or injected into a patient. Gamma rays travel out of the body and special cameras are used to monitor the flow of the source around the body. Doctors can then identify problems such as blockages or leaks within internal organs. A similar technique can also be used to detect leaks in underground pipes.
* Sterilising equipment. Gamma rays are used to sterilise medical equipment. The gamma rays are used to kill the bacteria on the instruments, making them safe for use in future operations.

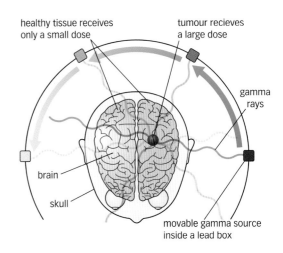

▲ A gamma knife is used to kill cancerous cells in a brain tumour

Key words

gamma knife

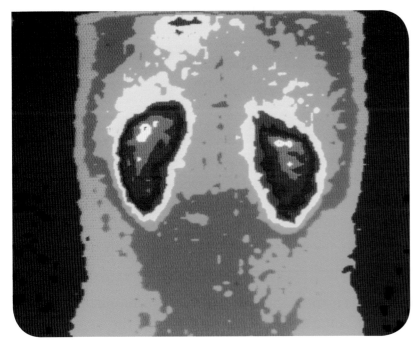

▲ This image of a patient's kidneys was obtained by using radioactive tracers injected into the body

Questions

1 Describe how smoke alarms work.

2 A similar arrangement to that used in paper mills is used to make sure steel sheets are kept at a constant thickness. Explain how this process might work, including the type of radiation you would use.

3 Give two reasons why gamma sources are used as medical tracers rather than alpha or beta sources.

4 Describe the advantages and disadvantages of using a radioactive medical tracer to diagnose a serious medical condition.

Learning objectives

After studying this topic, you should be able to:

✔ list the planets in order of distance from the Sun

✔ understand that the Sun's gravity keeps the planets in orbit

✔ describe the benefits and challenges of manned space exploration compared with using unmanned spacecraft

Key words

Solar System, planet, centripetal force, galaxy

▲ Saturn is one of the larger planets in orbit around the Sun.

Exam tip   OCR

✔ Astronomical objects vary greatly in size. In general, if we listed them in order from smallest to largest we would get:

Object	Typical Diameter (m)
Meteors	0.01–1
Comets	100–40000
Black Holes	30000
Planets	$5000–1 \times 10^8$
Stars	$10^9–10^{12}$
Galaxies	10^{20}

You should be able to list these in order of size.

The Solar System and the Universe

The Earth is part of the **Solar System**. In the same way that the Moon orbits the Earth, the Earth and all the other **planets** and dwarf planets (like Pluto) are in orbit around the Sun. It is the Sun's gravity which keeps them all in orbit.

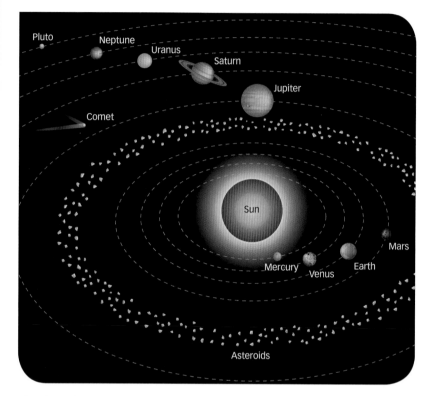

▲ The Solar System (not to scale)

Gravity and orbits

A force is required to keep all the planets in their almost perfectly circular orbits of the Sun. A force that makes an object move in a circular path is called a **centripetal force**. In this case the centripetal forces are due to the gravitational attractions between the Sun and the other planets.

As well as planets, there are icy comets orbiting the Sun that travel at over a million miles per hour, but the wider Universe is even more amazing. There are mysterious black holes, with gravity so strong nothing, not even light, can escape from them. The Universe contains immeasurable numbers of stars. Some of these are billions of kilometres away. We can only see them because their super-high temperatures mean they give out their own light.

Perhaps most amazing is the size of the Universe. We live in a **galaxy** called the Milky Way. This is a collection of 200 billion stars, and in total there are around 50 billion galaxies in the Universe. This means there are more stars in the Universe than grains of sand on every beach in the entire world.

Exploring space

Scientists have been exploring space since the 1960s. If the body being explored is nearby (like the Moon), samples are often brought back to Earth for further study. However, if the object being studied is much further away, a different technique is used. Spacecraft have been launched into space to collect a range of information. Probes have been sent to almost every planet, and to most large moons. They collect data on the temperature, magnetic field strength, atmosphere and the strength of gravity on the planet or moon. This data is then transmitted back to Earth for further analysis. All this information helps scientists understand more about the Universe.

Sending humans in spacecraft to explore space has many advantages, but also some significant risks. Large amounts of oxygen, food and water are needed. All this requires extra fuel and a much more complex spacecraft. As a result, manned spaceflight is much more expensive than sending unmanned spacecraft. Unmanned spacecraft need less maintenance and they can withstand conditions that would be lethal to humans.

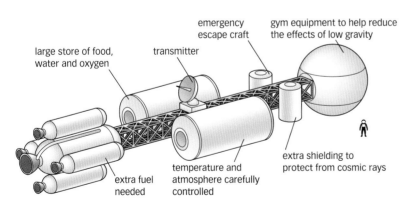

emergency escape craft

gym equipment to help reduce the effects of low gravity

large store of food, water and oxygen

transmitter

extra fuel needed

temperature and atmosphere carefully controlled

extra shielding to protect from cosmic rays

▲ A manned spacecraft of the future?

Even sending signals to spacecraft can be a problem. It takes time for signals to travel through space. A radio signal may take more than 15 minutes (between 4 and 20 minutes) to get to Mars (depending on where it is relative to the Earth). If there is a problem, this may be too late.

Did you know...?

It takes light from the Sun about eight minutes to get to the Earth. You can convert this into a distance and say the Sun is about eight light-minutes from the Earth. A light-year is a useful unit for measuring larger distances in space. One light-year is how far light travels in one year. This is 9 500 000 000 000 000 m (9.5 trillion km!). Our galaxy is around 70 000 light-years across.

A List four astronomical objects found in the Universe and sort them from largest to smallest.

B Give two examples of the information that can be sent back from spacecraft.

Questions

1 List the planets in order of distance from the Sun.

2 Describe how we are able to see stars even though they are far away from us.

3 State two advantages of unmanned spaceflight.

4 Look carefully at the diagram of the manned spacecraft, and describe some of the difficulties of manned space exploration.

5 Explain the meaning of the term light-year and give one advantage of its use.

Learning objectives

After studying this topic, you should be able to:

- ✔ outline the origin and location of asteroids in the Solar System
- ✔ describe the changes in a comet's orbit around the Sun
- ✔ describe the consequences of a collision between the Earth and an asteroid
- ✔ describe one theory that explains how the Moon was formed
- ✔ explain why the asteroid belt is found between Mars and Jupiter

Key words

asteroids, asteroid belt, comet, near-Earth object

A What is an asteroid, and where in the Solar System are most of them found?

Asteroids

Asteroids are pieces of rock that orbit the Sun. They are too small to be classed as planets. The largest asteroids have diameters of just 500 km; most are much smaller. Often they have unusual shapes. Most of them are not rounded, as gravity is not strong enough to pull them into spheres. It is thought that asteroids are left over from the formation of the Solar System. Most are found in between the orbits of Mars and Jupiter, inside the **asteroid belt**.

Formation of the asteroid belt

It is thought Jupiter's strong gravitational field (due to its large mass) prevented the asteroids in the asteroid belt from forming a planet. Jupiter's gravity disrupted this process, breaking up clusters of asteroids which would otherwise have eventually formed a planet.

Comets

A **comet** is a large ball of ice and dust. There are hundreds of comets orbiting the Sun, but unlike most asteroids their orbits are highly elliptical (squashed circles). This means that sometimes they are very far away from the Sun, further than even the most distant planets. At other times they are much closer to the Sun, and the closer they get the faster they move (as the Sun's gravitational attraction is stronger the closer you get to it). When they are near the Sun, the solar wind melts part of the comet, and its distinctive tail of debris is formed.

▲ An asteroid in orbit between Mars and Jupiter

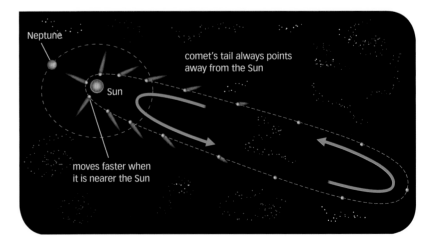

Neptune

comet's tail always points away from the Sun

Sun

moves faster when it is nearer the Sun

▲ The orbit of a comet

B Describe two differences between asteroids and comets.

Impact Earth

Asteroids and comets have hit the Earth in the past, and they will do so again in the future. Impacts from either of these throw large amounts of hot rock and dust into the atmosphere. Impacts are often explosive and so can lead to enormous countrywide (or larger) fires. This creates even more dust that may block out the Sun, with a devastating effect on life on Earth. The impact may lead to rapid climate change, resulting in the extinction of some species.

▲ The crater from a relatively small asteroid impact

Comets or asteroids that are on a possible collision course with the Earth are called **near-Earth objects** (NEOs). They reflect light from the Sun and so can be seen using powerful telescopes. However, making observations is difficult because they are so small and moving very fast. Observations of NEOs may be used to calculate their trajectories (paths). Once their trajectories are known it's possible to find whether it will collide with the Earth.

> Telescope surveys or satellite monitoring may be used to detect NEOs while they are still far enough away that they can be deflected using powerful explosions.

The Moon

The Moon is the Earth's only natural (not man-made) satellite. One popular theory about the formation of the Moon is that back when the solar system was very young, a planet about the size of Mars crashed into the Earth. The two planets merged together, with the heavier elements such as iron sinking into the middle. The lighter (less dense) elements were thrown into orbit. This material eventually formed the Moon.

Did you know...?

Perhaps the most famous large asteroid impact happened 65 million years ago. It is thought that an asteroid just 10 km wide crashed into Mexico, and this may have lead to the extinction of the dinosaurs. The impact threw up a gigantic cloud, containing large amounts of the rare metal iridium, that blocked out the Sun for several years. This dust eventually settled on the ground all over the world, and is now found as a layer in old rock layers. In younger rocks, above this layer, there are few dinosaur fossils. Below it (in older rocks) there are plenty of fossils.

Questions

1 Explain what is meant by a near-Earth object and describe how one might be detected in the future.

2 Draw a labelled diagram of a typical comet's orbit of the Sun. Describe any important features.

3 Outline the most popular theory on how the Moon was formed.

4 Describe the evidence supporting the idea that an asteroid impact led to the extinction of the dinosaurs.

5 Considering their orbits, give three reasons why comets are rarely seen with the naked eye.

↓ E

↓ C

↓ A*

▲ Most scientists think the Universe was created in the Big Bang

▲ Analysing the light from galaxies show most are moving away from us, and the further they are away, the faster they are moving.

It all started with the Big Bang

The **Big Bang** is at present the most widely recognised scientific theory on the origin of the Universe. It states that the Universe began from a very small, very dense and very hot initial point. It burst outwards in a giant explosion. All matter and space was created in the Big Bang. It is even thought this is the moment when time began.

This theory may seem a little strange, but there is some good evidence to support it.

> A Explain how the Universe was formed, according to the Big Bang theory, and describe what it was like in the past.

Where's the evidence?

There are two key pieces of evidence for the Big Bang. By observing light from distant galaxies scientists found out that most galaxies are moving away from us. Importantly, the galaxies furthest away are moving fastest. This suggests the Universe is expanding outwards, space itself is expanding. The galaxies are bit like the coloured sparks from an exploding firework. When the firework explodes, the sparks moving fastest travel the furthest.

◀ An exploding firework

If you could run time backwards you would see the sparks coming back closer together and all starting in one point. The same is true for galaxies. They all started out at one point in space, and then exploded outwards.

> Scientists found that the light from distant galaxies has been stretched. This happens because as the galaxies move away from us, the wavelength of the light increases. This is referred to as red shift. Red light has the longest wavelength of any colour. So when the

wavelength increases, the light shifts towards the red end of the spectrum. When you look at most galaxies, they are red-shifting and galaxies furthest away show the greatest red shift – meaning they are moving faster.

> **B** What does the motion of the galaxies suggest is happening to the Universe?

The second piece of evidence is even more compelling. In the 1960s, two scientists noticed that a form of microwave radiation was affecting their readings. No matter where they pointed their special telescope, they always detected the same background hum. This electromagnetic radiation was everywhere in the Universe. They had discovered the heat signature left over from the big bang (and won the Nobel Prize!).

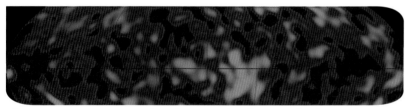

▲ Recent measurements show how cosmic microwave background radiation (CMBR) is distributed

It is now called cosmic microwave background radiation (CMBR). As the small, hot Universe expanded, it cooled, and the radiation was stretched out. Today this radiation is in the microwave region of the electromagnetic spectrum. It is the same everywhere you look because it fills the Universe.

By analysing distant galaxies, scientists are able to calculate how fast the galaxies are moving and the distance they have travelled since the universe began. This allows them to calculate the age of the Universe. However, this is a difficult process and the data are continually changing. Currently the Universe is thought to be 13.7 billion years old.

However, scientists cannot pinpoint where the universe began. The big bang theory says the Universe started at a small point (smaller than one atom). This tiny region expanded outwards to form the whole Universe. So really it began everywhere! There is no centre.

Key words

Big Bang, **red shift**, **cosmic microwave background radiation**

Questions

1 What are the two key pieces of evidence in support of the Big Bang theory? ↓ E

2 Explain the origin of cosmic microwave background radiation. ↓ C

3 How do observations of red shift support the Big Bang theory?

4 When a galaxy is moving away from us, in which direction is the light said to be shifted? ↓ A*

5 Explain why the Big Bang theory is currently the most widely accepted theory on the origin of the Universe.

Learning objectives

After studying this topic, you should be able to:

- ✔ describe how stars are formed
- ✔ describe what happens when a star approaches the end of its life
- ✔ describe the complete life cycle of a star

A What is the name given to a large cloud of gas in space?

B What force pulls the gas together to form a star?

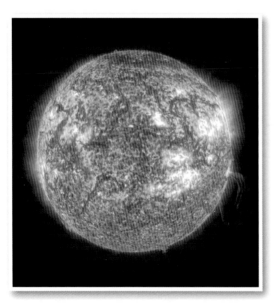

▲ The Sun is in the main phase of its life. This will last for billions of years.

Key words

nebula, proto-star, nuclear fusion, red giant, white dwarf, red supergiant, supernova, neutron star, black hole

Star birth and life

The Universe contains billions and billions of stars. Our Sun is an average star, some stars are smaller, and others are many, many times larger. Regardless of their size, all stars are formed in the same way. A huge cloud of gas (mainly hydrogen) called a **nebula** begins to be pulled together by gravity.

A large ball of gas forms in the centre of this cloud. As it gets denser, more gas is pulled in. The ball gets hotter and hotter, forming a **proto-star.** This continues to grow larger. Eventually, it gets so big, and its centre gets so hot, that atoms are squashed together in a process called **nuclear fusion.** A star is now born.

The energy released in nuclear fusion pushes out against gravity and keeps the star stable. This can last for billions of years, and is described as the main sequence of the star. Our Sun has been on its main sequence for around five billion years. It has another five billion to go before it starts to die.

Dying stars

All stars eventually die, but what happens to them depends on their mass. Small stars like our Sun gradually cool and expand to become a **red giant**. The outer layers of the star

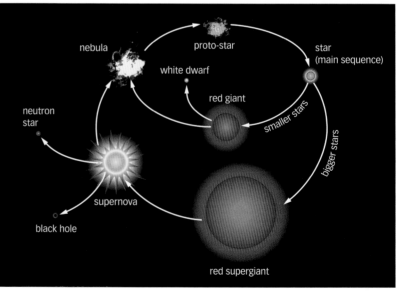

▲ The life cycle of stars

break away and form a planetary nebula. All that remains is the white-hot core of the star. This **white dwarf** gradually cools over time.

Stars that are much larger than our Sun have much more dramatic lives. They too eventually expand and cool, but grow much bigger. They turn into **red supergiants**. The star then explodes in a gigantic explosion called a **supernova**. When a star goes supernova, it often outshines all the other stars in the galaxy put together.

> **C** What is the name given to the explosion of a large star at the end of its life?

During a supernova, the core of the star is crushed down by immense gravitational forces. This can form a very dense kind of star just made up of neutrons. This **neutron star** spins very fast and sends pulses of radio waves to the Earth. If the star is even bigger, the core is crushed down into a tiny space – it forms a **black hole**.

Black holes have gravity so strong that nothing can escape from them, not even light.

Black holes and density
Black holes have near infinite densities due to their tiny volumes. All the mass of the core is crushed down into a space smaller than an atom. If you get too close to a black hole, you will be pulled in. The gravitational force is so large that nothing can escape.

▲ The Crab Nebula is left over from a star that went supernova in 1054

▲ Nothing can escape from a black hole

Questions

1 What is the name given to the hot remains of a red giant star?

2 Describe why our Sun will remain stable for billions of years.

3 Explain why nothing can escape from a black hole.

4 Describe the life cycle of a star that is:

(a) the size of our Sun

(b) much bigger than our Sun.

Exam tip   OCR

✔ What happens to a star depends on how big it is (its mass). Our Sun is too small to supernova and form a black hole. Only stars with much more mass explode at the end of their lives.

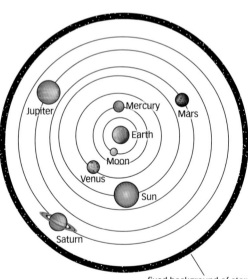

▲ Ptolemy's model had the Earth at the centre of the Universe, with everything else in orbit around it

Models from the past

Scientific ideas about the world around us are constantly changing. As more evidence comes to light scientific models change, and some even have to be completely re-thought. The history of ideas on the Universe is one example of a dramatic change in scientific theory. New evidence led to a completely different understanding of the Earth's place in the Universe.

The Universe has been studied ever since the earliest civilisations. In around 400 BC, the ancient Greek philosopher Aristotle proposed that the Earth was at the centre of the Universe. As astronomers began to use more powerful mathematics, the size of the known Universe began to grow. More and more was understood about the motion of the planets and Sun across the sky.

In around 100 AD, the Greek astronomer Ptolemy expanded on Aristotle's idea. He built up a model of the known Universe with the Earth at its very centre.

This **Earth-centred model** showed the Moon, the planets known at the time, and the Sun, all in orbit of the Earth.

Ptolemy's model (sometimes called the **Ptolemaic model**) was based on two key ideas:

• The Earth was at the centre of the Universe (the centre of everything).
• This Universe was surrounded by a background of fixed, unchanging stars.

Enter Copernicus and Galileo

Copernicus was a Polish astronomer and a very good mathematician. He used precise measurements of the planets to build models describing their motion. He found he could not explain their paths unless the Sun was at the centre of the Universe. He proposed a **Sun-centred model** of the Universe.

A Who first proposed the idea that the Earth was at the centre of the Universe?

B List the planets known when Ptolemy made his model.

C What was the idea proposed by Copernicus?

Copernicus realised the importance of this radical new idea and was scared of its potential impact. He did not publish his work until the year of his death. Galileo read Copernicus's work and decided to investigate further.

Galileo did not invent the telescope, but he worked hard to improve the technology behind it. He developed a telescope with very powerful magnification. This allowed him to see things that were previously too small to observe. Galileo used his telescope to observe moons in orbit of the planet Jupiter, uncovering revolutionary evidence. Galileo discovered that there were objects in the Universe that were not in orbit of the Earth. The Earth was not at the centre of everything.

Other observations of the stars showed that they could change. A supernova was observed and this brought more of Ptolemy's ideas into question.

Observations of stars and Galileo's evidence led to scientists changing their ideas about the Universe. The Earth-centred model of the Universe was eventually replaced by the Sun-centred model. We now know that the Sun is at the centre of our Solar System and is one of billions of stars in the Universe.

The ideas proposed by Copernicus and Galileo were extremely controversial. They went against the ideas of the church at the time. Speaking out against these ideas was considered blasphemy, and this was a very serious crime at the time. Scientists were scared to come out in support of the new ideas, despite the evidence. It took many years before the Sun-centred model was widely accepted.

▲ Galileo used his telescope to change the face of science

◀ Galileo saw moons in orbit of Jupiter

▲ The Hubble Space Telescope has enabled modern astronomers to find out even more about the nature of the Universe

Questions

1 Describe the Ptolemaic (Earth-centred) model of the Universe.

2 What key advance in technology allowed Galileo to make his observations?

3 Describe two key pieces of evidence in support of Copernicus's idea that Ptolemy's model was incorrect.

4 Explain why it took many years for the Sun-centred model of the Universe to be accepted.

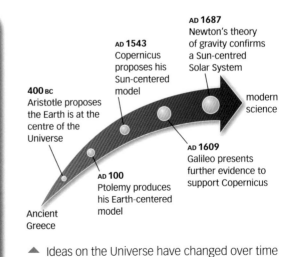

AD 1687
Newton's theory of gravity confirms a Sun-centred Solar System

AD 1543
Copernicus proposes his Sun-centered model

400 BC
Aristotle proposes the Earth is at the centre of the Universe

modern science

AD 100
Ptolemy produces his Earth-centered model

AD 1609
Galileo presents further evidence to support Copernicus

Ancient Greece

▲ Ideas on the Universe have changed over time

Module summary

Revision checklist

- The Sun is a renewable source of energy. Solar cells convert the Sun's energy directly into DC electricity.
- Kinetic energy from wind can be turned into electricity using turbines. They rely on wind speed, cause visual pollution, and require adequate space, but don't produce waste.
- The dynamo effect produces AC current using the movement of coils and magnets.
- Some power stations use fossil fuels, biomass, and nuclear fuels to heat water, generating steam to turn a turbine that drives an electrical generator.
- Power station efficiency can be calculated using the equation efficiency = total energy input/useful energy output (×100%)
- Carbon dioxide, water, and methane cause the greenhouse effect that traps infrared radiation in the atmosphere.
- CO_2 emissions, deforestation, dust from factories, and volcanic ash add to global warming and climate change.
- power = voltage x current, and is measured in watts and kilowatts.
- Transformers in the National Grid produce high-voltage electricity, reducing the energy lost in cables.
- Nuclear radiation can be useful or harmful, and different types (alpha, beta, gamma) have different penetrating powers.
- Radioactive waste from nuclear power stations can be hard to deal with, but the power stations do not contribute to global warming.
- The Moon orbits the Earth and the Earth orbits the Sun. The Universe consists of stars and planets, comets and meteors, black holes, and galaxies.
- Stars are very hot and give off their own light. They have life cycles with stages including red giant, planetary nebula, white dwarf, supernova, and neutron star/black hole.
- Manned and unmanned space travel both have advantages and disadvantages.
- A near-Earth object (NEO) is an asteroid or comet on a possible collision course with Earth. Asteroids have collided with the Earth in the past, causing craters, fires, climate change, and extinction.
- The red shift on light from distant galaxies is evidence for the Big Bang and expanding Universe.

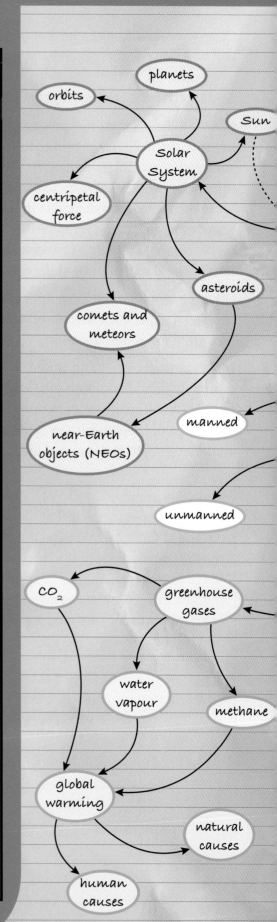

NOW USE THE P2 GRADE CHECKER ON PAGE 242

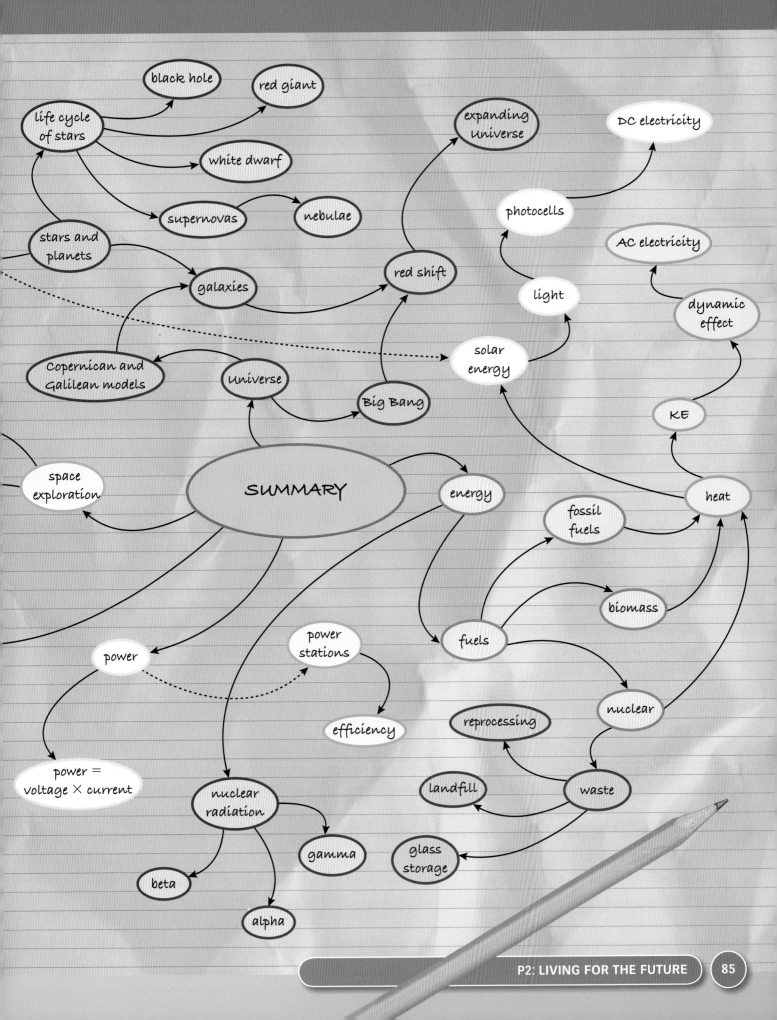

black hole

red giant

life cycle of stars

white dwarf

stars and planets

supernovas

nebulae

expanding Universe

DC electricity

photocells

AC electricity

red shift

light

dynamic effect

galaxies

solar energy

KE

Copernican and Galilean models

Universe

Big Bang

space exploration

SUMMARY

energy

heat

fossil fuels

biomass

power

power stations

fuels

nuclear

efficiency

reprocessing

power = voltage × current

nuclear radiation

landfill

waste

gamma

glass storage

beta

alpha

Answering Extended Writing questions

France relies on nuclear power to generate almost 80% of its electricity. In the UK, about 20% of electricity is supplied by nuclear power stations. Most of the rest of the electricity in Britain comes from power stations that burn fossil fuels.

Outline the advantages and disadvantages of generating electricity in nuclear power stations compared to power stations that burn fossil fuels.

The quality of written communication will be assessed in your answer to this question.

QUESTION

I am against nucleer power. If there is an acsident in a nuclear power station, millions of people can be affected, like in Chernobill. Acsidents in fossil fuel power stations is less bad. Nuclear power stations makes plutonium waste for nucleare bombs.

↓ **E**

Examiner: The answer makes two valid points, about the possible consequences of accidents at the two types of power station, and about using plutonium waste. Unfortunately, the candidate has not compared nuclear power to fossil fuel power stations. The first sentence is irrelevant. There are several spelling and grammar mistakes.

Fossil fule stations make carbon dioxide gass, which causes global warming, and sulfur dioxide gass, which causes acid rain. Nuclear power stations do not.

↓ **C**

Examiner: The points the candidate has made are correct, and the scientific vocabulary is used correctly, too. It is a shame the candidate did not make further comparisons between the two methods of generating electricity. There are three spelling mistakes.

Generating electricity in nuclear power stations does not produce carbon dioxide, and so does not contribute to global warming. But nuclear power stations generate dangerous radioactive waste, like plutonium, which stays radioactive for a long time, and is a terrorist risk. Fossil fuel power stations produce carbon dioxide gas, and so contribute to global warming, but do not make radioactive waste. Both uranium (for nuclear power stations) and coal are non-renewable.

↓ **A***

Examiner: This answer makes several valid points about the advantages and disadvantages of generating electricity by the two methods, and includes helpful comparisons. The answer is well organised, and includes scientific vocabulary. The spelling, punctuation, and grammar are faultless.

Exam-style questions

1 State whether each of the following is a renewable or a non-renewable source of energy.
[A01]

hydroelectricity
natural gas
solar
nuclear
biomass
coal
wind
tidal
oil
wave

2 The illustration represents a gas-fired power station.
[A01]

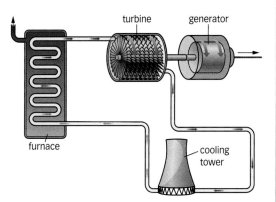

Explain what happens at each of the four stages illustrated above.

3 A kettle operates from the 230 V mains. The current is 13 A.

[A02] **a** What is the power of the kettle
  i in watts
  ii in kilowatts?

[A02] **b** The kettle takes 3 minutes to boil a litre of water. How many units of energy are transferred?

[A02] **c** A unit of electricity costs 12 p. What is the cost of boiling the kettle?

[A02] **d** Would it cost less to use a lower-powered kettle? Explain your answer.

4 **a** A coal-fired power station generates 140 million joules. The energy from burning the coal is 400 million joules. Calculate its efficiency.
[A02]

[A02] **b** A hydroelectric power station generates 540 million joules. It is 90% efficient. Calculate how much hydro-energy went into it.

[A02] **c** Suggest why a hydroelectric power station is so much more efficient than a coal-fired power station.

Extended Writing

5 Describe some of the ways in which we use energy that reaches the Earth from the Sun.
[A01]

6 Explain what is meant by the Big Bang theory, and the main points of evidence that support it.
[A01]

7 There are many nuclear power stations operating successfully worldwide. Explain the process involved; and discuss some of the arguments for and against building more nuclear power stations.
[A01]

A01 Recall the science
A02 Apply your knowledge
A03 Evaluate and analyse the evidence

P2: LIVING FOR THE FUTURE   87

P3

Forces and motion

Why study this module?

You can use physics to describe the motion of objects, and you can also use it to predict what will happen to an object in many different conditions. When objects move, energy transfers take place, for example from gravitational potential energy to kinetic energy when you drop an object and it falls to the floor. When engineers are designing cars, they need to be able to predict what will happen to the car and its occupants in order to minimise possible injuries if the car is in a crash.

In this module you will look at how the acceleration of an object is linked to the force acting on it, and how this can change its motion. You will learn how the motion of the object can be represented in graphs, and how the object's motion is affected by air resistance. You will also learn about the distance it takes to stop a car, and how this distance is affected by different conditions and by the state of the driver. You will learn about momentum, and how this influences the design of car safety features.

You should remember

1 When a force acts on an object it can cause it to move.

2 Friction is a force that tries to stop things from moving.

3 When an object is moving, air resistance tries to slow it down.

4 Energy cannot be created or destroyed.

5 Energy can exist in different forms, such as kinetic energy and gravitational potential energy.

The world's fastest roller-coaster is the Ring Racer at the Nürburgring race track in Germany. It has a top speed of 217 km/h and accelerates from 0 to 217 km/h in 2.5 seconds. It has been designed to simulate the speed of a Formula 1 racing car. It does not have any loops or banked turns and has been designed simply to travel at high speeds. Engineers will have considered the forces acting on the roller-coaster and riders to give the acceleration they need to reach the top speed. They will also have considered how to keep the riders safe by including many safety features.

The Ring Racer operated briefly in 2009 until it was damaged by an explosion in the control system. It is now scheduled to open to the public in 2011. There is an even faster roller-coaster under construction in Dubai – its top speed will be 240 km/h.

Learning objectives

After studying this topic, you should be able to:

- ✔ calculate the speed of an object
- ✔ explain how cameras are used to measure speed
- ✔ use average speed in calculations

Speed

Speed is a measure of how fast someone or something is moving. It is the distance moved in a certain time. It is calculated using the equation:

$$\text{average speed (metres/second, m/s)} = \frac{\text{distance (metres, m)}}{\text{time (seconds, s)}}$$

For example, in a sprint race the athletes run a measured distance and the time they take to run the distance is also measured. So you can work out their speed.

▲ We can work out the speeds of these athletes

Speeds can also be measured in other units. Speeds of cars and other vehicles are often measured in miles per hour (mph) or kilometres per hour (km/h).

If you know the speed of something, you can work out how long it will take to travel a certain distance.

Worked example 1

Usain Bolt ran 100 metres in 9.58 seconds. On average, how fast did he run?

$$\text{average speed} = \frac{\text{distance}}{\text{time}}$$

distance = 100 m and time = 9.58 s, so

$$\text{average speed} = \frac{100\ \text{m}}{9.58\ \text{s}}$$
$$= 10.4\ \text{m/s}$$

Worked example 2

A cyclist is travelling at 3 metres per second. How long does it take her to travel 180 metres?

$$\text{speed} = \frac{\text{distance}}{\text{time}}$$
$$\text{time} = \frac{\text{distance}}{\text{speed}}$$

distance = 180 m and speed = 3 m/s, so

$$\text{time to travel 180 metres} = \frac{180\ \text{m}}{3\ \text{m/s}}$$
$$= 60\ \text{s, or 1 minute.}$$

If you know the speed of something and for how long it has been moving, you can work out the distance it has travelled, by rearranging

$$\text{speed} = \frac{\text{distance}}{\text{time}} \text{ to:}$$
$$\text{distance} = \text{speed} \times \text{time}$$

A The cyclist in the worked example on the left increases her speed to 5 metres per second. How far will she now travel in 1 minute?

B What happens to the time taken to travel a certain distance when the speed increases?

Average speed

If the speed of something is changing, you can use the **average speed** to calculate the distance travelled:

distance   =   average speed   ×   time
(metres, m)   (metres/second, m/s)   (seconds, s)

If the speed is changing **uniformly**, then

$$\text{average speed} = \frac{\text{initial speed} + \text{final speed}}{2}$$

If u is the initial speed, and v is the final speed, then

$$\text{average speed} = \frac{u + v}{2}$$

Worked example 3

The initial speed of a car is 5 m/s. It travelled 300 m in 20 s. What was the car's final speed?

$$\text{distance} = \text{average speed} \times \text{time}$$

$$\text{average speed} = \frac{\text{distance}}{\text{time}}$$

distance = 300 m and time = 20 s

$$\text{average speed} = \frac{300 \text{ m}}{20 \text{ s}} = 15 \text{ m/s}$$

$\text{average speed} = \frac{u + v}{2}$ and initial speed $u = 5$ m/s, so

$$15 = \frac{5 + v}{2}$$

Rearranging, $v = (2 \times 15) - 5 = 25$ m/s

The final speed of the car is 25 m/s.

Speed cameras

Speed cameras are used to measure the speeds of vehicles that are travelling faster than the speed limit.

Some speed cameras are used together with lines painted on the road. As the car passes over the lines the camera takes two pictures 0.2 seconds apart. The distance travelled by the vehicle in that time is found by looking at the two photos. So the distance and time are known. The speed can then be calculated.

Average speed cameras use a pair of cameras to work out the average speed of a car. The cameras read the car's number plate and record the time when the car passes each camera. The distance between the two cameras is known, so the car's speed can be worked out using the average speed equation.

Questions

1 A cheetah runs 1.5 km in 100 seconds. What is its average speed?

2 A car travels 240 km in 3 hours. What is the speed of the car?

3 Explain how a speed camera is used to find the speed of a car.

4 A car is travelling at a speed of 25 m/s. How far does it travel in 40 s?

5 A train is travelling at 10 m/s. Its speed increases uniformly, until 40 s later it is travelling at 50 m/s. How far does the train travel in this time?

6 An aircraft travels 3750 m in 25 s. Its speed is changing regularly and at the end of 25 s, its speed is 100 m/s. What was its initial speed?

Learning objectives

After studying this topic, you should be able to:

✔ draw and interpret distance–time graphs

✔ understand that the gradient of a distance–time graph represents speed

✔ calculate the speed of an object from a distance–time graph

Key words

distance–time graph, gradient, stationary, positive gradient, negative gradient

Worked example

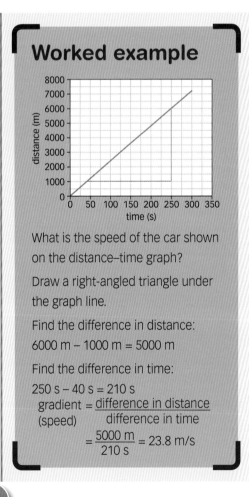

What is the speed of the car shown on the distance–time graph?

Draw a right-angled triangle under the graph line.

Find the difference in distance:

6000 m – 1000 m = 5000 m

Find the difference in time:

250 s – 40 s = 210 s

gradient = difference in distance
(speed)   difference in time

$= \dfrac{5000 \text{ m}}{210 \text{ s}} = 23.8$ m/s

You can record the distance that an object travels and the time taken to travel that distance. The table below shows the distance a car has travelled along a motorway. The distance and time are measured from where and when the car started.

You can plot this data on a **distance–time graph**. Time is usually plotted on the *x*-axis and distance on the *y*-axis.

Time (s)	Distance (m)
0	0
50	1500
100	3000
150	4500
200	6000
250	7500
300	9000

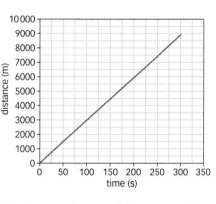

▲ Distance–time graph for a car on the motorway, using the data in the table

You can tell how fast something is moving by looking at the slope of the line. If the car is moving faster, it goes a greater distance in every 50 seconds and the slope of the line is steeper. If the car is slower, it moves a smaller distance every 50 seconds and the slope is less steep.

We call the slope (or steepness) the **gradient** of the graph. The gradient of a distance–time graph represents speed.

If a distance–time graph has a straight slope, this tells you that the object is moving at a constant speed. Where the line in a distance–time graph is horizontal, the object has not moved any distance – it is **stationary**.

A Look at this distance–time graph for two runners in a race. Which runner is faster?

Distance–time graph for two ▶ boys running in race

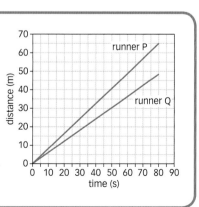

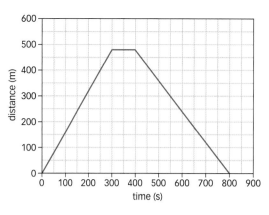

▲ A distance–time graph for Ben's trip from home to the shop and back again

Moving away and moving towards

The distance on a distance–time graph means the distance from a particular point. The graph can slope downwards as well as upwards. When an object is moving away from the fixed point, the graph slopes upwards to the right – it has a **positive gradient**. When the object is moving back towards the fixed point, the graph slopes downward to the right – the gradient is **negative**.

> **B** Describe Ben's trip to the shop as shown on the graph. In which direction does he travel faster?

Changing speed on a distance–time graph

When speed changes, so does the gradient or steepness of the graph. This graph shows another trip to the shop. At 600 seconds Ben begins to slow down: the graph becomes less steep, or the gradient decreases. At 1100 seconds, when he is 100 metres from home, he speeds up again: the gradient becomes steeper.

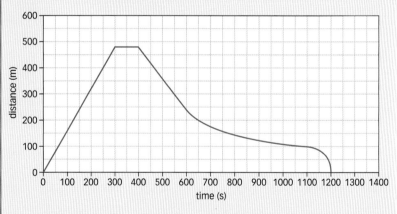

▲ Distance–time graph for another trip to the shop

Calculating speed from a distance–time graph

You can calculate the speed of an object by working out the gradient of a distance–time graph. You can work out the gradient using the equation:

$$\text{gradient (speed)} = \frac{\text{difference in distance}}{\text{difference in time}}$$

Questions

1 What does the gradient of a distance–time graph tell you?

2 What does a horizontal line on a distance–time graph tell you?

3 A cyclist sets out on a straight road. After 50 seconds he has travelled 200 m. He stops for 100 seconds to adjust his bike. He then travels 1000 m in 200 seconds. Draw the distance–time graph for his journey.

4 Find the speeds of the runners as shown in the graph in Question A.

5 Draw a distance–time graph for a train increasing its speed as it moves away from a station.

Exam tip OCR

✔ When calculating speed from a distance–time graph, remember to find the change (difference) in distance and the change in time.

▲ A cheetah can speed up from rest to 20 m/s in less than 2 seconds. That's a greater acceleration than most cars are capable of.

A moving object might speed up or slow down. This change in speed is called **acceleration**. The change can be negative as well as positive. When something is slowing down, it will have a negative acceleration. In everyday language, negative acceleration is called **deceleration**.

When a car is pulling away from traffic lights, the acceleration is in the same direction that the car is moving in, and it is positive. When the car slows down at another set of traffic lights, it is decelerating; the acceleration is in the opposite direction to the car's motion and it is negative.

Calculating acceleration

The size of the acceleration is the rate at which the speed changes. It depends on how much the speed changes and the time taken for the change in speed.

$$\text{acceleration (metres per second squared, m/s}^2) = \frac{\text{change in speed}}{\text{time taken for change}}$$

The change in speed is worked out by subtracting the initial speed from the final speed.

Worked example

The speed of a train increases from 15 m/s to 35 m/s in 10 seconds. What is the acceleration of the train?

$$\text{acceleration} = \frac{\text{change in speed}}{\text{time taken for change}}$$

initial velocity = 15 m/s, final velocity = 35 m/s

change in speed = 35 m/s − 15 m/s = 20 m/s

time taken for change = 10 seconds

$$\text{acceleration} = \frac{20 \text{ m/s}}{10 \text{ s}} = 2 \text{ m/s}^2$$

A A roller-coaster accelerates from 3 m/s to 18 m/s in 3 seconds. What is its acceleration?

B A car is moving towards a junction at a speed of 12 m/s. It slows down to a stop in 6 seconds. What is its deceleration?

Velocity and speed

Speed tells you how fast something is moving but it does not tell you what direction it is moving in. **Velocity** tells you the direction an object is travelling in as well as its speed. For example, you might say that a car was moving north at 30 km/h.

The two cars in the picture are both travelling at 40 mph; their speeds are the same. However, they are moving in different directions, so their velocities are different.

We might say that the red car has a velocity of +40 mph. The blue car is travelling at 40 mph in exactly the opposite direction, so then we would say that it has a velocity of –40 mph.

Relative velocity

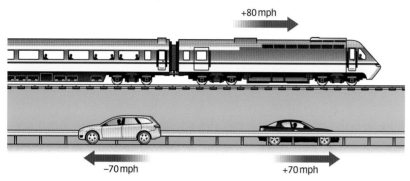

▲ The train seems to be going a lot faster to the people in the yellow car!

The black car in this picture is moving at +70 mph, and the train is moving in the same direction at +80 mph. For the people in the black car, the train is travelling past them at 80 – 70 mph, that is 10 mph. The difference in velocity, called the **relative velocity**, is 10 mph.

The yellow car is travelling at 70 mph in the opposite direction so its velocity is negative at –70 mph. The relative velocity of the train and the yellow car is 80 – (–70) mph, that is, 80 + 70 mph, 150 mph.

Acceleration is any change in velocity

When the velocity of an object changes, it is accelerating. A change in velocity can also mean a change in direction, such as a car going round a bend. Even if the speed stays the same, but the direction changes, the object is being accelerated.

▲ These cars may be travelling at the same speed, but they have different velocities

C What is the relative velocity of the black and yellow cars on the left?

Questions

1 What is acceleration?

2 What does it mean when an object has negative acceleration?

3 When an aeroplane lands, its speed is 65 m/s. The speed decreases to 10 m/s in 11 seconds. What is the deceleration of the aeroplane?

4 One car is travelling north at 70 mph. Another car is travelling at 70 mph east. Do the cars have the same velocity? Explain your answer.

5 A cheetah is moving at 5 m/s. It can accelerate at 10 m/s². How long will it take to increase its speed to 20 m/s?

Learning objectives

After studying this topic, you should be able to:

- ✔ draw a speed–time graph
- ✔ explain that the gradient of a speed–time graph represents acceleration
- ✔ state that the area under a speed–time graph represents the distance travelled
- ✔ calculate the acceleration of an object by using the gradient of a speed–time graph
- ✔ use a speed–time graph to calculate the distance travelled

Key words

speed–time graph

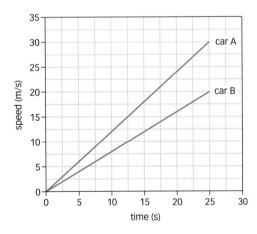

▲ Speed–time graph for two cars

A What does a horizontal line on a speed–time graph mean?

Speed–time graphs

In the same way that you can record an object's distance at different times, you can also record its speed at different times. The graph below shows the speed of a train that is travelling in a straight line between two stations. The speed is plotted at different times. The graph tells you how fast the train is moving and whether it is speeding up or slowing down. The area under the line of a speed–time graph shows the distance travelled.

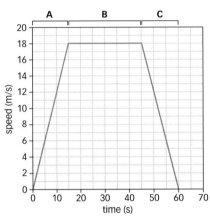

A Steady increase in speed from zero to 18 m/s.
Straight line sloping upwards (positive gradient).
B Constant speed of 18 m/s.
Horizontal straight line.
C Steady decrease in speed from 18 m/s to zero.
Straight line sloping downwards (negative gradient).

◀ Speed–time graph for a train

The graph on the left shows the speeds of two cars. Both are stationary to begin with, but after 25 seconds car **A** has reached a speed of 30 m/s and car **B** a speed of only 20 m/s. Car A has a greater acceleration, and this is shown by the higher gradient (steeper slope) of its graph.

Calculating acceleration

You can calculate acceleration by working out the gradient of a speed–time graph. The gradient is given by the equation:

$$\frac{\text{gradient}}{\text{(acceleration)}} = \frac{\text{change in speed}}{\text{time taken for change}}$$

Worked example 1

Calculate the acceleration of car **A**.

Use the equation above.

change in speed = 30 m/s – 0 m/s = 30 m/s

time taken for that change = 25 s – 0 s = 25 s

$$\text{acceleration} = \frac{30 \text{ m/s}}{25 \text{ s}} = 1.2 \text{ m/s}^2$$

Distance travelled

You can calculate the distance travelled by working out the area under a speed–time graph.

Worked example 2

This is a speed–time graph for a cyclist. Calculate the distance travelled by the cyclist.

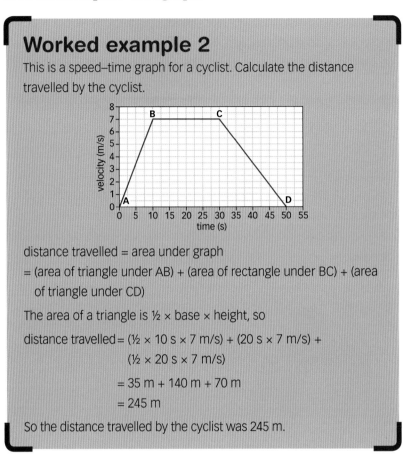

distance travelled = area under graph

= (area of triangle under AB) + (area of rectangle under BC) + (area of triangle under CD)

The area of a triangle is ½ × base × height, so

distance travelled = (½ × 10 s × 7 m/s) + (20 s × 7 m/s) +

(½ × 20 s × 7 m/s)

= 35 m + 140 m + 70 m

= 245 m

So the distance travelled by the cyclist was 245 m.

B Calculate the distance travelled by the train in the speed–time graph.

Change in acceleration

This graph shows the speed of a car moving off at traffic lights.

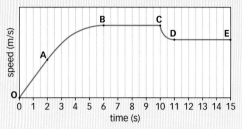

For 2 seconds, between **O** and **A** on the graph, the car's speed steadily increases. The gradient of the line is constant and so the acceleration is steady.

For the next 4 seconds, between **A** and **B**, the slope of the line becomes less and less steep. The acceleration is decreasing – the speed of the car is still going up, but not as quickly as before. Whenever you see a curved line on a velocity–time graph, the acceleration is changing.

From 6 seconds to 10 seconds, the slope of the line is zero: the car is not getting any faster: its speed is constant.

Questions

1 What does the gradient of a speed–time graph show?

2 Draw a speed–time graph for:
   (a) a person walking at a constant speed of 1 m/s for 10 seconds
   (b) an aircraft accelerating from 0 m/s to 60 m/s in 20 seconds.

3 Look at the speed–time graph for the train. Calculate the acceleration of the train as shown in each part of the graph.

4 Look at the speed–time graph for the car moving off at traffic lights. What happens to the car's speed between the points on the graph marked **C**, **D**, and **E**?

Key words

mass, resultant force

A What is needed for an object to accelerate?

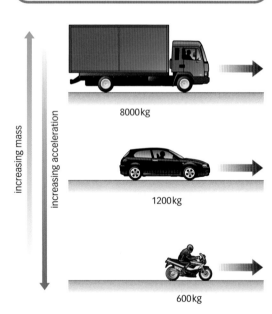

increasing mass

increasing acceleration

8000 kg

1200 kg

600 kg

▲ The greater the mass of an object, the lower its acceleration for a particular force

Exam tip   OCR

✔ You don't need to remember the equation – it will be given to you in the exam. But you do need to know how to apply it.

Forces and acceleration

Forces make objects change their motion. The change can be a change in speed, or direction, or both. For instance, when a football is volleyed, the force from the player's foot changes the ball's speed and direction. We can describe these changes as an acceleration. When a car accelerates away from traffic lights, the acceleration is caused by a thrust force from the engine. Forces make objects accelerate.

If the force acting on an object is in the same direction as the object is moving, the object's speed will increase. If the force acts in the opposite direction, the object will slow down. We see this in action when a book slides across a desk. If the forces acting on an object are balanced, its speed will remain the same.

◀ At the sound of the starter's gun, this sprinter's legs provide a force that accelerates him out of the blocks

If you apply the same force to different objects, they may accelerate at different rates. The greater the **mass** of the object, the lower its acceleration. Imagine the engines in the vehicles on the left can all provide the same force. The bike will accelerate at the greatest rate. This is because the bike has the lowest mass. The lorry has the greatest mass and so it will accelerate at the lowest rate.

If two cars have the same mass then the one with the higher driving force accelerates more quickly.

Calculating force, mass and acceleration

The force acting on an object, its mass and its acceleration are connected by this equation:

$$\underset{\text{(newtons, N)}}{\text{force}} = \underset{\text{(kilograms, kg)}}{\text{mass}} \times \underset{\text{(metres per second}^2, \text{m/s}^2)}{\text{acceleration}}$$

Worked example 1

A cyclist accelerates at 1.5 m/s². The mass of the bicycle and rider is 90 kg. What force is the cyclist producing?

$$\text{force} = \text{mass} \times \text{acceleration}$$
$$\text{force} = 90 \text{ kg} \times 1.5 \text{ m/s}^2 = 135 \text{ N}$$

Worked example 2

A passenger jet has mass of 320 000 kg and it has 800 000 N of thrust force from its engines. Calculate its acceleration.

$$\text{force} = \text{mass} \times \text{acceleration}$$
$$\text{acceleration} = \frac{\text{force}}{\text{mass}}$$
$$\text{acceleration} = \frac{800\,000 \text{ N}}{320\,000 \text{ kg}} = 2.5 \text{ m/s}^2$$

Resultant force and acceleration

Sometimes you need to work out the **resultant force** first, before calculating the acceleration. The resultant force is the sum of all the forces acting on an object, taking their directions into account.

Worked example 3

The engine of the car in the diagram is providing a thrust force of 1000 N. The friction and drag forces add up to 600 N. The mass of the car is 800 kg. What is the acceleration of the car shown in the diagram?

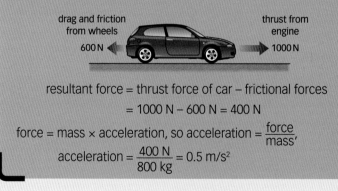

drag and friction from wheels — 600 N

thrust from engine — 1000 N

$$\text{resultant force} = \text{thrust force of car} - \text{frictional forces}$$
$$= 1000 \text{ N} - 600 \text{ N} = 400 \text{ N}$$
$$\text{force} = \text{mass} \times \text{acceleration, so acceleration} = \frac{\text{force}}{\text{mass}},$$
$$\text{acceleration} = \frac{400 \text{ N}}{800 \text{ kg}} = 0.5 \text{ m/s}^2$$

B A speedboat with a mass of 1500 kg accelerates at 2.5 m/s². What is the driving force produced by the engine?

C A car is braking and decelerating at 5 m/s². The mass of the car is 1200 kg. What force are the brakes providing?

Questions

1 The driving force of a train's engine is increased. What happens to the acceleration of the train? ↓ E

2 A tennis ball and a football are given the same acceleration. Which needs the smaller force?

3 A charging rhino has a mass of 1400 kg and accelerates at 1.5 m/s². Calculate the force providing the acceleration. ↓ C

4 A football of mass 0.5 kg is kicked with a force of 150 N. What is the acceleration of the football?

5 A small rocket has a weight of 200 N and a mass of 20 kg. When launched it accelerates at 5 m/s². Find:
   (a) the resultant (accelerating) force ↓ A*
   (b) the thrust from the engine.

Key words

braking distance, reaction time, thinking distance, stopping distance

A What is the stopping distance?

▲ Using a mobile phone in this way while driving can distract you. It is also illegal.

Stopping distances

The total distance needed to stop a car is not just the distance the car travels after the brakes have been applied, called the **braking distance**. There is also the time needed for the driver to react to seeing something. For example, the driver sees a red light and needs to move their foot onto the brake pedal. This is called the **reaction time**. During the reaction time, the car will have travelled a certain distance, called the **thinking distance**.

$$\text{total } \textbf{stopping distance} = \text{thinking distance} + \text{braking distance}$$

The Highway Code gives stopping distances under normal conditions, as shown in the diagram. The calculations assume that the acceleration is –6 m/s². (The minus sign means a negative acceleration, or deceleration. It is in the opposite direction to the direction of motion.)

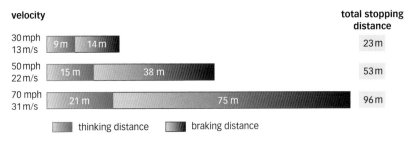

velocity			total stopping distance
30 mph 13 m/s	9 m	14 m	23 m
50 mph 22 m/s	15 m	38 m	53 m
70 mph 31 m/s	21 m	75 m	96 m

☐ thinking distance   ☐ braking distance

▲ Stopping distances from the Highway Code

Thinking distance

There are many factors that can affect your reaction time and the thinking distance. When you are tired, you react more slowly. If you have used drugs such as alcohol or marijuana, your reactions are slower. Some drugs that are available over the counter or prescription drugs can also increase the time it takes you to react.

Distractions, such as listening to music, using a mobile phone or a satellite navigation system, or even talking to passengers can increase reaction time. Also, people's reactions become slower as they get older.

The faster your speed, the further your car travels during your reaction time, so speed affects thinking distance too.

Braking distance

The braking distance does not only depend on the speed of the car. When you press the brake pedal, the brakes are applied to the wheel. If the brakes are worn, this can reduce the force that they can apply. If too much force is applied, the wheels can lock and the car skids.

Road conditions can also affect the braking distance. If the road surface is icy, there is less friction between the tyres and the road and the tyres may slip. The braking distance will increase. On wet road surfaces or if tyres are bald (worn), the friction between the tyres and the road is also reduced.

Stopping distances and safe driving

If the car in front of you stops or slows down suddenly, and you are nearer to it than the thinking distance, then you will inevitably crash into it. So you need to keep your distance, especially in poor road conditions.

Stopping distances are much greater at higher speeds, and this is one of the reasons for speed limits in built-up areas or where roads are hazardous because of bends, for example.

Effect of speed on stopping distances

The graph shows how thinking, braking and stopping distances change with speed. The thinking distance and speed are directly proportional. For example, if the speed doubles, so does the thinking distance.

But braking distance does not increase in direct proportion. For instance, at 30 mph braking distance is about 15 metres, but at 60 mph braking distance is about 55 metres – that is nearly four times as long. This is known as a squared relationship.

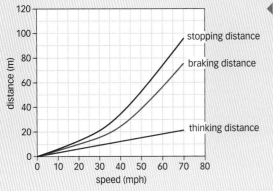

◀ Graph showing stopping distances against speed

▲ Stopping distances are longer in conditions like this

B Why do brakes need to be in good condition?

Questions

1 Use the graph to find out how much the stopping distance increases when speed increases from 30 mph to 50 mph.

2 What factors can affect the thinking distance?

3 What factors can affect the braking distance?

4 Using the data from the stopping distances in the Highway Code (page 100). Plot a graph of distance against speed (for both thinking distance and braking distance). Explain the shape of each line in as much detail as you can.

5 Look at the thinking distances shown in the diagram on the previous page. About how long is reaction time?

C From the graph, what is the braking distance, roughly, for 15 mph?

D From the graph, what is the braking distance, roughly, for 45 mph?

▲ Work is done when weights are lifted

A What is the relationship between work done and energy transferred?

B Give three examples of doing work.

Working hard?

In science, the term **work done** (or just 'work') has a very specific meaning. 'Work done' is another way of saying energy has been transferred or transformed. Lifting weights, as in the picture on the left, transfers energy to the weights. We can say work has been done on the weights.

$$\text{work done} = \text{energy transferred}$$

When you lift up the weights you might transfer 100 J of energy to them. This means the work done on the weights is 100 J. Work done, just like energy, is measured in **joules**. If no energy is transferred then no work is done.

Other examples of doing work include climbing stairs, pushing a trolley at a supermarket, or pulling a sledge along the ground. Work is always done when a force is used to move something through a distance against an opposing force.

How much work?

The amount of work done on an object depends on the force applied and the distance moved in the direction of the force.

$$\begin{array}{c}\text{work done} \\ \text{(newtons, N)}\end{array} = \begin{array}{c}\text{force} \\ \text{(metres, m)}\end{array} \times \begin{array}{c}\text{distance moved in the} \\ \text{direction of the force} \\ \text{(joules, J)}\end{array}$$

The distance moved must be in the same direction as the force. On the left of the diagram, the book has been lifted upwards against the gravitational force (weight) which acts downwards. On the right, the book has been lifted sideways and up, but it has been moved the same distance against the gravitational force of weight. The same amount of work has been done against the weight, so the same amount of energy has been transferred to the book.

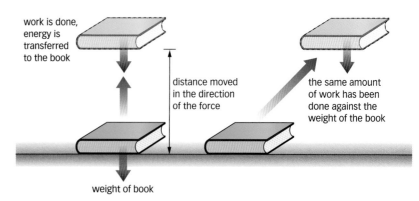

▲ When calculating work done, you use the distance moved in the direction of the force

Worked example

A TV with a weight of 300 N is lifted onto a wall mount 1.2 m from the ground. Calculate the work done.

work done = force × distance moved in the direction of the force

force = 300 N

distance moved in the direction of the force = 1.2 m

work done = 300 N × 1.2 m

= 360 J

'Watt' is power?

Power, like work, means something different in scientific language from its everyday use. A politician may be a very powerful person in terms of governing a country, but they are likely to be much less powerful physically than a honed athlete. In the scientific sense of transferring energy, a powerful person or device can do a lot of work in a short space of time. Power is the work done in a given time (or the rate of doing work).

A more powerful kettle will do more work in a certain time. It will transfer more electrical energy to heat every second. This means the water will boil quicker. A more powerful car transfers more chemical energy (in the fuel) into kinetic energy per second. This means it can accelerate more rapidly to a high speed.

Power is measured in **watts** (W). One watt is one joule of work done (or energy transferred) every second. A 1500 W hairdryer transfers 1500 J of energy every second. A large TV may have a power output of 120 W, an average family car 75 000 W, and an express train a huge 12 000 000 W.

◀ Express trains have a power output that is many times greater than that of a typical family car

Exam tip — OCR

✔ The distance moved must be in the direction of the force. For questions where objects are lifted, this is the vertical distance moved.

PRO*line*

MOD.:ST44

2450MHz

| 230V ~ 50Hz | MICROWAVE INPUT POWER | : 1550 W |
| | MICROWAVE ENERGY OUTPUT : | 950 W |

SERIAL NO.   81000138

MADE IN KOREA   CE

WARNING – HIGH VOLTAGE

▲ Different kettles have different power outputs. This one has a power of 950 W.

Questions

1 Name the units for work done and power. ↓ E

2 Calculate the work done to pull a sledge 80 m against a frictional force of 6.0 N ↓ C

3 How much work does a 200 W bulb do every second?

4 Explain why you do more work pulling a sledge uphill than along the flat.

5 A delivery driver lifts 20 boxes, each with a weight of 30 N, into the back of his truck 1.5 m above the ground. Find: ↓ A*

   (a) the work done on each box

   (b) the energy transferred to each box

   (c) the total work done lifting all the boxes into the truck.

Calculating power

The power of something depends on the work it can do in a certain time. A more powerful machine is one that does more work per second.

◄ A powerful sports car does more work per second than a standard car, allowing it to reach higher speeds more quickly

Learning objectives

After studying this topic, you should be able to:

✔ use the equation power = work done (or energy transferred) divided by time taken

✔ for an object moving at a steady speed use the equation power = force × speed

✔ relate the power of a car to its fuel consumption

A Calculate the power of a USB desk fan that does 300 J of work every 60 s.

If power is the work done in a given time (that is, the rate of doing work), then:

$$\text{power (watts, W)} = \frac{\text{work done (joules, J)}}{\text{time taken (seconds, s)}}$$

Exam tip  OCR

✔ When using the equations for power you must make sure time is in seconds. If it is in minutes, you will need to convert it to seconds.

Worked example 1

A man pushing a wheelbarrow does 400 J of work in 5 s. Calculate the power that he develops.

$$\text{power (W)} = \frac{\text{work done (J)}}{\text{time taken (s)}}$$

work done = 400 J, and time taken = 5 s, so

$$\text{power} = \frac{400 \text{ J}}{5 \text{ s}} = 80 \text{ W}$$

Worked example 2

An electric shower transfers 540 000 J of energy to the water in 1 minute. Calculate its power.

$$\text{power (W)} = \frac{\text{energy transferred (J)}}{\text{time taken (s)}}$$

energy transferred = 540 000 J and time taken = 60 s (as it took 1 minute)

$$\text{power} = \frac{540\,000 \text{ J}}{60 \text{ s}} = 9000 \text{ W or 9 kW}$$

▲ A cyclist does work against air resistance and friction just to maintain a constant speed

When an object moves at a steady speed, it has to push against resistive forces such as air resistance and friction. When you are cycling you can feel these forces. Cyclists have to do work – they have to pedal just to stay at the same speed. How much work does the cyclist have to do? You already know that:

$$\text{work done} = \begin{array}{c} \text{force provided by} \\ \text{the cyclist against} \\ \text{the resistive forces} \end{array} \times \begin{array}{c} \text{distance moved in} \\ \text{the direction of} \\ \text{the force} \end{array}$$

In any one second, the work done by the cyclist is the power (power = work done/time taken), and the distance moved in the direction of the force is given by speed × time taken (since speed = distance/time taken).

So for any one second, the work equation becomes:

$$\begin{array}{ccccc} \text{power} & = & \text{force} & \times & \text{speed} \\ \text{(watts, W)} & & \text{(newtons, N)} & & \text{(metres per second, m/s)} \end{array}$$

For any object travelling at a steady speed, the power needed to maintain this speed depends on the speed required and the resistive forces.

Travelling faster, or working against a larger force (for example if the cyclist is not streamlined), needs more power. The cyclist has to do more work per second.

Vehicle power

Different vehicles have different power outputs. A lorry will have a larger and more powerful engine than a typical car. This is because the lorry has to do more work to move its mass up hills, or to work against friction. Even cars have a wide range of engine sizes. Usually, the greater the engine size, the more powerful the car.

> **B** Explain why a lorry has a larger engine than a typical car.

In general, the more powerful the vehicle, the less economical it is. The engine does more work per second and so uses more fuel. More powerful cars have higher top speeds, but their extra fuel consumption is bad for the environment and results in a more expensive fuel bill.

Questions

1 List two disadvantages of having a car with a larger, more powerful, engine. ↓E

2 A hi-fi system does 24 000 J of work in 2 minutes. Calculate the power of the system.

3 A crane lifts a 50 000 N concrete block 20 m into the air in 40 seconds. Calculate the power of the crane. ↓C

4 A cyclist has a power meter on her bike to tell her about her performance. It is showing a steady reading of 200 W. How much work is she doing every second?

5 Calculate the power from an express train travelling at 25 m/s working against frictional forces of 10 000 000 N. ↓A*

6 A 40 W bulb is left on. Calculate the energy transferred in:
   (a) 10 seconds
   (b) 30 minutes
   (c) 24 hours.

▲ Horses can transfer more energy per second than a human being. They have an average power output of 750 W.

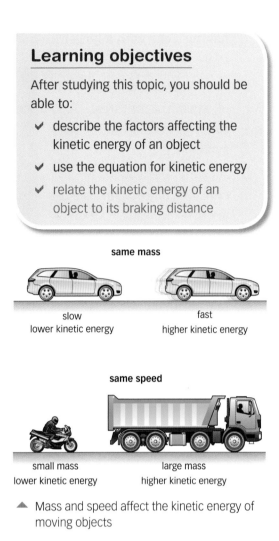

same mass

slow
lower kinetic energy

fast
higher kinetic energy

same speed

small mass
lower kinetic energy

large mass
higher kinetic energy

▲ Mass and speed affect the kinetic energy of moving objects

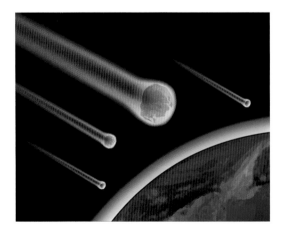

▲ Because of their large mass and high speed, meteorites can have enormous kinetic energy

Kinetic energy

Any moving object has energy due to its motion. This is its **kinetic energy** (or KE). Sprinters running the 100 metres, butterflies flying to the next flower, and fighter aircraft intercepting unknown radar contacts, all have kinetic energy. In fact, anything moving has kinetic energy. If an object is not moving it has zero kinetic energy.

▲ A faster moving sprinter has a higher kinetic energy

> **A** Give three everyday examples of objects with kinetic energy.

The size of an object's kinetic energy depends on the mass of the object and the speed at which it is travelling. The kinetic energy of the object will increase if the object has
• a greater mass
• a higher speed (moves faster).

> **B** Which two factors affect the kinetic energy of an object?

Calculating kinetic energy

This is the equation that links kinetic energy, mass and speed:

kinetic energy = $\frac{1}{2}$ × mass × speed²
(joules, J)   (kilograms, kg)   (metres per second, m/s)²

Worked example 1

Find the kinetic energy of a car of mass 1200 kg travelling at 20 m/s.

kinetic energy = $\frac{1}{2}$ × mass × speed²

mass of the car = 1200 kg and speed of the car = 20 m/s

kinetic energy = $\frac{1}{2}$ × 1200 kg × (20 m/s)²

= $\frac{1}{2}$ × 1200 × 400

= 240 000 J or 240 kJ

Did you know...?

If you increase the speed of an object, its kinetic energy increases much more dramatically. This is why if a car's speed doubles, it takes much more than double the distance to stop. As you know, the braking distance increases as any vehicle gets faster. For a typical car travelling at 30 mph the braking distance is 14 m; at 60 mph it has gone up to 55 m!

Worked example 2

A tennis ball has a mass of 60 g. A professional tennis player can serve the ball so that it leaves the racket with a kinetic energy of 75 J. Calculate the speed of the tennis ball when it leaves the racket.

kinetic energy = $\frac{1}{2}$ × mass × speed²

$$speed = \sqrt{\frac{kinetic\ energy}{\frac{1}{2} \times mass}}$$

mass of the ball = 60 g (0.06 kg) and kinetic energy of the serve = 75 J

$$speed = \sqrt{\frac{75\ J}{\frac{1}{2} \times 0.06\ kg}} = \sqrt{\frac{75}{0.03}} = 50\ m/s$$

Exam tip

✔ When using the equation for kinetic energy, that is, kinetic energy = $\frac{1}{2}$ × mass × speed², don't forget to square the speed!

Questions

1 Explain why a book placed on a shelf has a kinetic energy of 0 J.

2 Three identical cars all have the same mass. Car A is travelling at 10 m/s, car B at 30 m/s and car C at 12 m/s. Which one has the greatest kinetic energy? Explain your answer.

3 Find the kinetic energy of a football of mass 0.4 kg travelling at 20 m/s.

4 Explain why, in terms of energy, the braking distance of a vehicle increases dramatically as it gets faster.

5 Calculate the speed of a horse of mass 600 kg with a kinetic energy of 43 200 J.

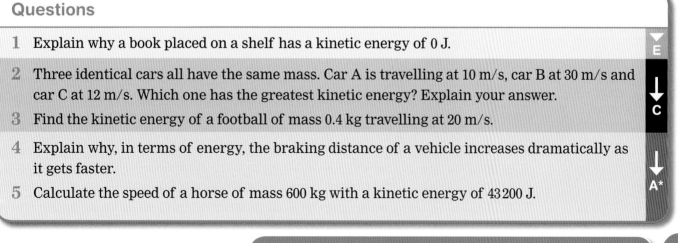

▲ Fossil fuels such as petrol and diesel are widely available in the UK

A Name two fossil fuels used in car engines.

B Give an advantage of using a vehicle powered by biofuels.

▲ Driving aggressively increases fuel consumption

Just stopping to get some fossil fuel …

Most of the cars you see on the road today use fossil fuels. They have either petrol or diesel engines. Both petrol and diesel are derived from crude oil and are forms of **fossil fuel**.

The fuel is burned inside the engine of the car. The heat released is converted into kinetic energy, to drive the car forwards, and electrical energy to power the radio, headlights and other electrical devices inside the car.

Using cars powered by fossil fuels increases the amount of carbon dioxide (CO_2) in our atmosphere. Cars are a major contributor to global warming. Some vehicles are now being designed to run on **biofuels** (such as biodiesel). Burning bio fuels also releases carbon dioxide into the atmosphere. However, unlike burning fossil fuels, this does not cause an overall increase in carbon dioxide. While it was alive, the plant that was used to make the biofuel absorbed the same amount of carbon dioxide that is released when it is burnt.

◄ Biofuels are being used more often to fuel vehicles

The amount of fuel used by a car is called its **fuel consumption**. Usually this is measured in miles per gallon (or mpg). A car which does 40 mpg will, on average, travel 40 miles for each gallon of fuel used. A more efficient car will travel further on the same fuel and so have a higher mpg.

The shape of a vehicle will affect its fuel consumption (and also the highest speed that it can reach). Sports cars are wedge-shaped for better streamlining, and lorries and cars pulling caravans often have deflectors for the same reason. Having a roof box on a car or driving with the windows open makes the car's shape less streamlined, increasing air resistance and fuel consumption.

Actual fuel consumption varies, depending on, for example:

- Energy needed to increase the kinetic energy of the car. This depends on the mass of the car and its contents. The greater the mass, the more fuel is required.
- Work done against resistive forces such as friction and air resistance. More streamlined cars have lower fuel consumption.
- Speed and driving style of the driver. Rapid acceleration increases the amount of fuel used.
- Road conditions. Driving in heavy rain tends to lead to more fuel being consumed per mile.

Electric vehicles

The number of electric vehicles is growing. These store energy in large batteries, and it is these batteries that power the car.

Instead of an engine, they have an electric motor which drives the car forward. As there is no burning involved, electric cars do not produce any pollution in the places where they are used. However, when the batteries run low, they must be recharged. As most of the electricity in the UK is produced by burning fossil fuels in power stations, powering an electric car still causes pollution, just not where the car is being used.

Solar-powered cars

There are several experimental cars that are powered by light from the Sun. These solar-powered cars have batteries which can be recharged directly from the Sun. They store enough energy during the day to allow the car to be driven at night.

Even though these cars do not pollute when they are being used, pollution is still produced when they are manufactured. Over the lifetime of a solar-powered car though, and even of a simpler electric car, less carbon dioxide might be emitted compared with a traditional car. This could lead to a reduction in our overall carbon dioxide emissions.

Key words
fossil fuel, biofuel, fuel consumption

Did you know...?

As the supply of fossil fuels becomes more limited, we may need to rely more and more on biofuels and solar-powered cars in future. Your first car might be powered by biodiesel, or even plain vegetable oil!

▲ An experimental car powered only by sunlight

Questions

1 Describe how fossil fuels are used to power some vehicles. ↓ E

2 Explain the differences in fuel consumption between a car which does 20 mpg and one which does 45 mpg. ↓ C

3 Explain what it means when we say that electric cars don't produce pollution at their point of use.

4 State and explain three factors which affect the fuel consumption of a typical car. ↓ A*

Learning objectives

After studying this topic, you should be able to:

✔ define and calculate momentum

✔ calculate the forces acting when an object stops suddenly

Key words

momentum

▲ The momentum of this runner depends on his velocity and his mass

A A woman with a mass of 60 kg is skydiving and has a velocity of 45 m/s. What is her momentum?

B A football has a momentum of 11 250 kg m/s and a mass of 450 g. What is its velocity?

Momentum of a body

A moving object does not just have kinetic energy. It has another property called **momentum**, which is related to the mass and the velocity of the object. You can calculate momentum using the equation:

$$\underset{\text{(kg m/s)}}{\text{momentum}} = \underset{\text{(kg)}}{\text{mass}} \times \underset{\text{(m/s)}}{\text{velocity}}$$

If an object is not moving, it does not have any momentum as it has no velocity. In the same way, an object cannot have momentum if it has no mass. The greater the mass or velocity of an object, the more momentum it has. Momentum has direction as well as magnitude. The momentum of an object takes the same direction as the direction of motion of an object. If a car is travelling forwards, its momentum will also be acting forwards.

Worked example 1

A person is cycling at 12 m/s. The mass of the person and the bicycle is 95 kg. What is the momentum of the person and bicycle?

momentum = mass × velocity

= 95 kg × 12 m/s

= 1140 kg m/s

Changing the subject of the momentum equation

The equation used to calculate momentum can be rearranged to calculate either the mass or the velocity of an object.

Worked example 2

A car has a mass of 1500 kg and a momentum of 37 500 kg m/s. What is the velocity of the car?

momentum = mass × velocity

$$\frac{\text{momentum}}{\text{mass}} = \text{mass} \times \frac{\text{velocity}}{\text{mass}}$$

$$\frac{\text{momentum}}{\text{mass}} = \cancel{\text{mass}} \times \frac{\text{velocity}}{\cancel{\text{mass}}}$$

$$\frac{\text{momentum}}{37\,500} = \text{velocity}$$

$$\frac{37\,500}{1500} = 25 \text{ m/s}$$

Change of momentum

When the momentum of an object changes, there is a force on the object that is given by the equation:

$$\text{force} = \frac{\text{change in momentum}}{\text{time}}$$

If change in momentum happens in a short time, the forces on an object can be very large. Using Newton's second law of motion, we can see that the deceleration of the object will also be high. This states $F = ma$ (see P3.5). If the change in momentum happens in a short time the object will experience a large acceleration or deceleration. From Newton's second law this requires a large force. If the acceleration is small, the change in momentum will take place over a longer time and so a smaller force is required.

Questions

1 What is the momentum of an object?

2 A ball has a momentum of 15 kg m/s and is travelling at 30 m/s. What is the mass of the ball?

3 (a) How does a crumple zone reduce the impact of a crash?

   (b) How does this protect the occupants of a car in a crash?

4 A car of mass 1200 kg is travelling at 15 m/s. It stops in 0.1 seconds. What is the force on the car?

5 A car is moving at 20 m/s and crashes. It comes to a stop in 0.02 seconds.

   (a) What is the force on a person with a mass of 75 kg?

   (b) A crumple zone increases the time an occupant takes to come to a stop to 0.1 seconds. How much does this reduce the force on a 75 kg person?

   (c) How does this link to Newton's second law of motion?

C A skydiver has momentum 375 kg m/s and stops in 0.75 seconds. What is the force on the skydiver?

Worked example 3

The bicycle in worked example 1 stops quickly in 0.5 seconds when it hits a wall. What is the force on the bicycle?

$$\text{force} = \frac{\text{change in momentum}}{\text{time}}$$

change in momentum = 1140 kg m/s

$$\text{force} = \frac{1140 \text{ kg m/s}}{0.5 \text{ s}} = 2280 \text{ N}$$

Worked example 4

The bicycle from the previous examples has a mass of 95 kg including its rider. What is its acceleration?

Newton's second law states:

$$\text{force} = \text{mass} \times \text{acceleration}$$

$$F = M \times a$$

force = 2280 N, mass = 95 kg

$$\frac{\text{force}}{\text{mass}} = \cancel{\text{mass}} \times \frac{\text{acceleration}}{\cancel{\text{mass}}}$$

$$\text{acceleration} = \frac{2280}{95} = 24 \text{ m/s}^2$$

Exam tip OCR

- ✓ Remember that momentum is mass multiplied by velocity, so the units are the units for mass (kg) multiplied by velocity (m/s), which gives kg m/s. Mass must also be given in kilograms, not grams.

Learning objectives

After studying this topic, you should be able to:

✔ describe some safety features of cars

✔ evaluate the effectiveness of safety features

✔ describe how anti-lock braking systems work

Key words

airbag, ABS brakes, traction control, paddle controls

> A What features of a car help to protect you in a crash?

▲ Car brakes absorb some of the energy of a collision as they slow the car down. They transfer the collision energy into heat.

Protecting passengers in a collision

In a collision such as a car crash, there is a sudden change in momentum. A large force can be exerted on passengers by rapid deceleration, causing injuries. Seatbelts, crumple zones, and airbags in cars help reduce injuries in a crash by reducing momentum more gradually. Each of these features also absorbs some of the energy of the collision and transfers it into a less dangerous form.

Safety feature	How it works in a crash	Use of collision energy
Seatbelt	Stretches, rather than holding a passenger completely rigid.	Used to stretch the seatbelt fibres.
Crumple zone	Bends, absorbing some of the energy of the collision rather than resisting it as a stiffer piece of metal would.	Used to bend the metal in the crumple zone.
Airbag	Creates an air filled cushion to slow the passenger gently, ensuring they don't hit the solid steering wheel or car interior.	Used to slowly force the gas in the air bag out once the passenger has hit it.
Collapsible steering column	Bends, absorbing some of the energy of the collision rather than resisting it as a completely rigid steering column would.	Used to bend the steering column.

Seatbelts have to be replaced after a crash because they stretch during the accident and do not return to their original shape. In another crash they would not stretch when needed, and as a result they would not be able to absorb any of the energy of the collision.

Sudden change in momentum means a greater resultant force. The car safety features in the table above allow the occupants to keep moving slightly longer. For example, the seatbelt takes time to stretch and bring the passenger to a stop, allowing the change in momentum to take place over a longer period. This reduces the force acting, and reduces the injuries the passenger may suffer. Airbags and crumple zones work on the same principle.

Preventing accidents

Cars now contain many safety features that are intended to help prevent accidents altogether.

Safety feature	How it prevents accidents
ABS (Anti-lock Braking System) brakes	Helps to stop the wheels of a car locking into a skid when too much force is applied by the driver, making sure the wheel remains in contact with the road.
Traction control	Compensates for any differences between the grip of the car's four wheels on the road surface, such as when one wheel hits some ice. Loss or differences in grip of one wheel of a car can lead to the driver losing control.
Electric windows	Stop a driver being distracted by winding a window handle, and reduce the amount of time the driver's hands need to be off the wheel.
Paddle controls	Found around the steering wheels of cars, these are usually used to control the radio or sometimes to change gear. They reduce the amount of time drivers need to take their hands off the wheel, and prevent the driver looking away from the road at the radio display while driving.

Car safety features – risks and benefits

Car safety features reduce the forces acting in a collision by
- increasing the time taken for the passengers to stop, or the time taken for the collision to happen
- increasing the stopping or collision distance
- decreasing the acceleration of passengers.

Seatbelts can save lives in road collisions. However, they can damage internal organs, and even fracture vertebrae. Many countries have laws requiring everyone to wear a seatbelt while driving. People had to weigh the benefits of wearing seatbelts against the potential risks.

To design new safety features, data is gathered at real crash sites and analysed. Scientists and engineers investigate accident cause and prevention. Data from crash test dummies is used to analyse the benefits and risks of new safety features.

B Why is a paddle control a safety feature?

ABS brakes

ABS brakes help drivers control cars in hazardous situations (such as when braking hard in an emergency or going into a skid). They sense that the wheels are about to lock and reduce the pressure on the brake pads for a fraction of a second, so that the wheel can keep moving. They then reapply the pressure. ABS brakes pump on and off like this repeatedly until the vehicle stops. ABS brakes can reduce stopping distances on dry and slippery surfaces. In some cases (such as on loose surfaces like gravel) they increase the stopping distance but can improve control of the vehicle.

Questions

1 List car safety features designed to prevent accidents.

2 Why do seatbelts have to be replaced after a crash?

3 How do car safety features reduce the forces on passengers in a crash?

E
C
A*

Worked example

A large bag of rice has a mass of 2 kg. What is its weight?

$$weight = mass \times \text{gravitational field strength}$$

$$= 2\,kg \times 10\,N/kg$$

$$= 20\,N$$

Exam tip OCR

✔ In everyday life, when you talk about someone's weight, you usually mean their mass. Make sure you use these terms correctly.

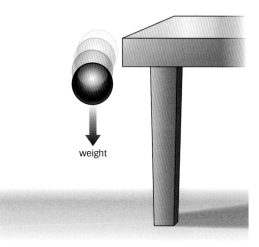

weight

▲ The resultant force on this ball is downwards

Weight

When you drop an object, it falls directly towards the ground. It falls because of the gravitational attraction between the object and the earth. The force from the Earth's gravitational field is called **weight**.

The weight of an object depends on

• its mass (the amount of matter) in kilograms (kg)

• the **gravitational field strength** in newtons/kilogram (N/kg).

The equation linking weight, mass, and gravitational field strength is:

$$\begin{array}{ccc} \text{weight of object} & = & \text{mass of object} \times \text{gravitational field strength} \\ \text{(newtons, N)} & & \text{(kilograms, kg)} \quad \text{(newtons per kilogram, N/kg)} \end{array}$$

The Earth's gravitational field strength is about 10 N/kg.

It is also called the **acceleration due to gravity**. It is the same for any object at a particular point on the surface of the Earth. It is often shown by the symbol g.

The gravitational field strength on Earth is not affected by changes in the atmosphere, such as wind or rain. It depends only on the mass of the Earth. However, it does vary slightly at different points on the Earth's surface.

A A car has a mass of 1450 kg. What is its weight?

Falling under gravity

If there is nothing to stop an object falling, the force of its weight, in other words gravity, will cause it to start moving downwards towards the Earth.

The ball in the diagram has just begun to fall from the table. The force of gravity makes the ball accelerate downwards. As the ball falls, its speed continues to increase.

Air resistance or 'drag'

However, when something is falling through the air, there is a frictional force in the opposite direction due to air resistance, called 'drag'. As the speed increases, the size of the opposing drag force increases.

The diagram on the right shows what happens to a falling leaf. When the leaf first begins to fall, the upward force due to air resistance, or drag, is low. As the speed of the leaf increases, so does the drag. The downward force from the weight of the leaf stays the same.

There is also an upward drag force on the ball described on the previous page, but because of the shape of the ball, the drag is not as noticeable.

Drag and moving through a fluid

Whenever an object moves through a **fluid** such as air or water, there is a drag force on the object due to friction. The faster an object moves through the fluid, the greater the frictional force which acts on it in the opposite direction.

Drag affects all objects moving through fluids, such as the leaf falling through air above, or a speedboat moving through water. For example, you can hit a badminton shuttlecock very hard. The shuttlecock will move quickly to begin with and then slow down rapidly because of drag.

No fluid, no drag

In places where there is no atmosphere, such as the Moon, there is no drag force on a moving object. This was famously shown by one lunar astronaut, who dropped a feather and a hammer at the same time. Both hit the ground simultaneously.

In the time-lapse picture on the right there is no upward force due to air resistance, which would affect the feather more than the ball. They are accelerating at the same rate.

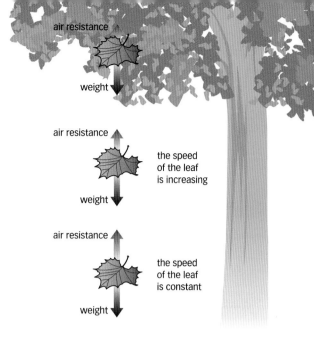

▲ As the leaf falls more quickly (accelerates due to gravitational attraction), the air resistance or 'drag' gets bigger

> **B** What happens to the drag as the leaf falls more quickly?

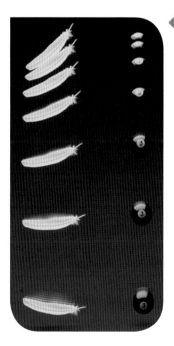

◀ The feather and ball are falling in a vacuum

Questions

1 What is the weight of an object?

2 Describe the motion of a pen falling to the floor.

3 Calculate the weight of each of the following:
   (a) a table with mass 25 kg
   (b) an elephant with mass 692 kg.

4 Alex says that his weight is 65 kg. Explain why he is wrong.

5 An object has a weight of 12 N. What is its mass?

Key words

weight, gravitational field strength, acceleration due to gravity, fluid

A What forces are acting on the skydiver in the pictures?

B What is the terminal speed of a falling object?

C What can you say about the forces acting on anything moving at a terminal speed?

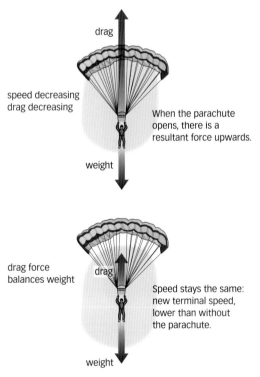

When the parachute opens, there is a resultant force upwards.

drag

speed decreasing drag decreasing

weight

drag force balances weight

drag

Speed stays the same: new terminal speed, lower than without the parachute.

weight

▲ Using a parachute reduces the terminal speed

Terminal speed

You already know that when something begins to fall downwards, it is accelerated due to gravity and its speed increases. As the speed increases, the upward force of drag or air resistance increases, as shown for the skydiver in the diagram.

The skydiver's weight stays constant, so the resultant force downwards decreases as the speed gets bigger. There is still a resultant force downwards though, causing acceleration, so the skydiver's speed is still getting bigger.

Eventually the speed and so the drag increase to a point where the skydiver's's weight is balanced by the upward drag force. The resultant force is zero and the skydiver will not accelerate any more. The skydiver will fall at the same speed. This steady speed is called **terminal speed**.

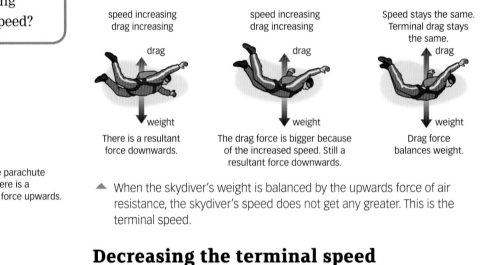

speed increasing drag increasing

drag

weight

There is a resultant force downwards.

speed increasing drag increasing

drag

weight

The drag force is bigger because of the increased speed. Still a resultant force downwards.

Speed stays the same. Terminal drag stays the same.

drag

weight

Drag force balances weight.

▲ When the skydiver's weight is balanced by the upwards force of air resistance, the skydiver's speed does not get any greater. This is the terminal speed.

Decreasing the terminal speed

When the skydiver opens a parachute, the upward force of air resistance increases. This means that there is a resultant force upwards, so there is also an acceleration upwards. The skydiver's speed decreases.

As the speed gets smaller, the upward drag force also decreases. So the resultant force upwards is less and the acceleration upwards also gets less.

The resultant upward force and upward acceleration are still there, though. The skydiver's speed still gets less and so the force of air resistance also keeps decreasing.

Eventually the air resistance and the weight of the skydiver are balanced. So the resultant force is zero again, and the skydiver's speed downwards now stays the same. This is a new terminal speed. The new terminal speed is much lower than the terminal speed without a parachute.

> **D** What effect does using a parachute have on terminal speed?

Moving horizontally

So far we have been looking only at falling objects. But cars or ships, for example, that move horizontally can also have a terminal speed.

The boat shown on the right reaches its terminal speed when the drag force from the water balances the driving force or thrust from the engine. If the thrust is the biggest force that the engine is capable of, then this terminal speed is the top speed that the boat can travel at.

Shape and drag

The shape of an object affects the amount of drag on the object. This affects its terminal speed. The larger the area, the greater the drag. Falling parachutists want their terminal speed to be very low, and so their parachutes have a very large area.

A racing driver might want the terminal speed of their car to be as high as possible. Racing cars are designed to minimise the forces due to drag. They have a streamlined shape so that air can flow over them more easily. This means that they can reach a higher terminal speed than a car that has the same thrust force but meets greater air resistance forces.

The drag on vehicles affects their fuel consumption. A more streamlined vehicle will use less fuel when travelling at the same speed as a less streamlined vehicle.

> **E** How does shape affect terminal speed?

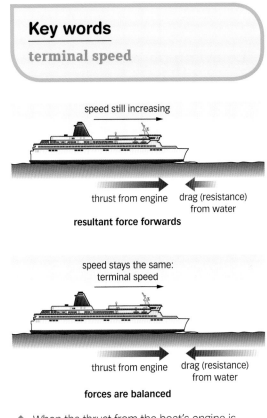

speed still increasing

thrust from engine   drag (resistance) from water

resultant force forwards

speed stays the same: terminal speed

thrust from engine   drag (resistance) from water

forces are balanced

▲ When the thrust from the boat's engine is balanced by the drag force from the water, the boat does not go any faster. It has reached a terminal speed.

Questions

1 What is drag?

2 A stone is falling down through pondwater at a constant speed. What do you know about the forces acting on the stone?

3 How does a parachute reduce a skydiver's terminal speed?

4 How will the shape of the ferry shown in the diagram affect its fuel consumption?

5 Explain how objects reach a terminal speed.

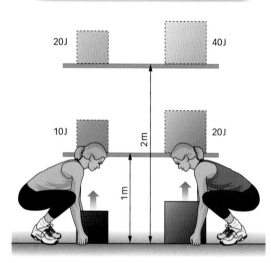

▲ The change in gravitational potential energy depends on the mass of the object and the change in height

◀ Bungee jumpers have a great deal of stored gravitational potential energy. When they jump this gets converted to kinetic energy at first. (What happens then to the kinetic energy?)

Gravitational potential energy

When you lift up a book and place it on a shelf, you are doing work on the book. The book gains **gravitational potential energy** (or GPE) as it is lifted away from the ground. The GPE of an object is the energy it has because of its position in a gravitational field, like the one around the Earth. This energy depends on the mass of the object, its height above the ground and the strength of the gravitational field.

> **A** Apart from gravitational field strength, which two factors affect the GPE of an object?

The higher you lift an object above the ground, or the greater the mass of the object, the greater its GPE.

- more mass = more GPE
- more height = more GPE

To calculate any change in GPE we can use this equation:

$$\begin{array}{c}\text{change in}\\\text{GPE}\\\text{(joules, J)}\end{array} = \begin{array}{c}\text{mass}\\\text{(kilograms, kg)}\end{array} \times \begin{array}{c}\text{gravitational}\\\text{field strength}\\\text{(newtons per}\\\text{kilogram, N/kg)}\end{array} \times \begin{array}{c}\text{change in}\\\text{height}\\\text{(metres, m)}\end{array}$$

On Earth, the gravitational field strength is 10 N/kg.

Worked example

Find the change in GPE when a book of mass 1.2 kg is lifted 1.5 m and placed on a shelf.

change in GPE = mass × gravitational field strength × change in height

change in GPE = $m \times g \times h$

mass of book = 1.2 kg, gravitational field strength on Earth = 10 N/kg, and change in height = 1.5 m.

change in GPE = 1.2 kg × 10 N/kg × 1.5 m
        = 18 J

> **B** A person of mass 60 kg runs up a flight of stairs 3.0 m high. Calculate their change in GPE.

GPE of falling objects

If you knock an object such as a book off the desk, you can see it accelerate towards the ground. It loses GPE as it gets closer to the ground. This energy is not lost; it is transferred to the kinetic energy (KE) of the book. The closer it gets to the ground, the lower the book's GPE and the greater its KE: the book gets faster as it gets nearer the ground.

Assuming that no energy is transferred to the surroundings, then the GPE an object has at the moment when it is dropped is equal to its KE just before it hits the ground.

If a ball has a GPE of 200 J when it is dropped, then it will have a KE of 200 J just before it hits the ground.

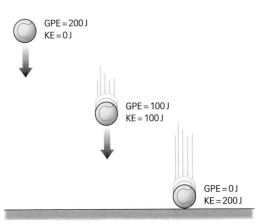

▲ When the ball is dropped, the gravitational potential energy is converted to kinetic energy

In most cases a small amount of energy is transferred to the surroundings. An extreme example of this is when a parachutist falls at their terminal speed. They are still losing GPE, but they are not gaining any KE as they are not getting faster. Where does the energy go? As the parachutist falls, friction with the air transfers the lost GPE to the surroundings. The air around the parachutist gains internal or thermal energy and so increases in temperature.

▲ At terminal speed, the gravitational potential energy is converted into thermal energy and transferred to the surroundings

Questions

1   State the equation for change in GPE and give all the units.

2   Calculate the change in GPE when a crane lifts a 3000 kg concrete block 40 m into the air.

3   Describe the energy changes when a tennis ball is dropped to the ground.

4   Explain what happens to the GPE of an object falling at its terminal velocity.

5   An escalator carries a person with a mass of 80 kg up from the lower level of a shopping centre. The person gains 24 000 J of GPE. Calculate the height of the escalator.

Key words

gravitational potential energy

Change in factor	Effect on kinetic energy
double the mass	double the kinetic energy
double the speed	increase kinetic energy by four times

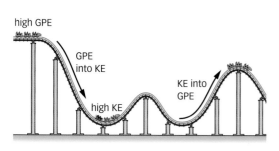

▲ An exciting way to convert GPE into kinetic energy!

▲ The energy changes on a simple roller-coaster

Changing kinetic energy

Any moving object has kinetic energy (or KE). The size of the kinetic energy depends on the mass of the object and the speed it is travelling at. An object with a greater mass will have more kinetic energy. An object that is moving faster will have more kinetic energy.

However, the relationship is not the same for each factor. Increasing the speed has a much larger effect on kinetic energy.

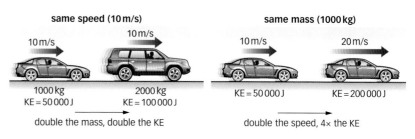

▲ Changing the mass or speed of the car changes the kinetic energy. However, changing the speed has the greater effect.

A What happens to the kinetic energy of an object if its mass doubles?

B What happens to the kinetic energy of an object if its speed doubles?

The roller-coaster

A ride on a roller-coaster is exciting because it is designed to provide large changes in kinetic energy. The changes in speed provide the thrilling ride.

All roller-coasters convert gravitational potential energy (GPE) into kinetic energy. The track has some large drops. When the roller-coaster cars move over these drops, their GPE is converted into kinetic energy. Bigger drops cause a larger change in GPE. They provide a greater increase in kinetic energy and so larger drops cause the cars to move much faster.

The opposite happens when the cars go up the slopes. Here the kinetic energy of the cars is converted back to GPE as they climb higher above the ground.

Calculations with GPE and kinetic energy

Mathematically, as the GPE is converted into kinetic energy we can say:

change in gravitational potential energy $=$ change in kinetic energy

$$mgh = \frac{1}{2}mv^2$$

where m is mass, g is acceleration due to gravity, h is height, and v is speed.

As mass is a common factor on both sides, it cancels to give

$$gh = \frac{1}{2}v^2$$

This can be rearranged to give

$$h = \frac{v^2}{2g}$$

Providing we know the speed of the object, we can use this equation to calculate the height from which it was dropped. This is often done using light gates, which can record the speed of an object passing through them.

The equation can be rearranged further to find the speed of a falling object dropped from any height.

Did you know...?

The Kinda Ka roller-coaster in the US is the fastest free fall roller-coaster in the world, with the biggest drops. It uses hydraulic ramps to push a car up to an eye-watering 120 mph before rolling them up an incredible 130 m and dropping them down the other side!

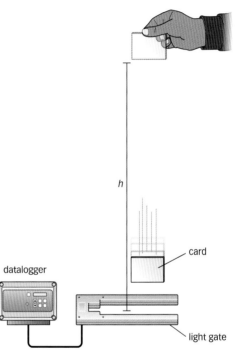

datalogger

card

light gate

▲ By measuring the speed of the card, we can calculate the height it was dropped from

Questions

1 Name the two factors that affect the kinetic energy of an object. Changing which one has the greatest effect on the kinetic energy of a moving object?

↓ E

2 Sketch a simple roller-coaster and label the energy changes that happen at different sections.

3 Explain why roller-coaster cars move faster after travelling down larger drops.

↓ C

4 A ball hits the ground at 16 m/s. Find the height it was dropped from.

5 Using the GPE and kinetic energy equations show, by rearranging them, how $h = \frac{v^2}{2g}$, where h is height, v is speed and g is acceleration due to gravity.

↓ A*

Exam tip

✔ Increasing the mass or the speed of an object increases its kinetic energy, and increasing the speed has the greatest effect.

Module summary

Revision checklist

- Speed can be calculated using the equation, speed = distance/time. This principle is used in speed cameras.
- Acceleration is a change in speed, and can be positive (speeding up) or negative (slowing down).
- Velocity describes the direction in which something is moving, as well as its speed. Two moving objects have relative velocity.
- The gradient of a speed–time graph represents acceleration. The area under a speed–time graph represents distance travelled.
- Forces change the way an object moves, and can affect both speed and direction. Force = mass × acceleration.
- Stopping distance (thinking distance plus braking distance) is affected by speed, road and vehicle conditions, and driver reaction time.
- Work done on an object (measured in joules) is equal to the energy transferred to it. Work done = force × distance moved in the direction of the force.
- Power (measured in watts) is the rate at which work is done. Power = work done/time taken.
- An object's kinetic energy is defined by its mass and its speed.
- Non-renewable fossil fuels increase the levels of CO_2 in the atmosphere. Biofuels used as alternative vehicle fuels also release CO_2 when burnt, but this is balanced by the amount of CO_2 absorbed by the plants used to make the bio-fuel.
- Electric vehicles may be powered using energy (from mains electricity or from the Sun) stored in large batteries.
- Momentum = mass × velocity.
- Force = change in momentum/time.
- Car safety features designed to protect passengers include seatbelts, crumple zones, air bags, and collapsible steering columns.
- Car safety features to prevent crashes include ABS brakes, traction control, electric windows, and paddle controls.
- Weight is the force from the Earth's gravitational field. Weight = mass of object × gravitational field strength.
- The speed of an object falling under gravity will increase until the upward force of air resistance (drag) balances the downward force of the object's weight at a terminal speed.
- An object's gravitational potential energy (GPE) is defined by its mass, height above the ground, and Earth's gravity. GPE is transferred into kinetic energy (KE).

thinking distance + braking distance

stopping distance

distance (m)

distance–time graph

average speed

speed (m/s)

cameras

ABS braking, paddle controls

NOW USE THE P3 GRADE CHECKER ON PAGE 244

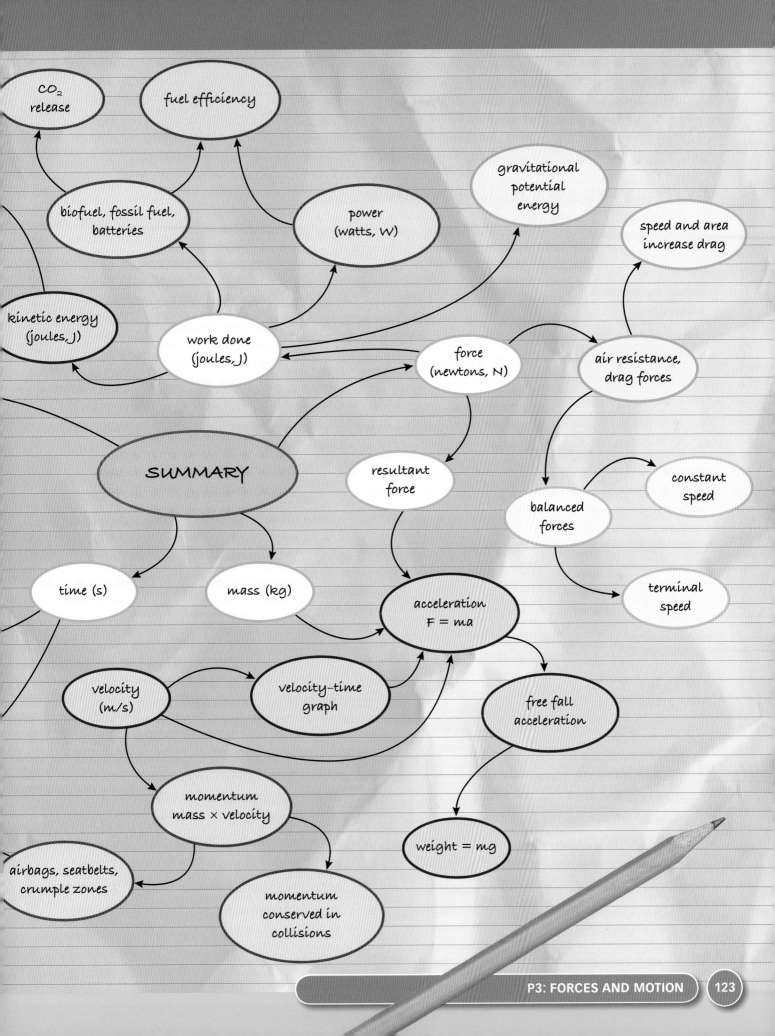

CO₂ release

fuel efficiency

gravitational potential energy

speed and area increase drag

biofuel, fossil fuel, batteries

power (watts, W)

kinetic energy (joules, J)

work done (joules, J)

force (newtons, N)

air resistance, drag forces

SUMMARY

resultant force

constant speed

balanced forces

time (s)

mass (kg)

acceleration F = ma

terminal speed

velocity (m/s)

velocity-time graph

free fall acceleration

momentum mass × velocity

weight = mg

airbags, seatbelts, crumple zones

momentum conserved in collisions

Answering Extended Writing questions

QUESTION

The graph shows the speed of fall of a skydiver at various stages of a descent.

Explain the motion of the skydiver at each of the stages A–E on the graph.

The quality of written communication will be assessed in your answer to this question.

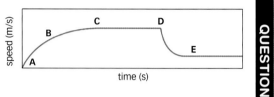

At A she has jumpd out and is speeding up At B are resistance is slowwing her down, C is terminal spede. At D she opens the parachute, goes up for a bit till her chute is fuly open and at E she comes down a good desent and lands.

E

Examiner: This answer shows only vague understanding of the physics, though some words are used correctly. There is again almost no mention of forces, and the actual motion at D is misunderstood. There is some irrelevant information. Spelling, punctuation, and grammar are erratic.

At A she has just left the aeroplane, speeding up. At B there is air resistence, so she slows down a bit. At C she has reached terminal speed. She opens her parachute at D, slows down. By E she has reached terminal speed with her parachute open.

C

Examiner: Most but not all of the physics is correct – at B she is not slowing down (though this is a common mistake). Answer includes little about forces acting, which is crucial to the explanations. There are occasional errors in spelling, punctuation, and grammar.

At A she is accelerating quickly, as air resistance is low. At B she is moving faster, so air resistance is higher, so resultant force and acceleration are lower. At C air resistance equals weight, she is at terminal speed. At D she opens parachute – area and so air resistance increase greatly, so she decelerates. At E she has reached new lower terminal speed.

A*

Examiner: This answer refers to both forces and consequent acceleration at each stage – sometimes by implication. No link is made between acceleration and the gradient of the graph, though this is implied. The physics explanations and the use of words are all correct. Spelling, punctuation, and grammar are all good.

Exam-style questions

1 Match these quantities with their units.

A01

force	m/s
mass	m
acceleration	J
velocity	m/s²
kinetic energy	N
distance	W
power	kg

2 This is a velocity/time graph for a tube train moving between stations.

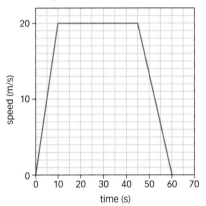

a How long did the journey take altogether?

b Calculate the acceleration in the time 0–10 s.

c Calculate the acceleration in the time 45 s–60 s.

d Describe what is happening in the time 45 s–60 s.

e Calculate the total distance the train moves between stations.

3 A weightlifter heaves a load of 30 kg from the floor to a height of 2 m. He then drops the bar, which hits the ground.

a Calculate the weight of the load.

b How much gravitational potential energy does the load have at the top of the lift?

c Calculate the speed at which the load hits the floor.

4 A model rocket has mass 5 kg. When it is fired vertically upwards, the initial thrust from the exhaust gas is 80 N.

a What is the resultant upward force accelerating the rocket?

b What is the initial acceleration of the rocket?

c Assuming that the thrust remains 80 N, explain why the acceleration of the rocket would increase.

Extended Writing

5 What is meant by the terms stopping distance, thinking distance, and braking distance? Explain why a car's braking distance is greater if the road is icy or wet.

6 Describe the advantages and disadvantages of fuelling a vehicle using biofuel or batteries.

7 Explain how airbags and paddle controls contribute to vehicle safety.

P4

Electricity, waves, and radiation

Why study this module?

What would the world be like without electricity? A flow of tiny, negatively charged, sub-atomic particles is vital to the operation of every electrical appliance, from small touch-screen mobile phones to large 3D TVs. An understanding of electric current is essential to all scientists, engineers and anyone interested in how things work. In this module you will learn about the dangers of all forms of electricity, and the differences between static, current, and mains electricity.

We will revisit waves, learning how high frequency sound waves produce images of unborn babies, and how high energy X-rays pass through your body to show doctors images of broken bones. You will also learn more about the atom, and how radiation from unstable nuclei breaking down surrounds us all of the time, continuously bombarding the cells in our bodies. Finally, you will learn how scientists have been able to split the atom to devastating effect, while they have yet to master fusing it back together.

You should remember

1. Electricity can produce a variety of different effects, including heating.

2. Electric circuits can be used to control an electric current.

3. All materials are made up of atoms.

4. Some atoms are unstable, and break down in radioactive decay.

5. The wavelength of a wave affects its properties.

Lightning is one of nature's most impressive and terrifying uses of electricity. Each strike only lasts around 30 millionths of a second, but in that time it transfers a massive 5 billion joules of energy to its surroundings. The voltage in a strike can be as high as 100 million volts – that's the same as 66 million AA batteries.

Even more frightening is what happens to the air around this giant electric spark. The air is heated to almost 30000 °C, which is five times hotter than the surface of the Sun. The heating takes place so rapidly that the air expands in a supersonic shock wave. We hear this explosion as thunder.

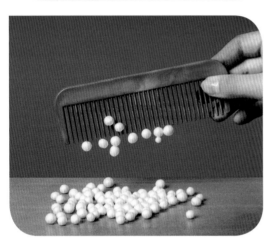

▲ The polystyrene balls are attracted to the comb

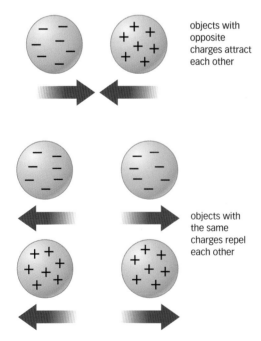

objects with opposite charges attract each other

objects with the same charges repel each other

▲ Attraction and repulsion of charged particles

Attracting paper, dust and other materials

When you rub some materials, they become charged with **static electricity** and attract other materials. For example, a comb or strip of plastic that has been rubbed will attract small pieces of paper or cork. When expanded polystyrene packaging is broken up into small pieces, it is attracted to many things.

This effect is used in some dusting brushes. The brush becomes charged and then attracts the dust as it passes over it.

Electrostatic charge

You have experienced static electricity if you have ever had a shock when touching a metal door knob or getting out of a car.

When you rub certain types of **insulating materials** together, they can become charged. This is sometimes known as an **electrostatic charge**.

Insulating materials can be charged with positive charge or negative charge. The charge is caused by electrons, which have a negative charge, being transferred from one insulating material to the other.

A Why might rubbing an insulator cause it to become charged?

Opposite charges attract, like charges repel

If two bodies are both positively charged, they will **repel** each other, or push each other away. If both bodies are negatively charged, they will also repel each other. However, if the two bodies have opposite charges, they will **attract** each other.

B Will the charges on the comb and polystyrene balls in the photograph be the same?

This boy has gained an electrostatic charge while sliding down. His hair is sticking out because the charges on the hairs are all the same type, so they are repelling one another.

Transfer of electrons

When a polythene rod is rubbed with a woollen cloth, electrons move from the cloth to the polythene rod. The polythene rod becomes negatively charged, as electrons have a negative charge.

When an acetate rod is rubbed with a woollen cloth, electrons move from the acetate rod on to the cloth. The acetate rod becomes positively charged, as it has lost negatively charged electrons.

So a negative charge means there are extra electrons. A positive charge means there is a lack of electrons.

The atoms or molecules that have become charged are ions.

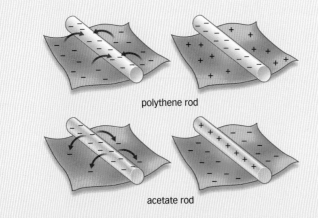

polythene rod

acetate rod

The rods become negatively or positively charged when electrons are transferred

Exam tip

✓ Remember that you can charge something with static electricity by rubbing two insulators together.

C Has a positively charged object gained or lost electrons?

Questions

1 Name the two types of charge.

2 What kind of material can become charged when you rub it?

3 Do like charges attract or repel each other?

4 Describe how a plastic comb can be used to pick up small pieces of paper.

5 (a) Describe how an acetate rod becomes charged when you rub it with a cloth.

(b) A polythene rod is rubbed with a conductor. Will it become charged? Explain your answer.

↓ E

↓ C

↓ A*

A What is an electrostatic shock?

B How does lightning happen?

Electrostatic shocks

Conductors such as metals allow charge to move freely. Insulators, such as polythene, don't allow charged electrons to move freely and charge can build up.

You can become charged, for example, by wearing clothing made from synthetic materials, or by walking over a floor that is covered with an insulator such as synthetic carpet. If you then touch a conductor connected to earth, like a water pipe or metal door handle, the built-up charge is conducted away very quickly – you get an **electrostatic shock**.

You can also get an electrostatic shock if you touch something that is charged. The charge is conducted to earth through you.

Dangers

Static electricity can be dangerous. When charge is transferred between two objects, a spark can jump across the gap between them. This spark can have a high temperature and could cause an explosion where flammable gases or vapours are being used. For example, when fossil fuels are being pumped into large tanks, static electricity can build up and the tank can become charged.

Static electricity is also responsible for lightning. Static electricity builds up on clouds. A lightning bolt happens when a very large amount of the charge flows very quickly to the Earth. If a lightning bolt strikes you it could kill you.

▲ Lightning is the discharge of static electricity from clouds to the Earth

Static electricity can also be a nuisance. The screens of TVs and computer monitors can become charged, attracting dust.

Static electricity can also cause clothing made of synthetic materials to cling to you.

Avoiding problems and dangers of electrostatic charge

You can reduce the chance of electrostatic discharge by connecting to earth through a conductor so that charge does not build up in the first place. Alternatively, insulating mats or shoes with insulating soles will prevent the rapid flow of charge to earth.

Vehicles that contain flammable gases, liquids or powders must be connected to earth before the substance is loaded or unloaded.

For example, when an aircraft is refuelled, friction can cause a build-up of charge. So both the fuel truck and the aircraft are connected to earth before refuelling starts.

You can buy anti-static liquids, sprays and cloths that all contain something that will conduct electricity and prevent the build-up of charge. Some fabric conditioners contain a chemical that coats clothing with a thin layer that will conduct charge.

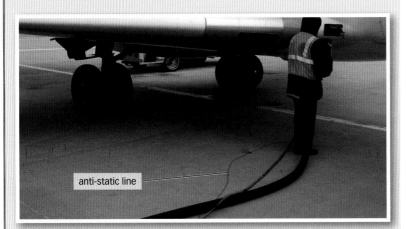
anti-static line

▲ The aircraft and the truck are connected to earth with an anti-static line

> **C** How can you reduce the chances of receiving an electrostatic shock?

▲ A charged TV screen attracts dust

Exam tip　OCR

✓ If a question asks about the dangers of static electricity, think about the properties of insulators and conductors, and include these in your answer. Insulators can gain electrostatic charge, but only conductors can conduct charge.

Questions

1. How can you get an electrostatic shock? ↓ E

2. When can static electricity be dangerous?

3. When can static electricity be a nuisance? ↓ C

4. Explain what an anti-static line does.

5. How does a fabric conditioner help to prevent clothes clinging due to the build-up of static electricity? ↓ A*

Learning objectives

After studying this topic, you should be able to:

✓ describe some of the uses of static electricity in removing smoke particles from waste gases, for spraying paint, and in heart defibrillators

A Why do the grid and metal plates have opposite charges?

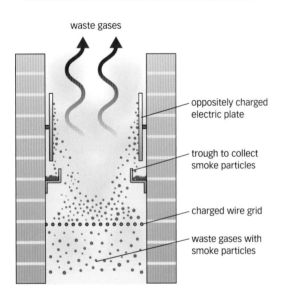

waste gases

oppositely charged electric plate

trough to collect smoke particles

charged wire grid

waste gases with smoke particles

▲ The electrostatic precipitator removes smoke particles from waste gases

B Why are the paint particles attracted to the object?

Key words

electrostatic dust precipitator,
induce, defibrillator

Removing smoke particles

An **electrostatic dust precipitator** is used to remove smoke particles from waste gases coming out of chimneys.

Inside the chimney there is a charged wire grid or a series of charged rods. When soot or dust travels up the chimney it passes through the grid, or travels past the rods. The dust becomes charged. Further up the chimney there are metal plates on each side. These plates are either oppositely charged to the grid or earthed. The charged dust particles are attracted to the plates and stick to them. This reduces the amount of dust released into the atmosphere. Several times during the year the plates are struck by metal hammers and the dust falls back to the bottom of the chimney, where it is collected.

To make sure that as much dust and soot is collected as possible, the grids have a very high voltage. The dust particles either gain or lose electrons as they pass through the high voltage metal grids. They become either positively charged (losing electrons) or negatively charged (gaining electrons). As they approach the earthed plates they **induce** an opposite charge in the plates. They either attract or repel electrons inside the plates, leading to a small opposite charge on the surface of the plates. The dust particles are attracted to this charge and stick to the plates. This is the same process that allows a charged balloon to stick to a neutral wall or ceiling.

Paint spraying

A paint spray gun has a charge, and the paint particles become charged as they pass through the gun. The object that is being painted has an opposite charge and so the paint particles are attracted to it.

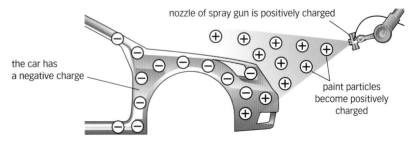

nozzle of spray gun is positively charged

the car has a negative charge

paint particles become positively charged

▲ How electrostatic paint spraying works

The paint particles all have the same charge, so they repel one another, making a finer spray. The object to be sprayed has an opposite charge to the paint so that the paint is attracted to more parts of the object, even those that are not directly facing the spray gun. This ensures an even coat of paint with less waste than there would be in spraying without the use of electrostatics.

The same principle is used in crop spraying.

Electrostatic charge is also used in photocopiers and laser printers. A laser printer has a drum which becomes negatively charged where the laser shines on it. The toner is negatively charged and so sticks to the parts of the drum that have stayed positively charged, The image is then transferred to a piece of paper.

A photocopier works in a similar way.

Defibrillators

A **defibrillator** is used to restart a person's heart when it has stopped beating, for example after a heart attack or an electric shock.

Two paddles are electrostatically charged using a high-voltage supply. They are placed on the patient's chest and discharged. The charge passes through the patient's chest to make the heart contract and start beating again.

There has to be a good electrical contact with the patient's chest.

The paddles have insulated handles so that the operator does not get an electrostatic shock.

A defibrillator must now always be available in large public buildings.

▲ These people are using a special dummy to practise using a defibrillator

Did you know...?

Electrostatic charge can make a stream of water bend, as shown in the photo.

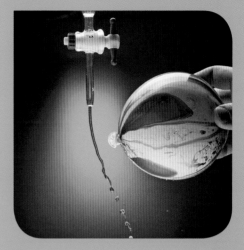

▲ The balloon has been charged by rubbing, and is bending the stream of water

C Why does there need to be a good electrical contact between the paddles and the patient's chest?

Questions

1 What is a defibrillator?

2 Describe how a patient's heart is restarted.

3 Why do we need to remove smoke particles from waste gases?

4 Explain how an electrostatic precipitator works.

5 Explain how electrostatic charge is used in paint spraying.

A How will the brightness of the lamp in the circuit in the photograph change if the resistance of the variable resistor is increased?

B Which of the resistors in this diagram has the largest resistance? Explain how you worked out your answer.

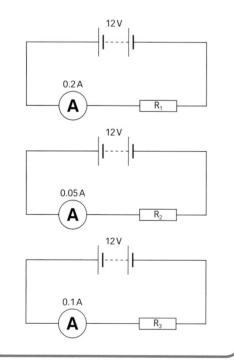

Current and charge

A complete loop is required for a circuit to work.

When an electric **current** flows in a circuit, the current is a movement of **charge** around the circuit. The charge is carried by electrons. The size of the current is given by the charge passing a point in a circuit each second. The higher the current, the higher the number of electrons moving past the point each second.

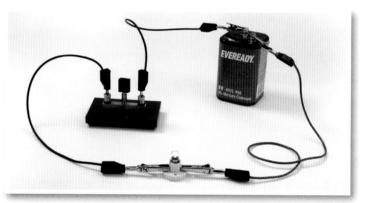

▲ A simple circuit with a battery, lamp, and switch

Resistance, voltage and current

Resistors can be used to change the current in a circuit. When the **voltage** or potential difference is constant, the current through a component depends on the resistance of the component. As the resistance increases, the current through the component decreases.

Variable resistors can be used to change the resistance and hence the current in a circuit. Increasing the resistance decreases the current and decreasing the resistance increases the current.

Resistance can also be changed by using different wires. Longer wires have a higher resistance than shorter wires. Thinner wires have a higher resistance than thicker ones.

If the resistance is kept the same and the voltage is increased, the current in the circuit increases.

◀ A rheostat is a variable resistor. It is a long piece of wire wound into a coil. You can change the resistance by moving the slider on the top of the coil. This changes the length of the wire.

Calculating resistance

You can calculate current, voltage or resistance using the equation:

$$\text{resistance (ohms, } \Omega\text{)} = \frac{\text{voltage (volts, V)}}{\text{current (amperes, A)}}$$

Resistors often have resistance values that are thousands of ohms. So resistance is often given in kilo ohms ($k\Omega$), with $1\ k\Omega = 1000\ \Omega$. When the resistance is large, the current will be small – much less than 1 A. When this happens, currents are given in milliamps (mA), with $1\ A = 1000\ mA$.

Questions

1   Explain why a circuit with a break in it will not work.

2   What happens to resistance if:
    (a) a longer wire is used
    (b) a thicker wire is used.

3   Calculate the resistance of resistors A, B and C from the graph.

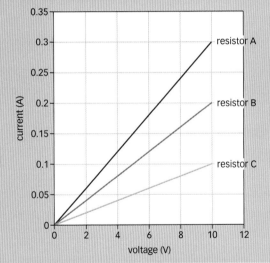

4   The current through a 8 Ω resistor is 1.5 A. What is the voltage across the resistor?

5   The voltage across a resistor is 12 V. Calculate the current through the resistor for the following resistances:
    (a) 6 Ω (b) 24 Ω (c) 1.2 $k\Omega$

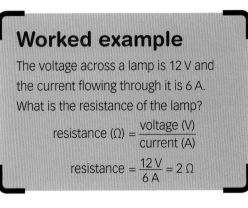

Worked example

The voltage across a lamp is 12 V and the current flowing through it is 6 A. What is the resistance of the lamp?

$$\text{resistance } (\Omega) = \frac{\text{voltage (V)}}{\text{current (A)}}$$

$$\text{resistance} = \frac{12\ V}{6\ A} = 2\ \Omega$$

Exam tip

✓ Take care with the units of current and resistance when using them in calculations. Always make sure you are using ohms and amps instead of kilo ohms and milliamps.

Did you know...?

Variable resistors are used in dimmer switches and volume controls to control the current flowing in the circuit. Increasing the size of the variable resistance reduces the current and dims the lights.

▲ This dimmer switch contains a variable resistor

Key words

current, charge, resistor, voltage, variable resistors, rheostat

Learning objectives

After studying this topic, you should be able to:

- ✔ describe the structure of a UK three-pin plug
- ✔ explain what the different wires do and know their colours
- ✔ describe how fuses protect electrical devices
- ✔ use the equation
  power = current × voltage

Key words

fuse, live, earth, circuit breaker, double-insulated

▲ Fuses usually come as replaceable cartridges. The wire inside the fuse heats up and melts if there is too much current. This prevents the wires connected to the appliance heating up and leading to a fire or damaging the appliance.

A How many pins are there on a standard UK plug?

B Which wire is the fuse connected to?

The UK plug

If you've ever been on holiday abroad, you know that you had to take a plug adapter to use or recharge any of your electrical appliances. Different countries use different plug designs depending on their own electrical systems. The UK plug is unusual as it contains three connections (or pins).

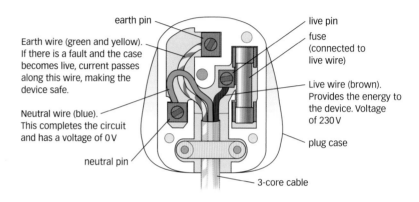

earth pin

Earth wire (green and yellow). If there is a fault and the case becomes live, current passes along this wire, making the device safe.

Neutral wire (blue). This completes the circuit and has a voltage of 0 V

neutral pin

live pin

fuse (connected to live wire)

Live wire (brown). Provides the energy to the device. Voltage of 230 V

plug case

3-core cable

▲ A standard UK three-pin plug

Safety devices

There are several devices designed to improve the safety of the mains electricity supply. In the UK, each plug contains a **fuse**. This is connected to the **live** wire and is usually a small cylindrical cartridge.

Each fuse has a rating, and if the current passing through it exceeds this rating, the wire inside the fuse heats up, melts, and breaks the circuit. This protects your electrical appliances from surges of current – the fuse melts before the wires in the computer. A fuse with a rating of 13 A would melt if 13 A were to pass through it. A 3 A fuse contains a thinner wire which melts when the current reaches just 3 A. It is important to select the correct fuse rating for each appliance.

The power of an appliance depends on the voltage and current it needs to operate.

$$\underset{\text{(watts, W)}}{\text{power}} = \underset{\text{(amperes, A)}}{\text{current}} \times \underset{\text{(volts, V)}}{\text{voltage}}$$

This equation can be used to calculate the current drawn by an appliance (the current it needs to operate) and so to select a suitable fuse. Usually a fuse just above, but close to, the operating current is selected. The table on the next page gives a few examples.

Device	Power (W)	Voltage (V)	Current (A)	Fuse rating
kettle	2300	230	10	13 A
small lamp	10	5	2	3 A
cooker	8050	230	35	40 A

The **earth wire** is another important safety device. One end of this wire is connected to the metal case of the appliance. If the live wire were to come loose and touch the case, the case would become live. If you were then to touch the case, you could receive a very dangerous shock. With the earth wire attached, the case cannot become live as the current passes down the earth wire. This causes a surge in current, and this melts the fuse.

Another type of safety device is the **circuit breaker**. Like the fuse, this is connected to the live wire of a device, but rather than heat up it detects tiny changes in current when there is a fault and breaks the circuit.

Despite being more complex than fuses, circuit breakers have a number of advantages. They switch the current off much faster than fuses, and they can be easily reset and used again.

Questions

1. Explain why plugs are made of rigid plastic.

2. List the three wires found in a UK plug, state their colour, and explain what they do.

3. Give two advantages of using circuit breakers compared with fuses.

4. Calculate the power of a speaker which draws a current of 1.5 A at 12 V.

5. Explain how the earth wire protects you if there is a fault with your device.

6. A TV has a power rating of 115 W. Calculate the current through the TV when connected to the mains at 230 V, and suggest a suitable value for the fuse.

Did you know...?

Some devices don't have an earth wire. These are usually made from non-conducting materials (such as wood or plastic) and so the case cannot become live. Even some metal devices are **double-insulated**. The live components are sealed away from the case and so there is no chance of the case becoming live.

▲ The square symbol in the photo indicates that a device is double-insulated.

Learning objectives

After studying this topic, you should be able to:

✔ describe the features of longitudinal waves

✔ explain that ultrasound waves are sound waves above human hearing, above 20 000 Hz

✔ describe the motion of the particles in a longitudinal wave

Key words

oscillation, longitudinal wave, compression, rarefaction, frequency, ultrasound

▲ Sound is an example of a longitudinal wave

A Give one example of a longitudinal wave.

B What is the region of a longitudinal wave called where the air is more spread out?

Longitudinal waves

If you look closely at a speaker, you can see the small paper speaker cone behind the grille moving in and out. It is this kind of movement that creates a sound wave.

A sound wave is a series of **oscillations**, or vibrations, which travel through air in the same direction as the speaker movement. A sound wave is an example of a **longitudinal wave**, and the p-waves formed in earthquakes are another. You may remember that the other type of wave is the transverse wave, including all electromagnetic and water waves.

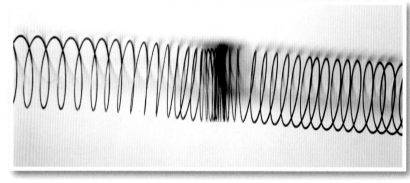

▲ This is a longitudinal wave on a slinky

In longitudinal waves the oscillations are parallel (in the same direction) as the wave movement. This means drawing a longitudinal wave can be a little complicated. They are usually drawn like the one in the diagram below:

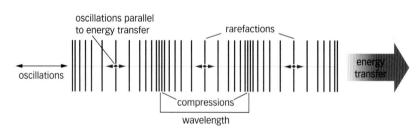

▲ A longitudinal wave

When the speaker cone moves out it creates a **compression** as the air is bunched up (this is a region of higher pressure). When it moves back in it creates a **rarefaction**, where the air is more spread out (this is a region of lower pressure). It is these compressions and rarefactions which make up a longitudinal wave.

Like all waves, longitudinal waves have a wavelength and a **frequency**. The wavelength of a longitudinal wave is the distance between each compression. A wave with a shorter wavelength has compressions that are closer together. The frequency is the number of compressions which pass a given point each second. If 20 compressions pass a point in one second, then the wave has a frequency of 20 Hz.

The particles in a transverse wave vibrate at right angles to the direction of wave motion. The particles in a longitudinal wave vibrate very differently. Instead of vibrating up and down, they vibrate from side to side. They are closer together at a compression and further apart at a rarefaction.

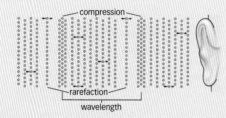

▲ When a longitudinal wave travels through the air, it causes the particles to bunch up then spread out

If the frequency of the wave increases, the air particles vibrate more rapidly. If the sound is louder, the particles vibrate with a greater amplitude. For louder sounds the maximum distance each particle moves from its central position increases. They vibrate further in each direction.

Ultrasound

The human ear can detect a very wide range of frequencies. Humans can hear sounds with a frequency up to 20 000 Hz. Sound waves above this frequency are called **ultrasound**.

◀ The frequency of a dog whistle is too high for humans to hear but it's fine for dogs!

Different animals can hear different ranges of sound frequencies. The frequency of a dog whistle is too high for humans to hear. Dogs can hear much higher frequency sounds.

Questions

1 Sketch a diagram of a longitudinal wave and label the key features. ↓ E

2 Describe how to measure the wavelength of a longitudinal wave. ↓ C

3 Define what is meant by ultrasound.

4 Describe how a speaker produces compressions and rarefactions.

5 In terms of particles, describe the differences between a quiet, low frequency sound wave and a louder, higher frequency one. ↓ A*

Exam tip

✔ When describing ultrasound waves don't forget to say they are sound waves, with a frequency above the range human hearing, that is, above 20000 Hz.

Ultrasound scans

You've probably already had an ultrasound scan, but you would have been too small to remember. In fact, you were not even born.

Ultrasound waves have a high frequency and a short wavelength. This means they are able to travel inside the body and produce images that are useful for doctors. Ultrasound scans measure the speed of blood flow in the body.

These **ultrasound body scans** are generally used as a non-invasive means of checking that babies are developing properly whilst still inside their mother. But they can also be used to check on a patient's heart, kidneys or liver.

Ultrasound waves are beamed into the body of a patient from a special transmitter. These waves **reflect** from different layers inside the body of the patient. The waves return at different times, depending on the depth of the layer. A computer processes this information to build up a picture of the inside of the body.

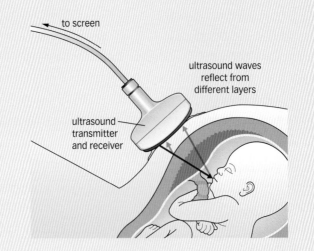

to screen

ultrasound waves reflect from different layers

ultrasound transmitter and receiver

▲ Ultrasound reflects from different layers within the mother and baby

Ultrasound scans have advantages over X-ray scans. An ultrasound scan does not damage living cells as some higher energy X-rays can. This makes them suitable for scanning unborn children.

X-rays are very penetrating, and this makes it difficult to see any soft tissue on an X-ray photograph. Ultrasound scans produce much clearer images of soft tissues such as the liver and heart.

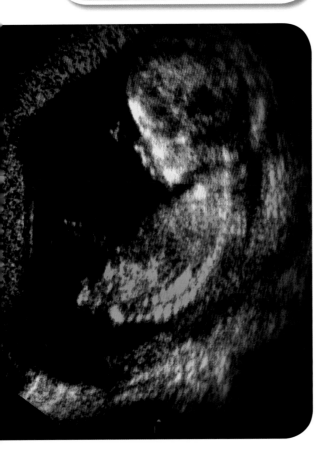

▲ Ultrasound images are used to check the health of newborn babies

A Give three examples of things which might be scanned as part of an ultrasound body scan.

Other uses of ultrasound

Ultrasound has a number of other medical uses. Special ultrasound scanners can even monitor the blood flow inside your veins!

One of the common medical uses of ultrasound is to break up kidney stones. These sometimes form in a patient's kidney. They can block important ducts and can be very painful.

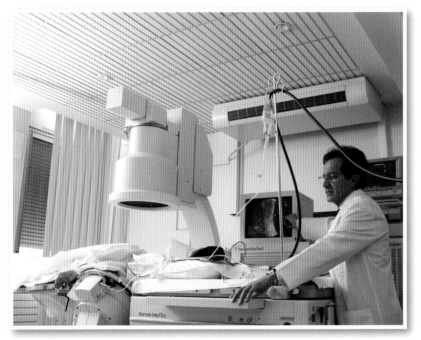

▲ Ultrasound is used to break up painful kidney stones

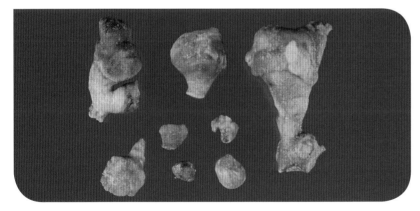

▲ Kidney stones

Ultrasound can break up the kidney stones inside the body, avoiding the need for surgery. Ultrasound is directed at the kidney stone. This makes the stone vibrate at a very high frequency, causing it to break up into pieces that are small enough to pass out of the body in the patient's urine.

Exam tip

✔ When describing a use of ultrasound don't just say 'an ultrasound'. Be more precise, say 'an ultrasound body scan, for example a prenatal scan'.

B What is a kidney stone, and why is it a problem?

Questions

1 Other than body scans, give two examples of how ultrasound might be used in hospitals.

2 What property of ultrasound waves allows them to penetrate inside the body?

3 Describe how ultrasound is used to break up kidney stones.

4 Explain how ultrasound is used to produce an image of an unborn baby.

5 Give two reasons why an ultrasound body scan might be used instead of an X-ray image.

↓ E

↓ C

↓ A*

Learning objectives

After studying this topic, you should be able to:

- ✔ describe the processes involved in radioactive decay
- ✔ describe the three different forms of nuclear radiation
- ✔ explain the process of ionisation

Key words

nucleus, radioactive decay, ionising radiation, activity, ionisation

▲ Water, like all substances, is made up of billions of atoms

A Which part of the atom emits nuclear radiation?

B If the activity of a radioactive substance is measured as 100 000 decays per second, how many atoms decay each second?

Radioactive decay

Everything around us is made up of atoms. There are billions and billions of them in a tiny drop of water. Each atom has a tiny central **nucleus**, with electrons in orbit around it.

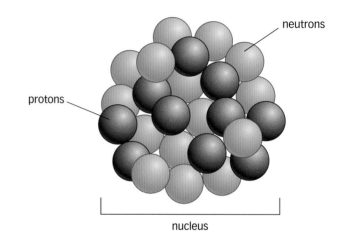

▲ The nucleus of every atom contains protons and neutrons

Thankfully, the nuclei found in most atoms are perfectly stable. The nucleus in a small number of atoms is unstable. **Radioactive decay** occurs when this nucleus breaks down and emits one of the three types of **ionising radiation**.

All forms of ionising radiation come from the nucleus of unstable atoms, but the three types are all very different.

alpha particles α_2^4	These are very ionising particles made up of two protons and two neutrons. This is the same as a helium nucleus. Alpha particles have a positive charge.
beta particles β_{-1}^0	A beta particle is fast electron from the nucleus. Beta particles have a negative charge.
gamma rays γ_0^0	A gamma ray is a high frequency electromagnetic wave. This kind of radiation is not very ionising, but travels very far and is very penetrating.

The number of radioactive decays per second is called the **activity**. A radioactive substance might have an activity of 20 000 decays per second. Inside this substance, the nucleus of 20 000 atoms breaks down each second.

What is ionising radiation?

Alpha particles, beta particles and gamma rays are all described as **ionising** radiations. They ionise the atoms of any material they pass through.

Atoms are usually neutral. They have no overall charge, as the positive charge from the protons is exactly cancelled out by the negative charge from the electrons. When an atom gains or loses an electron, it becomes charged as the charges are no longer balanced. An atom charged in this way is called an ion.

When ionising radiation passes through a spark chamber, it ionises the gas inside by removing some electrons from the atoms. This causes an electric current, which is seen as a spark between the metal plates.

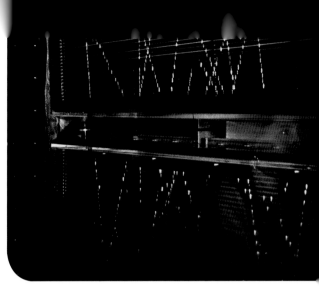

▲ Radiation ionises the gas inside a spark chamber, leading to an electric current seen as a spark

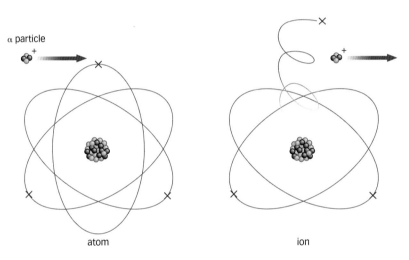

▲ An alpha particle ionises an atom by removing one of the atom's electrons

Both alpha and beta particles have a charge. When they pass close to atoms they either attract or repel electrons away from the atom, ionising them. Alpha particles have a greater mass and greater charge; this makes them the most ionising form of radiation.

Questions

1 Name the three types of nuclear radiation.

2 If a substance has an activity of 50 000 decays per second, how many nuclei break down in 4 minutes?

3 Describe the three types of nuclear radiation.

4 Explain how ionisation of a material takes place.

5 Explain why alpha radiation is the most ionising form of nuclear radiation.

Key words

half-life

A What happens to the activity of a radioactive substance with time?

B Name a unit for the measurement of activity.

Radioactivity and time

A substance that contains radioactive atoms gives out radiation all of the time. The nuclei within it decay. As you know, the number of these decays per second is called the activity.

In a radioactive substance, atoms are decaying all of the time. As time passes, the activity gradually decreases. An example can be seen in the table below:

Activity (decays per second)	Time (years)
2000	0
1520	10
1150	20
880	30
650	40
500	50
370	60

Half-life

As the radioactive atoms within a substance decay, fewer and fewer radioactive nuclei remain. This leads to the drop in activity as time passes. The time taken for half of the radioactive nuclei in a sample to decay is called the **half-life**. This is the time it takes for the activity to halve.

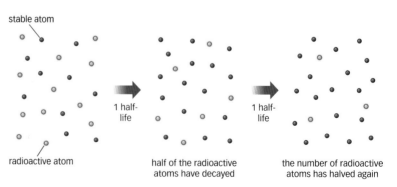

▲ Half of the radioactive atoms have decayed after each half-life

In each half-life, the number of radioactive atoms remaining halves. Starting with 400 atoms (a very small number), after one half-life 200 will remain. After another, just 100 are left. Then 50, and so on.

If you plot a graph of the number of radioactive atoms remaining (or the activity) against time, you can use it to find the half-life of a substance. After one half-life, the number of radioactive atoms remaining (or the activity) will have halved.

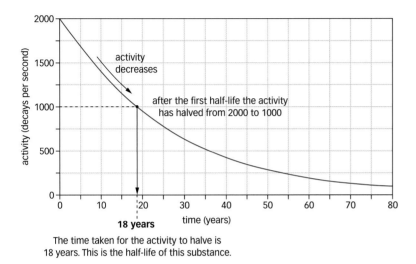

The time taken for the activity to halve is 18 years. This is the half-life of this substance.

▲ The half-life can be found by plotting a graph of activity against time

Different substances have different half-lives. These range from milliseconds to billions of years. The table on the right shows a few examples.

C What is meant by the half-life of a radioactive substance?

▲ Half-life means that radioactive waste remains harmful long after it is used, and needs to be carefully stored. Here high-level radioactive waste is being turned into glass for storage under the black circular lids in the floor.

Isotope	Half-life
nitrogen 17	4 seconds
radon 220	3.8 days
carbon 14	5700 years
uranium 238	4.5 billion years

Questions

1 Explain why the activity from a radioactive material decreases with time.

2 Plot a graph of activity against time using the data in the table on the previous page. Use your graph to find the half-life of the substance.

3 How many radioactive nuclei remain in a sample after:

(a) one half-life

(b) two half-lives

(c) six half-lives?

4 Carbon 14 is a radioactive material. What proportion of carbon 14 will be left in a sample after 28 500 years?

Learning objectives

After studying this topic, you should be able to:

✔ describe the changes in the nucleus caused by the three types of radioactive decay

Key words

atomic number, **mass number**, **neutron**, **alpha particle**, **beta particle**, **gamma ray**

▲ Uranium eventually decays into lead

Describing the nucleus

All atoms have an **atomic number** and a **mass number**. The atomic number is the number of protons in the atom. All atoms of the same element have the same number of protons, and so the same atomic number. For example, all carbon atoms contain six protons.

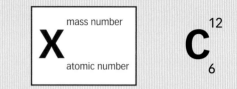

$$X \quad \text{mass number} \atop \text{atomic number} \qquad C^{12}_{6}$$

▲ Each atom has a mass number and an atomic number

The mass number refers to the number of protons plus the number of **neutrons**. A carbon 12 nucleus contains six protons and six neutrons (12 particles in total).

How radioactive decay changes the nucleus

When a nucleus breaks down during radioactive decay, this changes the make up of the nucleus. This leads to change in atomic number, mass number or both. If the atomic number changes, a new element is created.

An **alpha particle** is a helium nucleus: it is made up of two protons and two neutrons. After a nucleus breaks down by emitting an alpha particle (alpha decay), both the mass number and the atomic number change.

unstable nucleus | new nucleus (lost 2 protons + 2 neutrons) | alpha particle (2 protons + 2 neutrons)

▲ A large nucleus might emit an alpha particle

The mass number drops by 4 and the atomic number drops by 2. This means the element changes. For example, uranium 238 becomes thorium 234 after emitting an alpha particle.

This can be shown in the decay equation:

$$U^{238}_{92} \rightarrow Th^{234}_{90} + \alpha^{4}_{2}$$

A What effect does emitting an alpha particle have on the mass number and atomic number of a nucleus?

Exam tip OCR

✔ When using decay equations, the atomic numbers and mass numbers must always balance. They must add up to the same value on both sides.

In beta decay, a neutron breaks up into a proton and a **beta particle**.

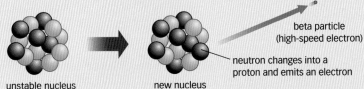

unstable nucleus   new nucleus
(1 less neutron but 1 more proton)

beta particle
(high-speed electron)

neutron changes into a
proton and emits an electron

▲ In beta decay, a neutron changes into a proton and emits an electron

The nucleus has lost one neutron but gained one proton. As a result, the mass number of the atom stays the same and the atomic number goes up by 1. As with alpha decay, a new element has been formed when the atomic number changes.

For example, when carbon 14 undergoes beta decay, it forms nitrogen 14. This can be shown in the decay equation:

$$C^{14}_6 \rightarrow N^{14}_7 + \beta^0_{-1}$$

B What happens to the number of protons in a nucleus after a beta decay?

In gamma decay, the nucleus emits a high frequency electromagnetic wave. This **gamma ray** has no mass and no charge, and so it has no effect on the mass number or atomic number of the nucleus. The element stays the same.

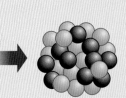

unstable nucleus   nucleus unchanged
(same number of protons
and neutrons)

gamma ray
(high frequency
electromagnetic wave)

▲ The nucleus is unchanged after emitting a gamma ray

Questions

1 Describe what happens in the nucleus during beta decay.

2 Explain why the emission of a gamma ray does not change the element.

3 Give one example of an alpha decay equation.

4 Explain what happens to the mass number and atomic number during beta decay, and give one example.

5 Complete the following decay equations:

(a) $Pu^{239}_{94} \rightarrow U^{?}_{?} + \alpha^{?}_{?}$

(b) $Pb^{210}_{82} \rightarrow Bi^{?}_{?} + \beta^{?}_{?}$

A*

Learning objectives

After studying this topic, you should be able to:

- ✔ explain what background radiation is and describe some of its sources
- ✔ describe some uses of radiation including tracers and radioactive dating
- ✔ explain how the decay of carbon 14 is used to date organic material

Key words

background radiation,
radioactive dating

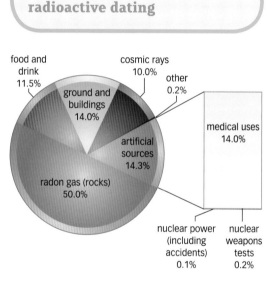

▲ Sources of UK background radiation

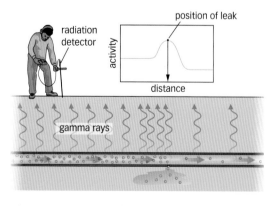

▲ A gamma source is used to find leaks in an underground pipe

Background radiation

The radiation around us every day is called **background radiation**. It comes from a variety of sources such as hospitals, nuclear weapons testing or from nuclear power (including radiation released in accidents). However, most of it occurs naturally due the breakdown of radioactive atoms within rocks. Less than 15% comes from man-made activities.

> A Give the three most common sources of background radiation.
>
> B How much background radiation comes from man-made sources?

Your exposure to radiation depends on where you live and, for example, on the nature of your job. Different parts of the country have different levels of background radiation, and an airline pilot or someone working in a hospital can receive a higher dose than other people.

Some more uses of radiation

We have already looked into some of the uses of ionising radiation. You may remember that a source of alpha radiation is used in smoke alarms. When smoke enters the alarm, it stops the alpha particles ionising the air. This leads to a drop in current and the alarm sounds.

As well as their medical applications, radioactive tracers may be used to map out the path of underground pipes or to track how material is dispersed when it enters the water supply. Radiation can even be used to find blockages or cracks in pipes very deep underground.

Finding a leak

A source of radiation is mixed into the fluid flowing through the pipe. A worker can then detect the radiation at the surface. If there is a blockage or a leak, the activity detected after the leak will fall. This allows the worker on the surface to pinpoint where to dig. The source used must emit gamma radiation, as alpha or beta particles would not reach the detector above.

Radioactive dating

Radioactive atoms within a substance decay with time. This process can be used to determine the age of rocks or ancient materials, using a method called **radioactive dating.** Scientists take careful measurements of the amount of carbon in ancient objects such as clothing, bones, or wooden machinery. This can be used in carbon dating to precisely determine the age of the object.

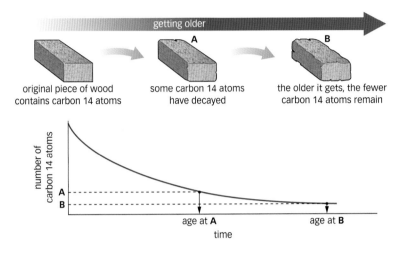

▲ The number of carbon 14 atoms decreases as organic materials age

A similar technique is used to date rocks, by studying the ratio of uranium atoms to lead atoms. As a rock ages the uranium inside it decays, eventually ending up as lead. Over the time the number of uranium atoms decreases as the number of lead atoms increases. The older the rock, the lower the ratio of uranium to lead.

How carbon dating works

Carbon dating relies on the amount of carbon 14 in the air not having changed for thousands of years.

Carbon dating only works with organic material (such as wood, cotton or bone). When an organism is living, it continuously absorbs more carbon 14 through biological processes such as gaseous exchange. However, when the organism dies, no new carbon 14 is absorbed and so, as the carbon 14 atoms decay, the amount found in the material drops. The amount of carbon 14 in the sample is compared to the amount found in living things to determine the age of the sample.

▲ Carbon dating can be used to work out the age of this ancient Egyptian mummy

Questions

1   Give two examples of a source of background radiation.

2   Other than medical uses, give three examples of how radioactive tracers might be used.

3   Explain how a smoke alarm uses radiation to detect smoke.

4   Describe how radiation may be used to detect a leak in a pipe. Use a diagram to help illustrate your answer and state the type of radiation used.

5   Explain how the decay of carbon 14 can be used to determine the age of ancient materials.

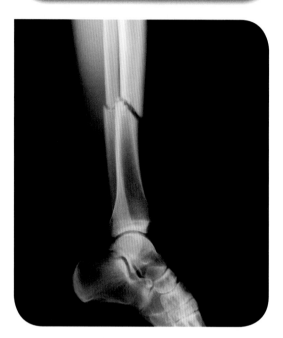

▲ X-rays are used to obtain photographs of broken bones

A X-rays and gamma rays are examples of which type of wave?

Did you know...?

X-rays have tiny wavelengths. Some are just 0.000 000 000 01 m long (0.01 nm). This means you could fit around one billion of them across your finger nail!

What are X-rays?

If you've ever been unlucky enough to break a bone, you will have gone for an X-ray scan. Scans like these allow the doctor to treat your injury or disease without having to cut you open and take a look.

X-rays are similar to the gamma rays produced in radioactive decay. They are both ionising and are both types of **electromagnetic wave** (other examples include radio, light and microwaves). All electromagnetic waves, including X-rays and gamma rays, travel very fast and can travel through a vacuum such as space.

X-rays and gamma rays have very high frequencies and have very similar, very small **wavelengths**. This means they are able to travel easily through flesh and even through denser materials such as bone.

In spite of their similarities, they are made in different ways. Gamma rays come from the radioactive decay of unstable nuclei, while X-rays are produced by fast-moving electrons.

In hospitals X-rays are used by radiographers to produce an image, usually of part of a patient's skeleton, as a photograph. Most X-rays pass through the patient, but the denser material inside the patient (such as bones) absorbs some of the radiation. This causes a variation in the X-rays received by the photographic film, and so an image is produced.

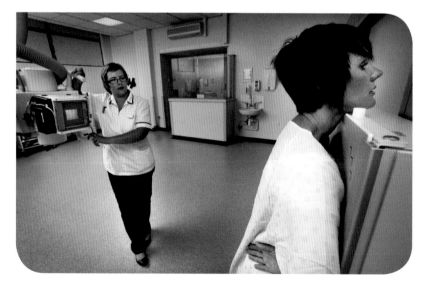

▲ Radiographers, who work all day with X-rays, must take precautions to reduce their own exposure

A large X-ray machine is operated by a radiographer. It is their responsibility to ensure that X-rays are used safely. X-rays can be dangerous, particularly if you are exposed to them on a regular basis. To reduce their own exposure, the radiographer leaves the room or stands behind a large lead screen whenever the machine is used.

> **B** What is the name given to the person who takes X-ray images in a hospital?

How are X-rays produced?

In hospitals X-rays are produced by firing high-speed electrons at angled metal targets inside the X-ray machine. Very high voltages are needed to accelerate the electrons to a high enough speed to produce X-rays. When the electrons smash into the plate, X-rays are emitted.

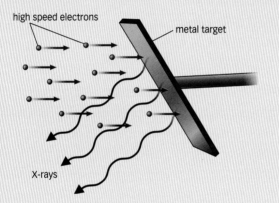

high speed electrons

metal target

X-rays

▲ High-speed electrons are smashed into metal plates to produce X-rays

X-rays are much easier to control than gamma rays. To stop an X-ray machine emitting X-rays, all the radiographer has to do is turn off the electricity. It is not possible to stop a nucleus emitting gamma rays.

Unlike gamma rays, the wavelength of X-rays used in hospitals can be varied slightly. Changing the voltage used to accelerate the electrons alters the wavelength of the X-rays. A higher voltage will produce smaller, more penetrating X-rays.

Key words

X-ray, electromagnetic wave, wavelength

Exam tip

✔ As when describing an ultrasound body scan, be precise when writing about X-rays. For example, don't just say 'an X-ray'; instead say 'producing an X-ray image of a broken bone'.

Questions

1 Give one use of X-rays.

2 Give one similarity and one difference between X-rays and gamma rays.

3 Describe how X-rays are produced.

4 Explain why a radiographer leaves the room whenever X-ray photographs are being taken.

E ↓ C ↓ A*

Learning objectives

After studying this topic, you should be able to:

✔ describe the properties of gamma radiation that make it useful for medicine

✔ describe how sources of gamma radiation are used as tracers

✔ explain other uses of gamma radiation medicine, including the gamma knife

Key words

radioisotope, sterilisation, gamma knife, medical tracer

A What part of the atom emits gamma rays?

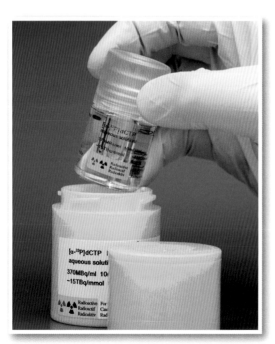

▲ Radioactive sources are widely used in hospitals

Gamma radiation and cancer

Gamma rays are a very important tool for doctors. However, atoms emitting gamma radiation are decaying all the time, so most hospitals have to produce their own **radioisotopes**. A radioisotope is a radioactive version of a normally stable element.

To produce medical radioisotopes, materials are placed inside nuclear reactors. Inside the reactor they absorb neutrons (their mass number increases). This forms a radioisotope – the normally stable element has too many neutrons in its nucleus and so may emit gamma rays.

We have already learnt that gamma rays are very high-frequency, short-wavelength electromagnetic waves. They are emitted from the nucleus of some radioactive atoms.

Gamma rays have a lot of energy and, as they are a type of ionising radiation, they can damage or even kill cells. Gamma rays are used to kill microorganisms on medical equipment. This process, called **sterilisation**, makes equipment safe to use and reduces the risk of infection after an operation.

Gamma rays can kill human cells too. Exposure to too many gamma rays can lead to cancer or even death. Despite these dangers, they have some very important medical uses. To ensure safety, sources of gamma radiation must be handled very carefully.

One of the main uses of gamma rays is in the treatment of cancer. Machines such as the **gamma knife** fire gamma rays into the body to kill cancerous cells.

▲ A gamma knife machine is used to kill cancerous cells

Using gamma rays to kill only certain cells is a complex process. Doctors must ensure that the tumour receives a high enough dose to kill the cancerous cells, while limiting the damage to the healthy tissue around the tumour.

With the gamma knife, a wide beam of low-intensity gamma rays is fired into the body. This is focused onto the tumour as the source moves around the patient.

Medical tracers

Radioactive **medical tracers** are often used to help diagnose problems without the need for an operation.

A special sample is produced which contains radioactive atoms. This is then either eaten by or injected into the patient. An image of the patient's internal organs can then be produced. The radioactive source selected must emit gamma radiation (or very occasionally beta radiation) as alpha radiation is not penetrating enough to leave the body.

The source used must also have a short half-life (a few hours). This means it does not stay radioactive for long and reduces the risks to the patients and their families.

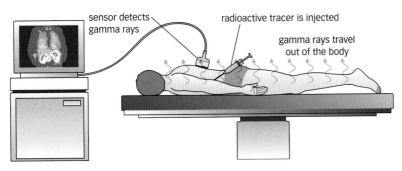

sensor detects gamma rays

radioactive tracer is injected

gamma rays travel out of the body

▲ Injecting a patient with a radioactive tracer allows doctors to diagnose problems

When a radioactive tracer is injected or ingested, the doctor must allow a short time for the tracer to travel around the body. When the source has spread throughout the body, special cameras are used to monitor the radiation which leaves the body. If there is a blockage or a tear inside an organ, the radiation emitted from this area will be different. Specially trained doctors look for these differences.

B Give two examples of medical uses of gamma rays.

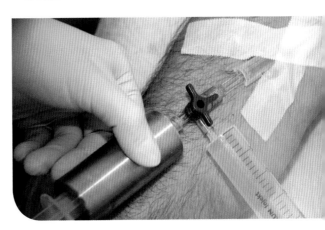

▲ Radioactive tracers must be carefully prepared before they are injected

Questions

1 What is the name of the machine used to kill cancerous cells using gamma rays?

2 Give two ways in which a radioactive medical tracer may enter the body.

3 Explain why a source of gamma radiation is used in a medical tracer, rather than an alpha or beta source.

4 Explain how a gamma knife may be used to kill cancerous cells whilst avoiding damage to the healthy surrounding tissue.

5 Describe how a radioactive medical tracer might be used to diagnose a problem with a patient's digestive system.

↓E

↓C

↓A*

Learning objectives

After studying this topic, you should be able to:

- describe how a nuclear power plant generates electricity
- describe the process of nuclear fission
- describe what happens to materials when they absorb neutrons, leading to radioactive waste

Electricity from nuclear fission

You may remember that we generate around 13% of our electricity using nuclear power. Inside a nuclear power station the heat from a nuclear reaction is used to turn water into steam. This travels along pipes to a turbine which is made to spin by the passing steam. The turbine is connected to a generator which also spins and generates electricity. This process is very similar to how electricity is generated in fossil fuel power stations; the only difference is the source of heat.

Nuclear fission is the splitting of atoms. This is the reaction which takes place inside all nuclear reactors. Fission releases energy in the form of heat.

Most nuclear reactors use uranium as their fuel. Uranium atoms are split into two smaller nuclei. These smaller nuclei are often very radioactive, and make up some of the **radioactive waste** produced by all nuclear reactors.

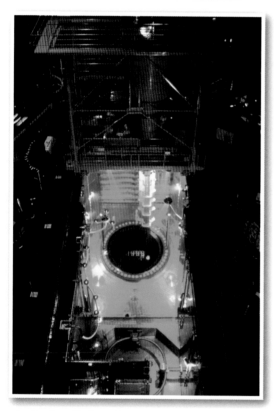

▲ Nuclear fission takes place inside nuclear reactors

▲ Nuclear reactors are used to power some submarines

A What is the name of the reaction which takes place inside a nuclear reactor?

Nuclear reactors can also be used to power some submarines and aircraft carriers. They not only generate all the electricity needed by these giant machines, they also power the engines, produce clean drinking water and generate supplies of fresh oxygen.

B   Other than power stations, give another example of where nuclear reactors are used.

Splitting the atom

Not all atoms undergo nuclear fission. Uranium 235 and plutonium 239 are described as fissionable substances as they can both be split easily.

To split one of these atoms in nuclear fission, a nucleus must first absorb an extra neutron. This makes the nucleus spin and distort. After a few billionths of a second it splits into two smaller nuclei. It is this process which releases the energy used to power nuclear reactors.

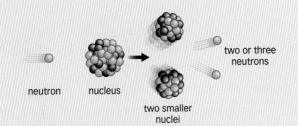

neutron   nucleus

two or three neutrons

two smaller nuclei

▲ When a fissionable nucleus absorbs a neutron, it splits into two smaller nuclei, and fires out two or three neutrons in its turn

When an atom splits as part of nuclear fission, it also releases two or three extra neutrons. These are absorbed by other atoms in the materials that make up the nuclear reactor. Some of the new atoms which are created are radioactive. Absorbing the extra neutron changes their nucleus and can make it unstable.

The production of radioactive waste, both from fission and from reactor materials that absorb neutrons, means that it is very expensive to dismantle a nuclear power plant. This process is called decommissioning the reactor. Specially trained engineers work for decades to carefully remove all the radioactive material.

Key words

nuclear fission, radioactive waste

Did you know...?

The first nuclear reactor was built in a squash court at the University of Chicago in 1942. With the Italian physicist Enrico Fermi leading, the reactor was completed as part of the US's top secret project to build the first nuclear bomb.

Exam tip

✓ Do not confuse nuclear fission with radioactive decay (alpha, beta or gamma) – nuclear reactors or nuclear bombs are not an example of a use of radioactivity.

Questions

1   What is the fuel used in most nuclear reactors?

2   Describe how nuclear reactors generate electricity.

3   What particle is absorbed by materials in nuclear reactors to make them radioactive?

4   Draw a diagram showing a nuclear fission and describe the process.

15: Chain reactions

Learning objectives

After studying this topic, you should be able to:

- describe how the fission of uranium atoms can lead to a chain reaction
- describe the differences between chain reactions in nuclear reactors and nuclear weapons
- explain how the chain reaction in nuclear reactors is kept under control

A In terms of energy, why is splitting just one single atom not very useful?

B Give two examples of where a nuclear chain reaction takes place.

A nuclear explosion releases massive amounts of energy

What is a chain reaction?

Splitting a single atom does not release very much energy, not even enough to power the smallest of electrical devices. Instead, a very large number of nuclear fissions are needed.

When uranium atoms are split they release two or three neutrons. If there are enough uranium atoms in a sample of material, a **chain reaction** may start. Neutrons released in the first fission go on to make more fissions. These fissions release more neutrons, which lead to even more fissions, and the process continues.

The greater the number of fissions, the greater the amount of energy released. In nuclear reactors there are billions of fissions every second.

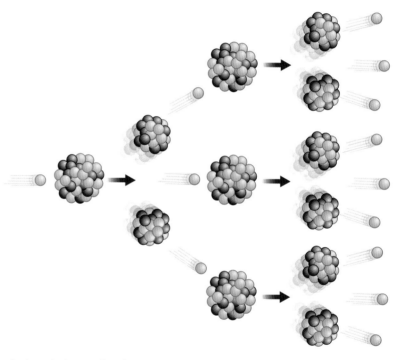
In a chain reaction the neutrons from one fission go on to create further fissions

Nuclear reactors and nuclear weapons

Both nuclear weapons and nuclear reactors use the energy released in a chain reaction of uranium atoms. In a nuclear reactor this chain reaction is carefully controlled. In a nuclear weapon the reaction is allowed to go out of control, releasing massive amounts of energy.

Controlling nuclear fission

When a nuclear weapon explodes, the number of fissions rapidly increases. After the first atom has been split, the neutrons it has released go on to split three more atoms. These three release enough neutrons to split nine more atoms. After just 30 cycles, more than 68 000 billion atoms have been split and the process keeps growing. This releases huge amounts of energy in a very short space of time.

In a nuclear reactor the fissions are carefully controlled so that, on average, one fission leads to one more fission, leading to one more. This maintains a steady, and constant, reaction.

Special rods called **control rods** are raised and lowered into the reactor. They are made of a special material that absorbs neutrons, reducing the number available to go on and split more atoms. They are very carefully positioned to ensure that there are enough neutrons left to create further fissions, but not enough to cause the reaction to go out of control.

▲ Control rods absorb neutrons inside nuclear reactors, helping to maintain a steady reaction

Questions

1 How many neutrons are released when one atom of uranium is split?

2 Draw a diagram to show a chain reaction, and describe how it is formed.

3 Explain the differences between the chain reaction in a nuclear power station and the one in a nuclear weapon.

4 Explain how the chain reaction is controlled inside a nuclear reactor.

5 Assuming all three neutrons go on to split three more atoms, how many atoms are split on the:

(a) third cycle

(b) tenth cycle

(c) 20th cycle?

Did you know...?

The Russian Tsar bomb, released the energy equivalent to exploding 50 million tonnes of TNT. That is an incredible 2.1×10^{17} J, enough to power over 55 million TVs for whole year.

Key words

chain reaction, **control rods**

Learning objectives

After studying this topic, you should be able to:

- ✔ describe the process of nuclear fusion
- ✔ know that nuclear fusion is the process of energy release in stars and hydrogen bombs
- ✔ describe the differences between nuclear fission and nuclear fusion
- ✔ know why cold fusion is not accepted as a method of nuclear fusion

Key words

nuclear fusion, hydrogen bombs, cold fusion

▲ Stars release energy via nuclear fusion in their core

Exam tip   OCR

- ✔ Be careful not to mix up fission and fusion. In nuclear *fusion* nuclei are *fused* together. Nuclear fission is the splitting of atoms.

B Why is it difficult to fuse two small nuclei together?

Nuclear fusion

Nuclear fusion is another kind of nuclear reaction, but it is very different from nuclear fission. In nuclear fusion two small nuclei of hydrogen are joined (or fused) together. This forms a single heavier nucleus of helium.

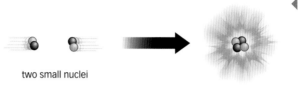

two small nuclei

one larger nucleus

◀ In nuclear fusion two smaller nuclei fuse together to make a larger nucleus

A In nuclear fusion, what are fused together?

A nuclear fusion reaction releases energy in the form of heat (just like nuclear fission).

Fusion in stars and bombs

Nuclear fusion is the process by which energy is released in all stars, including our Sun. It is also the main way energy is released in **hydrogen bombs** (H-bombs). In both stars and bombs, isotopes of hydrogen are fused together to make helium. This releases vast amounts of energy.

It is very difficult to sustain a nuclear fusion reaction on Earth. Atomic nuclei are positively charged due to their protons. This means they repel each other when they get close together. The nuclei must be moving very, very fast to get close enough to fuse. This is achieved in the core of stars like our Sun as the core is so hot and is under very high pressure. At extremely high temperatures the nuclei are moving around at very high speeds and so they smash together. Reproducing this reaction on Earth requires exceptionally high pressures and temperatures. This is very difficult to do safely and offers significant engineering challenges.

A typical fusion reaction involves the fusing of two isotopes of hydrogen. For example, hydrogen 1 and hydrogen 2 can fuse to form helium 3 in the reaction below:

$$H_1^1 \ + \ H_1^2 \ \rightarrow \ He_2^3$$

The cold fusion controversy

Using nuclear fusion to generate electricity in the future would have the same advantages as using traditional nuclear power. No carbon dioxide is produced and very large amounts of electricity can be generated. Yet, unlike nuclear fission, nuclear fusion does not produce radioactive waste.

Safely controlling the high temperatures needed for fusion is proving very difficult. Several experimental fusion reactors are being built. These are very expensive and so countries work together to share costs, expertise, and the future benefits. Some use superstrong magnetic fields to try to squeeze the nuclei together. Others use incredibly powerful lasers to heat up a tiny volume of gas to enormous temperatures.

◀ The interior of the experimental JET Tokamak fusion reactor in Oxfordshire

In 1989, a group of scientists claimed to have achieved **cold fusion**. They claimed they were able to fuse atoms together at room temperature.

This would have been an incredible breakthrough. Other scientists used their data and tried to repeat their findings. All scientific ideas and theories are thoroughly tested by other scientists to check any claims.

Despite several attempts, no-one could recreate the original findings. This led scientists to believe that the claims made by the original team were false. All their findings were disputed and so cold fusion is not now accepted as an energy production method.

The hydrogen bomb

In a hydrogen bomb, the immense temperatures needed to fuse the atoms of hydrogen together are created by a nuclear fission explosion. The bombs contain a core of uranium 235 or plutonium 239 surrounded by hydrogen. When it explodes, it creates an uncontrolled chain reaction which releases vast amounts of heat. This heat in turn causes the hydrogen atoms to fuse together, releasing even more energy.

Questions

1 Name the two nuclear reactions which release energy.

2 Draw a diagram to show a nuclear fusion reaction and describe the process.

3 Explain how stars are able to sustain nuclear fusion reactions in their cores.

4 Describe the differences between nuclear fusion and nuclear fission.

5 Describe how a hydrogen bomb works.

↓ E

↓ C

↓ A*

Module summary

Revision checklist

O Some materials gain an electrostatic charge when rubbed together. Electrons are transferred to produce a charge. Opposite charges attract, like charges repel.

O You can receive an electrostatic shock when built-up charge is conducted away from you, or when charge from a charged object is conducted to earth through you.

O Static electricity causes lightning, and can cause explosions in flammable gases. It is useful in separating smoke particles from waste gases, in paint spraying, and in debribrillators.

O Resistors are used to change the current in a circuit. Current decreases as resistance increases.

O UK three-pin plugs contain a live wire (brown), a neutral wire (blue), an earth wire (green and yellow), and a fuse.

O Electrical safety devices include fuses, earth wires, and circuit breakers.

O Power = current × voltage.

O The oscillations in longitudinal waves are parallel to the wave movement and feature compressions and rarefactions.

O Sound waves above human hearing (20 000 Hz) are called ultrasound. Ultrasound has various medical uses.

O Radioactive decay occurs when an unstable nucleus breaks down and emits ionising radiation. Radioactivity decreases with time.

O Alpha particles, beta particles, and gamma rays are ionising radiation.

O Radiation is used in medical tracers and radioactive dating.

O X-rays and gamma rays are both types of electromagnetic wave, with high frequencies and small wavelengths.

O Gamma rays are ionising and have a lot of energy. They can damage or kill cells, making them useful in sterilising medical equipment and treating cancerous tumours.

O In a nuclear power station nuclear fission reactions produce steam to drive turbines.

O Nuclear fusion is the fusion of two hydrogen nuclei to form a helium nucleus, releasing energy. It takes place in stars and hydrogen bombs.

O Nuclear fusion could be a sustainable means of electricity generation for the future as no CO_2 or nuclear waste is generated, but the cost and technical challenge involved is currently too high.

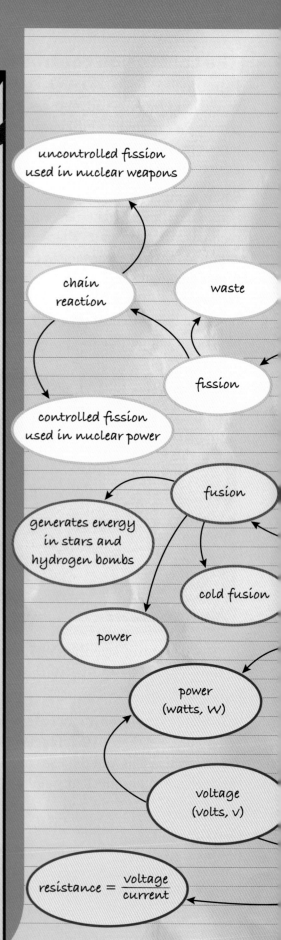

NOW USE THE P4 GRADE CHECKER ON PAGE 246

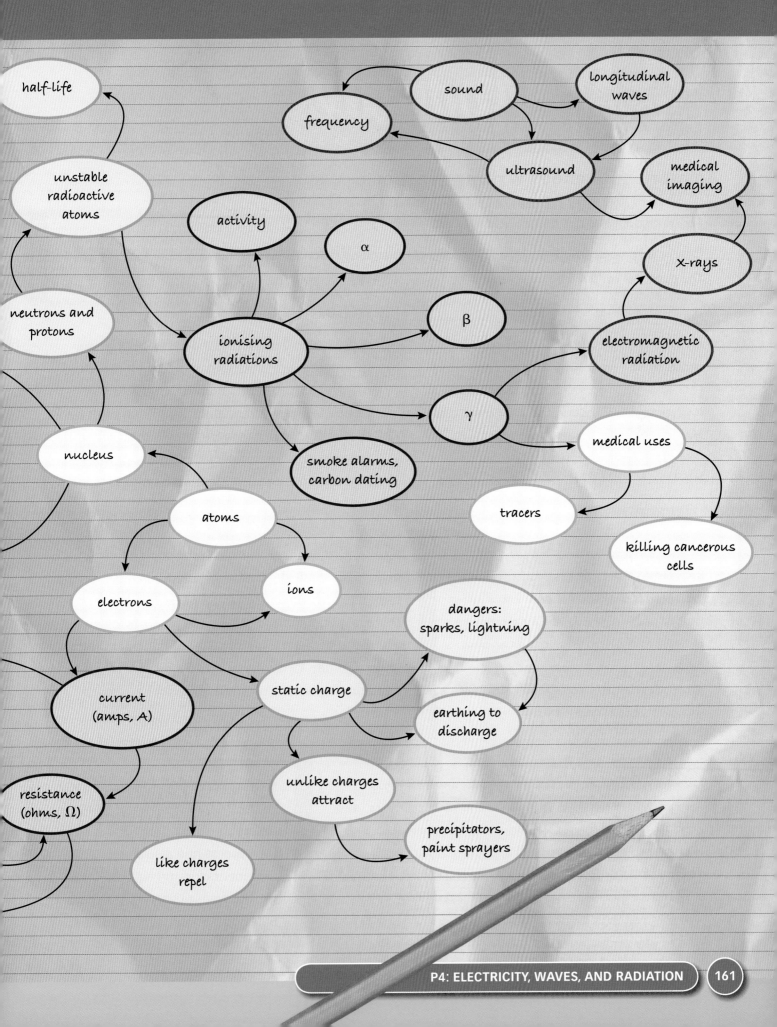

half-life

unstable radioactive atoms

neutrons and protons

nucleus

activity

α

β

γ

ionising radiations

smoke alarms, carbon dating

atoms

electrons

ions

current (amps, A)

resistance (ohms, Ω)

like charges repel

static charge

unlike charges attract

precipitators, paint sprayers

dangers: sparks, lightning

earthing to discharge

frequency

sound

longitudinal waves

ultrasound

medical imaging

X-rays

electromagnetic radiation

medical uses

tracers

killing cancerous cells

Answering Extended Writing questions

There are many nuclear power stations operating successfully worldwide.

Explain the process involved; and discuss some of the arguments for and against building more such stations.

The quality of written communication will be assessed in your answer to this question.

QUESTION

Nuclear power gets electricity from radioactivity from uranum there are lots of α, β, and γ flying around hiting things and geting hot. The stuff is dangerous becos if it leaks out an you eat it you get sick and die. I don't want it near me! But its good becose it doesn't make grenehous gas.

↓ E

Examiner: The facts given here about power production are mostly wrong, though there is mention of uranium and heat. One reason in favour is given, although lacking detail; but the reasoning against is more tabloid than scientific. Physics words are not used properly. Spelling, punctuation, and grammar are erratic.

In nuclear power, atoms hit each other and brake apart. This is called fision. This makes the fuel get very hot, and that is used for the power. The electricity is chepe and clean. But It is dangerous because they can explode, and poison a lot of people, also terorists can steal the radioactive fuel and make a bomb.

↓ C

Examiner: This answer has some correct ideas, and deals with some key points. But detail is missing: the fission process is not accurately described; nor is there any explanation of why the power is 'clean'. There are occasional errors in spelling, punctuation, and grammar. Crucially, the word 'fission' is ambiguously spelt – could the student have meant 'fusion'?

Nuclear power uses fission. A moving neutron hits a uranium nucleus; this splits into two smaller atoms, and more neutrons are released. They hit other uranium nuclei, and a chain reaction happens. It causes heat, which makes the power. It doesn't use fossil fuel, and no greenhouse gas is produced. But there is radioactive waste material which is difficult to store safely; and there is a risk of dangerous material leaking like at Chernobyl.

↓ A*

Examiner: This is a good answer. In the limited space available it covers most key points, addressing the process and also some arguments for and against. Physics words are used correctly, except for 'atom'. Spelling, punctuation, and grammar are fine.

Exam-style questions

1 Which colour wire should be attached to each of the pins in a three-pin mains plug?

Choose from:

red   red/yellow

yellow   green/yellow

green   green/blue

blue   red/green

brown   yellow/brown

A01   **a**   live

A01   **b**   neutral

A01   **c**   earth.

2 You have a bulb labelled 12 V, 2 A.

A02   **a**   Calculate its resistance.

A02   **b**   Calculate its power output.

A02   **c**   Suppose you are now given another bulb with half the resistance. What would its power output be?

3 The graph shows the activity of a sample of bismuth-210 against time.

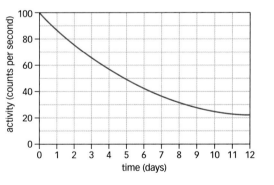

A02   **a**   What is the half-life of bismuth-210?

A02   **b**   You have a sample of bismuth-210 with activity 300 counts per second. What will its activity be after 10 days?

A02   **c**   You have a sample of bismuth-210 containing 8×10^6 atoms. How many atoms will be left after 20 days?

A02   **d**   You have a sample of bismuth-210 with activity 200 counts per second. What will its activity be after 5 years?

4   **a** $^{241}_{95}$Am describes the nucleus americium-241, used in smoke alarms. How many protons and neutrons are in this nucleus?

A02

A02   **b**   Americium-241 decays into a nucleus of nepturium (Np) by emitting an α-particle. Write a nuclear equation for this decay.

A02   **c** $^{90}_{38}$Sr describes the nucleus strontium-90. It decays into a nucleus of yttrium (Y) by emitting a β-particle. Write a nuclear equation for this decay.

Extended Writing

5 Explain how fuses, circuit breakers, and the earth wire help to keep mains electricity safe.

A01

6 Explain what is meant by ionising radiation, and explain which of α, β, and γ radiations is the most ionising of the three.

A01

7 Describe the process of fusion; and explain why scientists do not believe that the claimed cold fusion discovery was correct.

A01

P5

Space for reflection

Why study this module?

We have only started to use satellites in the last 50 years. They are now an essential part of communication, scientific research, navigation, and even home entertainment. As part of this module you will learn about forces and motion. You will study how satellites stay in orbit, learning about some of their uses, and you will find out what happens to the path of a tennis ball or a bullet fired from a gun.

In this module you will also learn more about how electromagnetic waves travel through our atmosphere, how they reflect off invisible layers, and how we communicate with satellites. You will find out why at the bottom of a valley you can still get a good radio signal but not a clear picture on your television.

Finally you will learn more about light, how it is refracted by different materials, how rainbows are formed, and how simple lenses can focus light into a point. You will learn the history of ideas about the nature of light and how the most famous physicist of all time, Sir Isaac Newton, was wrong!

You should remember?

1. The meaning of speed, velocity, acceleration, and momentum.
2. How the forces acting on an object effect its motion.
3. How waves can be used to communicate.
4. The properties of electromagnetic waves.
5. How waves are refracted when they travel from one medium to another.

Sputnik was the first ever satellite. Launched by the former Soviet Union back in 1957, the satellite itself did not do much. It just sent out a regular beep which could be picked up on the ground when the satellite was overhead. However, its impact has been enormous.

Sputnik ushered in the space age. This was a series of political, military, technological, and scientific developments that led to landing a man on the moon and the development of countless modern technologies. There are now thousands of satellites in orbit, including the International Space Station, pictured. They perform a wide variety of jobs. Some are used to beam down TV signals, others peer into distant galaxies. Some are used to spy on other countries and satellites are even used in sat nav to help you drive from A to B. All this and more, thanks to Sputnik!

Key words

satellite, natural satellite, orbit, artificial satellite, gravitational attraction, gravity, weight, inverse square law

▲ The International Space Station is an artificial satellite

> **A** What kind of satellite is the Hubble Space Telescope?

◀ The moon is a natural satellite of the Earth

Natural and artificial satellites of the Earth

A **satellite** is an object that orbits a larger object in space. For example, the Moon is a satellite of the Earth. It is a **natural satellite**.

Along with the Moon, the Earth has over 20 000 man-made objects in **orbit**. These are called **artificial satellites**. Some are very small, just a few metres across. Others are much larger commercial or military satellites, perhaps the size of buses. The Hubble Space Telescope and the International Space Station are examples of larger artificial satellites. If you look up at night you can often see them passing overhead.

Artificial satellites perform a number of very important roles, including:
- telecommunications (eg satellite TV)
- weather prediction
- military uses (eg spy satellites)
- satellite navigation systems (eg GPS found in some cars and mobile phones)
- scientific research (eg Hubble Space Telescope)
- producing images of the Earth.

What keeps satellites in orbit?

As you may recall, any two masses attract each other. The force between them is called **gravitational attraction** or **gravity**.

Satellites are kept in orbit by this universal force of attraction. The Moon stays in orbit around the Earth because of the gravitational attraction between them – otherwise it would fly off into space! The Earth and other planets stay in orbit around the Sun because of the gravitational force between them and the Sun.

The bigger the masses of any two objects, the bigger the attraction between them. The Earth is more massive than the Moon, so the force of attraction between you and the Earth would be greater than the attraction between you and the Moon.

The gravitational attraction force is called **weight**.

B Give two examples of uses of artificial satellites.

C What is the name of the force that keeps satellites in orbit?

Exam tip OCR

✔ Learn the examples of uses of satellites – this can be an easy way to pick up marks.

✔ You may remember that you can calculate an object's weight using this equation: weight = mass × gravitational field strength.

Orbit and distance

The gravitational force of attraction varies with the distance between two objects. It varies in proportion to an **inverse square law**. This means that if the distance between the objects is trebled, for example, the force between them is nine times smaller (3^2). It is reduced to one-ninth of what it was previously.

Comets have highly elliptical orbits around the Sun. The furthest distance of a comet from the Sun can be more than 50 times its closest distance from the Sun. The change in the distance means that the gravitational force of attraction between a comet and the Sun also varies enormously. It is higher when the comet is closer to the Sun. This means that the speed of the comet in its orbit also varies. It is higher when it is closer to the Sun.

The time taken for a planet to orbit the Sun depends on its distance from the Sun. The further away a planet is from the Sun, the longer its time period to orbit the Sun.

The times for some objects to complete an orbit are shown in the table.

Object	Time to orbit the Sun	Distance from Sun
Halley's comet	75 years	Between 88 million km (closest) and 5270 million km (furthest)
Mercury	116 days	Between 46 million and 70 million km
Earth	1 year	150 million km
Jupiter	11.9 years	780 million km

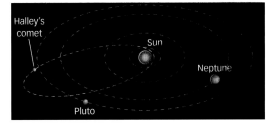

▲ The orbit of Halley's comet

Questions

1 What is the difference between a natural satellite and an artificial satellite?

2 How does the International Space Station stay in orbit around the Earth?

3 Explain why the Moon is in orbit of the Earth, not the other way around.

4 Explain how the speed of a comet varies in its orbit of the Sun.

5 How much stronger is the gravitational force of attraction on Halley's comet when it is closest to the Sun than when it is furthest away from the Sun?

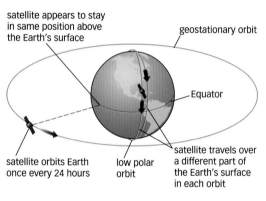

satellite appears to stay in same position above the Earth's surface

geostationary orbit

Equator

satellite orbits Earth once every 24 hours

low polar orbit

satellite travels over a different part of the Earth's surface in each orbit

⏶ Different types of satellite orbit

A What type of orbit is used for a satellite that takes pictures of the Earth's surface?

B What force is needed to keep a satellite in orbit?

How high are satellites above the Earth?

Satellites are carefully placed into different orbits at different heights, depending on their use. They can be as low as just a few hundred kilometres above the Earth's surface, or tens of thousands of kilometres high. The International Space Station (ISS) is just 340 km above the Earth. Satellites used for satellite television are 36 000 km up (over 100 times further away).

The height of a satellite affects its orbital **time period**. This is how long it takes to orbit once around the Earth. The higher a satellite is above the Earth, the longer its time period. The ISS takes just 90 minutes to complete one orbit. Satellites used for television take 24 hours. Satellites used in satellite navigation systems (such as GPS) have low orbits, so they can easily send and receive signals. Their low orbit means they travel very fast. There are normally 5 or 6 navigational satellites overhead at once.

Types of orbit

Satellites are placed in different orbits as well as at different heights. The **trajectory** of a satellite is the name given to the path it follows around the Earth. There are two main trajectories followed by artificial satellites:

- low **polar orbit**
- **geostationary orbit**.

Satellites in low polar orbit have a short time period. As the Earth rotates, satellites in low polar orbit can observe any part of the planet over a few days. This makes them ideal for taking pictures of the Earth's surface, and for military purposes. They are closer to the Earth than satellites in geostationary orbit, so can produce much clearer images of the surface and need less powerful communications systems to send and receive signals.

Satellites in geostationary orbit are much further away. A satellite in geostationary orbit:

- orbits the Earth once in 24 hours
- remains in a fixed position above the Earth's surface
- orbits the Earth above the Equator.

As they stay fixed above the same position on Earth, geostationary satellites are always overhead in certain places. This makes them useful for communications (TV and radio broadcasts) and weather forecasting.

They are always pointing at the same place, so they don't miss anything. Satellite dishes on Earth can be directed straight at the satellite and don't need to move.

Whatever orbit a satellite is in, it moves in a circle. Any object following a circular path requires a **centripetal force** to keep it moving in a circle. For satellites this centripetal force is provided by gravity, which pulls the satellite towards the centre of the Earth.

Exam tip **OCR**

✔ Remember that the closer to the Earth the satellite is, the shorter the time period of its orbit.

✔ Don't say that geostationary satellites do not move. They are moving very fast!

More on satellite orbits

The centripetal force acting on an artificial satellite is always at right angles to its motion and is always directed towards the centre of the Earth. As the direction of the satellite is continually changing, its velocity is also changing, so it is accelerating (although it continues to travel at a steady speed). The satellite is continually accelerating towards the Earth.

Despite being pulled towards the Earth, a satellite stays in orbit because it is moving so fast. At point A, the satellite's velocity is at right angles to the acceleration and the centripetal force. The force causes the satellite to change direction, but it stays at the same height. This happens at all points in the orbit and leads to a circular path. The satellite's high velocity keeps it in a stable orbit. If it were to stop, it would accelerate towards the Earth.

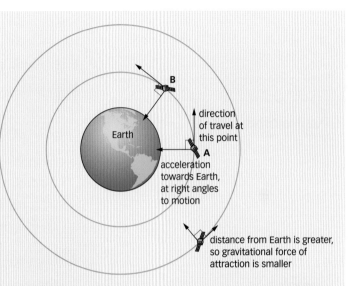

▲ The direction of motion at B has changed, but is still at right angles to the acceleration

The distance between the Earth and artificial satellites in lower orbits is smaller, so the gravitational attraction is greater. This means that they travel faster. Low polar orbit satellites orbit the Earth with a time period of about 2 hours. Geostationary satellites orbit with a period of 24 hours. The satellites in low polar orbit have a much shorter time period because the gravitational force on them is larger, so they travel much faster than those in geostationary orbit.

Questions

1 How does the height of a satellite above the Earth's surface affect its period of orbit?

2 What are the differences between a geostationary orbit and a low polar orbit?

3 Why are TV satellite dishes in a fixed position?

4 Why does a satellite in a geostationary orbit travel more slowly than one in a low polar orbit?

5 Explain how the force of gravity keeps artificial satellites in orbit around the Earth.

E
↓
C
↓
A*

Learning objectives

After studying this topic, you should be able to:

✔ describe the difference between scalar and vector quantities

✔ add up parallel vectors to find the vector sum

✔ find the resultant of vectors that are at right angles to each other

Key words

size, scalar, direction, vector, velocity, resultant

Relative speed

🔺 These three cars are travelling on a straight road. The speed of the green car relative to the red car is 10 km/h to the right. The speed of the blue car relative to the red car is 100 km/h to the left.

A Give two examples of scalar quantities.

B What two things does a vector quantity have?

C Is weight a scalar or a vector quantity?

What direction?

Some quantities only tell us how big something is. For example, a bag of flour may have a mass of 1 kg, or the temperature outside might be 16 °C. A quantity that only has a **size** is called a **scalar** quantity. Time is another example.

For some quantities, the **direction** is just as important. For instance, with a force we need to know the direction and the size of the push or pull. A quantity that has a direction as well as a size is called a **vector**. Acceleration is vector quantity.

A car is travelling at 50 km/h. This tells us how fast the car is moving, but not which direction it is travelling in. The speed of the car is 50 km/h and it is a scalar quantity.

Now imagine a car travelling north at 50 km/h. We know how fast the car is moving and we know what direction it is going in. The **velocity** of the car is 50 km/h northwards and this is a vector quantity.

Vector sums

Worked example 1

Sam is walking at 1.75 m/s. He steps on a moving walkway that is going in the same direction, but carries on walking as before. The moving walkway is travelling at 1.25 m/s. What is Sam's total velocity?
The velocities are parallel, so we can add them together.

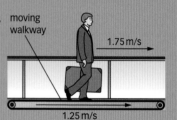

total velocity = 1.75 m/s + 1.25 m/s = 3.0 m/s

Worked example 2

What is the total force on the box?

The forces are parallel, so we can add them together. Assume that the positive direction is left to right, so the right-hand force is –10 N.

Add forces together: 40 N + (–10 N) = 30 N

Finding a resultant vector

Sometimes vectors are at an angle to each other. For example, if an aircraft is flying in a cross wind, there are two velocity vectors at an angle to each other. The **resultant** velocity of the plane is the sum of the two velocities.

When the two velocities are at right angles to each other, you can calculate the resultant of the two vectors by drawing a scale diagram or by calculation.

Worked example 3

A microlight is flying at 40 m/s to the east in a cross wind from the south of 10 m/s. What is the resultant velocity of the microlight?

To draw a scale diagram, draw an arrow representing the velocity of the microlight to scale. Then draw, to the same scale, an arrow representing the cross wind starting at the point of the arrow for the velocity of the microlight, as shown in the diagram. Then measure the length of the resultant arrow and its angle, θ, with the horizontal.

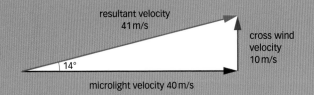

resultant velocity 41 m/s
cross wind velocity 10 m/s
14°
microlight velocity 40 m/s

Or calculate the size of the resultant velocity using Pythagoras' theorem:

$$(\text{resultant velocity})^2 = 40^2 + 10^2 = 1600 + 100 = 1700$$
$$\text{resultant velocity} = \sqrt{1700} = 41.2 \text{ m/s}$$

Calculate the size of the angle using trigonometry:

$$\tan \theta = \frac{10}{40} = 0.25$$
$$\theta = \tan^{-1} 0.25 = 14°$$

The resultant velocity is 41 m/s at an angle of 14° north of east.

Questions

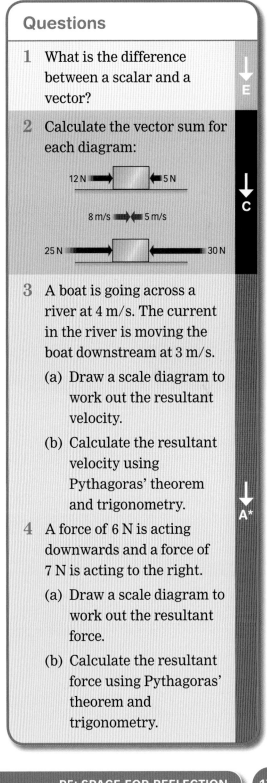

1 What is the difference between a scalar and a vector?

2 Calculate the vector sum for each diagram:

12 N → ☐ ← 5 N

8 m/s →→ ← 5 m/s

25 N → ☐ ← 30 N

3 A boat is going across a river at 4 m/s. The current in the river is moving the boat downstream at 3 m/s.

  (a) Draw a scale diagram to work out the resultant velocity.

  (b) Calculate the resultant velocity using Pythagoras' theorem and trigonometry.

4 A force of 6 N is acting downwards and a force of 7 N is acting to the right.

  (a) Draw a scale diagram to work out the resultant force.

  (b) Calculate the resultant force using Pythagoras' theorem and trigonometry.

Learning objectives

After studying this topic, you should be able to:

✔ use the equations of motion
$s = \dfrac{(u + v)}{2}$ and $v = u + at$

✔ use the equations of motion
$v^2 = u^2 + 2as$ and $s = ut + \frac{1}{2}at^2$

▲ You can use the equations of motion to calculate distances, speeds, and other quantities

Exam tip

✔ When answering questions involving the equations of motion, write down all the quantities that you know, and the one you are trying to find. Then select the equation that contains all of these quantities.

Average speed and distance

During a journey, speed can change. If acceleration is constant we can easily calculate the average speed. If the initial speed is u and the final speed is v, then:

$$\text{average speed} = \frac{(u + v)}{2}$$

Distance travelled is speed × time, so if the distance travelled is s, and the length of time of the journey is t, then:

$$s = \frac{(u + v)}{2} \quad \text{or} \quad s = \tfrac{1}{2}(u + v)t$$

If the steady acceleration is a and the time the acceleration lasts for is t, then the initial and final speeds are connected by the equation:

$$v = u + at$$

These equations work when something is moving in a straight line and any acceleration is constant (steady).

Worked example 1

An aeroplane accelerates to a final velocity of 200 m/s over 20 s. Its acceleration is 4 m/s².

i   What was the initial velocity of the aeroplane?

ii How far did it travel?

i $v = u + at$
$v = 200$ m/s, $t = 20$ s, $a = 4$ m/s²
$$200 \text{ m/s} = u + 4 \text{ m/s}^2 \times 20 \text{ s}$$

Rearranging the equation:
$$u = 200 \text{ m/s} - 4 \text{ m/s}^2 \times 20 \text{ s}$$
$$= 200 \text{ m/s} - 80 \text{ m/s}$$
$$= 120 \text{ m/s}$$

ii $s = \tfrac{1}{2}(u + v)t$
$$s = \tfrac{1}{2}(120 \text{ m/s} + 200 \text{ m/s}) \times 20 \text{ s}$$
$$= 160 \text{ m/s} \times 20 \text{ s}$$
$$= 3200 \text{ m}$$

A   Which equation would you use to calculate the distance an object travels?

B   A train accelerates at 2 m/s² for 20 seconds. Its final velocity is 40 m/s. What was its initial velocity?

More equations of motion

We can combine and rearrange the two equations of motion to get two more:

$$v^2 = u^2 + 2as$$
$$s = ut + \tfrac{1}{2}at^2$$

Worked example 2

A car travels 216 m. Its final velocity is 12 m/s and initial velocity is 6 m/s. What is its acceleration?

$s = 216$ m

$v = 12$ m/s

$u = 6$ m/s

We use the equation $v^2 = u^2 + 2as$

$$(12 \text{ m/s})^2 = (6 \text{ m/s})^2 + 2 \times a \times 216 \text{ m}$$

Rearranging the equation:

$$a = \frac{(144 - 36)}{(2 \times 216)\,\text{m/s}^2} = \frac{108}{432\,\text{m/s}^2} = 0.25 \text{ m/s}^2$$

Worked example 3

A train travels 200 m while it accelerates at –2 m/s² for 5 seconds. What was the train's initial velocity?

$s = 200$ m

$a = -2$ m/s² (the minus sign tells us the train is slowing down or decelerating)

$t = 5$ s

Use the equation $s = ut + \tfrac{1}{2}at^2$

$$200 \text{ m} = u \times 5 \text{ s} + \tfrac{1}{2} \times -2 \text{ m/s}^2 \times (5 \text{ s})^2$$

Rearranging the equation:

$$u = \frac{200 \text{ m} - (\tfrac{1}{2} \times -2 \text{ m/s}^2 \times (5 \text{ s})^2)}{5 \text{ s}} = \frac{225 \text{ m}}{5 \text{ s}} = 45 \text{ m/s}$$

C   The initial velocity of a car is 5 m/s. It accelerates at 1.5 m/s² for 8 seconds. How far does it travel?

D   An aeroplane is stationary. It accelerates down a runway at 2 m/s². It travels 900 m. What is its final velocity?

Questions

1   A car's initial velocity is 5 m/s. It accelerates at 1.5 m/s² for 6 seconds. What is its final velocity?

2   An aeroplane's initial velocity is 120 m/s. It accelerates at –3 m/s² for 10 seconds. What is its final velocity?

3   An object is dropped from the top of a cliff. It takes 2 seconds to reach the bottom. The acceleration due to gravity is 10 m/s².

   (a) What is the object's final velocity?

   (b) What is the height of the cliff?

4   A train travels 168 m as it accelerates from an initial velocity of 5 m/s over 12 s. What is the acceleration of the train?

5   An aeroplane travels 1200 m while it accelerates at 2 m/s². Its final velocity was 150 m/s. What was its initial velocity?

▲ The aircraft is accelerating down the runway

Key words

projectile, trajectory, parabolic, range, optimum angle

▲ The long jumper is a projectile and his path, or trajectory, is parabolic in shape

▲ The range of this football depends on the launch angle

A Give three examples of projectiles.

B What is meant by the range of a projectile?

The path of a projectile

When you kick a football, it takes a curved path through the air. The path of the football has this curved shape because of the Earth's gravitational field.

Anything that is thrown (or 'projected') through the air has a curved path, and is called a **projectile**. Other examples of projectiles are missiles and cannonballs, and all balls that are hit, thrown, or kicked in sports. A dart is a projectile when it has been thrown. Long jumpers are projectiles from the moment when their feet leave the ground.

The curved path of a projectile is called its **trajectory**. The shape of the path of a projectile is said to be **parabolic**.

When a projectile is moving through the air, gravity is the only force acting on it, apart from air resistance.

The diagram below shows a football that is kicked horizontally off a cliff. If air resistance is ignored, the football has a constant horizontal velocity. The football is accelerated downwards towards the sea by the force of gravity. This acceleration only affects the vertical velocity of the football. Its vertical velocity increases steadily while the horizontal part of its motion stays the same.

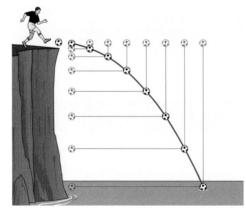

◀ After this football has been kicked, the only force acting on it is gravity

How far a ball travels when it is hit – its **range** – depends on the angle at which it leaves the ground. This is called the launch angle. If the launch angle is high, the ball will not travel as far, because the horizontal velocity will be smaller. If the launch angle is low, the ball will fall back to the ground in less time. The greatest range is achieved when the launch angle is 45° – this is the **optimum angle**.

Horizontal and vertical velocity vectors

The horizontal and vertical velocities of a projectile are vectors. The resultant velocity of a projectile is the resultant vector of these horizontal and vertical components.

> **C** Why are the vertical and horizontal velocities vectors?

You can use the equations of motion from spread P5.4 to work out how long it will take for a projectile to hit the ground and work out how far it has travelled. You use the equations separately for the horizontal and the vertical parts of the motion.

Worked example

A stunt car drives horizontally off a small cliff with a velocity of 12 m/s. The cliff is 1.25 m high.

i How long does the car take to hit the ground?

ii How far from the base of the cliff will the car land?

i Looking at the vertical part of the motion, height of the cliff, $s = 1.25$ m, initial vertical velocity, $u = 0$ m/s (as the car is travelling horizontally when it leaves the cliff, it has no vertical velocity), and vertical acceleration, $a = 10$ m/s^2 (just acceleration due to gravity).

$$s = ut + \tfrac{1}{2}at^2$$
$$1.25 \text{ m} = 0 \text{ m/s} \times t + \tfrac{1}{2} \times 10 \text{ m/s}^2 \times t^2$$
$$t^2 = \frac{1.25 \text{ m}}{5 \text{ m/s}^2} = (0.25) \text{ s}^2$$
$$t = \sqrt{(0.25)} \text{s}^2 = 0.5 \text{ s}$$

ii Looking at the horizontal part of the motion, horizontal velocity of the car = 12 m/s (and this stays the same), and the car lands at the foot of the cliff after 0.5 s (from calculation above).

Distance car lands from the base of the cliff = horizontal velocity × time
= 12 m/s × 0.5 s
= 6 m

Exam tip

✔ Remember to read the question properly. In a recent exam, students were asked to identify the projectile in a photo – many identified the sport instead!

Questions

1 What is a projectile?

2 Explain why a long jumper is a projectile.

3 Explain why the horizontal velocity of a projectile remains constant (ignoring air resistance).

4 What is the vertical velocity of the car in the worked example when it hits the ground?

5 A stone is fired horizontally from a catapult off the top of a building, with a horizontal velocity of 25 m/s. The stone takes 2.5 seconds to hit the ground.

(a) What is the height of the building?

(b) What is the stone's vertical velocity when it hits the ground?

(c) How far from the base of the building does the stone hit the ground?

(d) Calculate the resultant velocity of the stone as it hits the ground.

Key words

action, reaction

▲ The wall pushes against Tom with an equal and opposite force

A In the example of Tom and the wall, which force is the action?

B What pairs of forces act on a book sitting on a table?

C What is the reaction to the pull of the Earth's gravity on the person in the diagram on the right?

Simple actions and reactions

Tom is leaning against a wall with a force F. He does not fall over because the wall pushes back on Tom with an equal force F that acts in the opposite direction. There is a pair of forces – the force exerted on the wall by Tom and the force the wall exerts on Tom. This is an important principle of physics – forces always appear in pairs. Each **action** has an equal and opposite **reaction**. It is known as Newton's third law of motion.

When a person stands on the ground, there are two forces acting: a pair of contact forces between the person's feet and the ground, and a pair of forces due to the gravitational attraction between the Earth and the person. The push of the person's feet on the ground is equal and opposite to the push of the ground on the person's feet. The pull of Earth's gravity on the person is equal and opposite to the pull of the person's gravity on the Earth.

The action forces are the push of the person's feet on the ground and the pull of the Earth's gravity on the person. The reaction forces are the push of the ground on the person's feet and the pull of the person's gravity on the Earth.

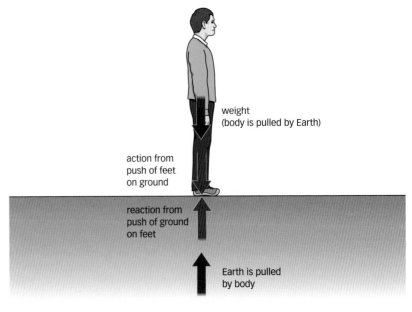

▲ Pairs of forces acting on a person standing on the ground

When an object is hanging from a crane, there are two pairs of forces acting on the object. The first pair of forces involves tension in the wire that is lifting the object. The object is pulling on the wire. There is an equal and opposite force from the pull of the wire on the object.

The second pair of forces involves the gravitational attraction between the Earth and the object. The pull of the Earth on the object is equal and opposite to the pull of the object on the Earth.

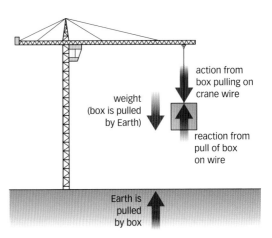

action from box pulling on crane wire

weight (box is pulled by Earth)

reaction from pull of box on wire

Earth is pulled by box

▲ There are pairs of action and reactions acting on the object the crane is lifting

> **D** What is the reaction force to the weight of the object on the crane?

Collisions

When two objects collide, they exert equal and opposite forces on each other. This is another example of Newton's third law. For example, when this car collided with the post, the car exerted a force on the post. The post exerted a force on the car that was equal and opposite to the force the car exerted on the post.

▲ The car and post exerted equal and opposite forces on each other

Questions

1 What is the direction of a reaction force?

▼ E

2 (a) What forces are acting on a parked car?

(b) Which of these forces are reactions?

3 A light is suspended from the ceiling.

↓ C

(a) Draw a diagram to show the pairs of forces acting on the light.

(b) The weight of the light is 15 N. What is the size of the reaction force?

4 (a) Describe what happens when a car collides with a wall in terms of the action and reaction forces.

↓ A*

(b) The car exerts a force of 7500 N to the right on the wall. What is the size and direction of the reaction force?

Exam tip OCR

✓ When explaining something in an answer, remember to use the correct scientific language – if you don't, you could lose marks.

▲ Equal and opposite forces act on the football and the foot

◀ There is a collision between the cricket bat and the ball

Simple collisions

When two things collide they exert equal and opposite forces on each other.

Collisions happen all the time in sporting activities. For example, there is a collision between a footballer's foot and a football when the ball is kicked. The force exerted by the footballer's foot on the ball is equal and opposite to the force exerted by the ball on the footballer's foot.

The action of these forces changes the motion of the objects. When kicked, the football moves at a different speed in a different direction: its velocity changes. The momentum of the football is its mass multiplied by its velocity. The force applied during the collision changes the momentum of the football.

> **A** Give three other examples of sporting activities where there are collisions.

Recoil, explosions, and rockets

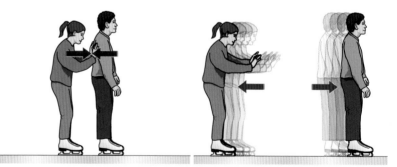

▲ The skater on the right recoils when the skater on the left pushes on them

The diagram shows two ice skaters. At first the skaters are not moving. Then Sadie pushes Ben in the back and Ben moves forwards. But Ben's back exerts an equal and opposite force on Sadie's hands, so Sadie will **recoil** backwards. Both skaters now have momentum, but in opposite directions.

Similarly when you fire a gun, the bullet travels out of the gun barrel at high speed, and the gun recoils in the opposite direction to the bullet.

Rockets work on the same principle. Rocket fuel is burned in the combustion chamber, which means that the particles have a high energy and move very fast.

Inside the chamber the particles crash into the sides, causing a high pressure. The hotter the gas gets, the faster the particles move and the higher the pressure (the pressure can also be increased by reducing the volume of the gas, but this is not practical). Some of the particles escape out of the bottom of the chamber. The force pushing these particles out is the same as the force pushing the rocket up, so the rocket accelerates upwards.

> **B** What is recoil?
>
> **C** How does a rocket move?

Inside the combustion chamber of large rockets, the pressure is very high. As the particles strike the walls of the chamber they bounce off, changing their momentum. There are a large number of collisions each second. This high frequency of collisions leads to a high rate of change of momentum, so a large force is created. In order to ensure that this force is large enough to lift the massive rockets carrying satellites into orbit, the exhaust must contain a large number of gas particles moving at very high speeds. This is achieved by rapidly burning a large volume of fuel at very high temperatures.

Did you know...?

For rockets that take people and objects into space, the mass of fuel is a very large proportion of the total mass of the rocket. The total mass of the Space Shuttle at take-off is about 2030 tonnes. The total mass of fuel is about 1750 tonnes.

Gas particles leave a shuttle's engine at over 4000 m/s at temperatures of over 3000 °C, and the shuttle burns over 1000 litres of fuel per second!

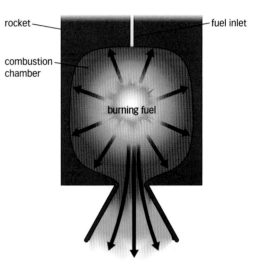

rocket — combustion chamber — burning fuel — fuel inlet

▲ The fast moving particles collide with the walls of the combustion chamber. Some particles escape backwards.

Questions

1 What are the action and the reaction forces when a cricketer hits a ball?

2 How do action and reaction forces help to explain why a tennis ball changes direction when it is hit?

3 Explain how a gun recoils when it is fired.

4 Explain how a rocket motor works.

5 Explain why large numbers of particles moving at high speed are needed to put a rocket into orbit.

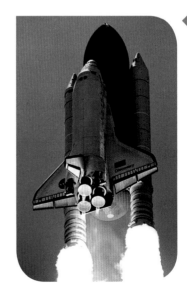

◀ At take-off over 85% of the mass of the Space Shuttle is fuel

Key words

law of conservation of momentum, **coalesce**

Did you know...?

The law of conservation of momentum can be used to predict how the balls in a game of pool will behave when the cue ball hits them.

Law of conservation of momentum

The total amount of momentum stays the same. For example, if two moving objects collide, their total momentum does not change. This is the **law of conservation of momentum**.

$$\text{total momentum before collision (or explosion)} = \text{total momentum after collision (or explosion)}$$

The law only applies if the forces involved come from the objects themselves. If any external forces act on the objects, such as friction, then momentum is not conserved.

You can use the law of conservation of momentum to describe explosions, the recoil of a gun, and rocket propulsion:

Before you fire a gun, the total momentum of the gun and bullet is zero. When you fire a gun, the gun moves in the opposite direction to the bullet. The momentum of the gun is equal and opposite to the momentum of the bullet. As the gun has a much larger mass than the bullet, its velocity is much less than that of the bullet, and in the opposite direction.

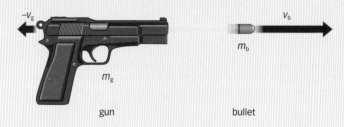

gun   bullet

▲ The total momentum of the gun and bullet is zero

Similarly, you can use the law of conservation of momentum to explain how rockets work. The momentum of the gases coming out of the rocket is equal and opposite to the momentum of the rocket. The total momentum of the rocket and exhaust gases is zero.

> **A** Why is the velocity of the gun much less than that of the bullet?

Momentum calculations

You can use the law of conservation of momentum to solve problems involving, for example, the collision of two cars. When two objects moving in the same direction collide, and then **coalesce** (join together) after the collision, you can use the following equation:

$$m_1u_1 + m_2u_2 = (m_1 + m_2)v$$

where m_1 and m_2 are the masses of the two objects in kg, u_1 and u_2 are the velocities of the two objects before the collision in m/s, and v is the velocity of the two objects after the collision in m/s.

> **B** How does the law of conservation of momentum help in solving the worked example?

Worked example

A car of mass 1250 kg is travelling at 20 m/s. It collides with a car in front of it of mass 1000 kg that is travelling at 10 m/s in the same direction. The two cars coalesce after the collision and move at the same velocity. What is the velocity of the two cars after the collision?

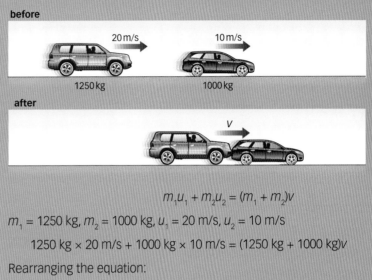

before

20 m/s   10 m/s

1250 kg   1000 kg

after

v

$$m_1u_1 + m_2u_2 = (m_1 + m_2)v$$

$m_1 = 1250$ kg, $m_2 = 1000$ kg, $u_1 = 20$ m/s, $u_2 = 10$ m/s

1250 kg × 20 m/s + 1000 kg × 10 m/s = (1250 kg + 1000 kg)v

Rearranging the equation:

v = (1250 kg × 20 m/s + 1000 kg × 10 m/s)/(1250 kg + 1000 kg)

= (25 000 kg m/s + 10 000 kg m/s)/2250 kg

= 15.6 m/s

So the two cars move in the positive direction (to the right) at 15.6 m/s.

Questions

1 What is the law of conservation of momentum?

2 A model car of mass 0. 3kg is moving at 5 m/s. It collides with a second model car of mass 0.2 kg that is stationary. The two cars move off together. What is the speed of the two cars?

3 A car has a mass of 750 kg and is travelling at 20 m/s. A second car is travelling in the same direction and has a mass of 1250 kg. The two cars collide and coalesce. They move on at 14 m/s. What was the initial velocity of the second car?

4 Use the law of conservation of momentum to explain how a rocket works.

5 A ball of mass 0.5 kg is moving at 4 m/s. Another ball of mass 0.5 kg is moving with a velocity of –4 m/s. The balls collide head on and come to a stop.
Show that momentum is conserved in the collision.

A*

Learning objectives

After studying this topic, you should be able to:

✔ understand how only some frequencies of radio waves pass through the atmosphere

✔ describe how information is transmitted to and from satellites

Key words

atmosphere, electromagnetic wave, microwave, aerial

A Give an example of a type of electromagnetic wave that cannot travel through our atmosphere.

B Which part of the electromagnetic spectrum is used for both terrestrial and satellite TV signals?

▲ A satellite dish receives microwaves beamed down from a satellite in orbit. Why do all satellite TV dishes in the UK point southwards? Which way do they point in Australia?

Waves and our atmosphere

We've already learnt how parts of the **atmosphere** protect us from high energy ultraviolet radiation from the Sun. This thin layer of air surrounding our planet is essential for life. It acts like a shield, not only protecting us from ultraviolet, but also stopping higher energy parts of the electromagnetic spectrum, such as X-rays and gamma rays, from reaching the surface.

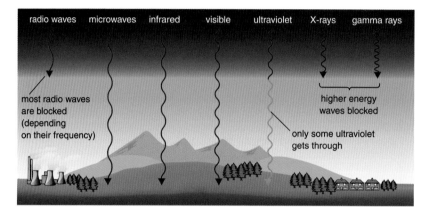

▲ Only certain frequencies of electromagnetic waves can pass through our atmosphere

Only some **electromagnetic waves** are able to pass through our atmosphere. Some waves are absorbed by one of the many gases, others by water droplets. Whether an electromagnetic wave passes through depends on its wavelength and its frequency.

If you don't have cable TV at home then the pictures you receive are all beamed through the air. The TV signal might consist of **microwaves** sent from your local transmitter. This is called a 'terrestrial' TV signal. These waves travel at the speed of light through the air and are received by your TV **aerial**. For the best quality image, your aerial needs to be pointing towards the transmitter.

Satellite TV works in a similar way, but there is one crucial difference. Instead of the TV signal being sent from a transmitter tower to your aerial, the signal is beamed down from a satellite in orbit. For this, higher frequency microwaves are used: they have a shorter wavelength than normal TV signals.

To receive a signal from a satellite you need a satellite dish. A normal TV aerial is not sensitive enough to pick up the signal. The satellite dish has to be very carefully aligned. A few millimetres out and it won't be able to pick up the signal.

Communicating with satellites

All signals sent to and from satellites are digital. This allows the signal to be processed by computers and any interference can be removed. The signal is sent as a series of microwave pulses. Relatively low frequency microwaves are used to communicate with nearby satellites. To communicate with satellites much further away, higher frequency microwaves are used.

Satellites can be used to bounce a signal around the world. The signal is sent up to a satellite. The satellite then processes the signal, before it re-transmits it to another receiver. The signal can be made to travel further by using more than one satellite. Instead of transmitting the signal to another receiver on the ground, the satellite could transmit it to another satellite, then another, then another. Finally, the signal is sent back to a receiver on Earth.

▲ Satellites can be used to relay signals around the world

Did you know...?

Satellites that transmit satellite TV signals are in a geostationary orbit. They beam the signal from a height of over 30 000 km from the Earth's surface. If you could drive to one, the journey would take around four weeks, driving for 10 hours every day.

More on microwaves

Microwaves have a shorter wavelength than radio waves. As a result they don't spread out, or diffract, as much as radio waves. This is the reason the dishes need such careful alignment. The microwave beam travels in a straight line, not spreading out very much at all. The dish needs to be at precisely the correct angle to reflect the signal onto the receiver.

▲ Satellite dishes must be carefully aligned. The signal from the satellite does not spread out very much.

To increase the quality of the signal, dishes with sizes many times that of the wavelengths of microwaves are used. They reflect the signal to a central receiver. This signal is then processed by your TV.

Questions

1 List the parts of the electromagnetic spectrum whose waves are able to pass through the atmosphere.

2 What type of signal is used to communicate with satellites?

3 Describe how a satellite might be used to transmit a signal from the UK to the other side of the world.

4 Explain, in terms of diffraction, why a satellite dish needs to be very carefully aligned.

↓ E
↓ C
↓ A*

Key words

ionosphere, amplitude modulation, diffraction

Did you know...?

Information is sent in most longer wavelength radio waves by a technique called **amplitude modulation** (or AM for short). The amplitude of the 'carrier' radio wave is changed according to the amplitude of the original signal. The information is encoded in the height of the wave transmitted.

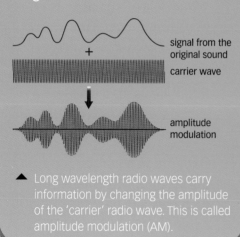

▲ Long wavelength radio waves carry information by changing the amplitude of the 'carrier' radio wave. This is called amplitude modulation (AM).

The ionosphere

Our atmosphere is made up of several different layers. Each layer has different properties. One of these is the **ionosphere**, and it is very important for longer range communications.

The ionosphere is at a height of around 400 km from the surface of the Earth. It is unusual as it contains a large number of ionised gases.

Radio waves are part of the electromagnetic spectrum. They have the longest wavelength and the lowest frequency. When radio waves approach the ionosphere they are reflected back from it, like light reflecting off a mirror.

Radio waves with a frequency lower than 30 million Hz (30 MHz) are reflected back towards the Earth. Some higher frequency electromagnetic waves, such as microwaves, are able to pass through the ionosphere unaffected.

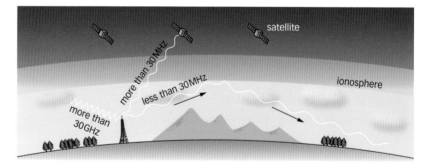

▲ Lower frequency waves such as radio waves are reflected by the ionosphere, but higher frequency waves pass through

It's not just low frequencies that meet obstacles. Higher frequency microwaves above 30 GHz (30 000 MHz) also have difficulty passing through the atmosphere. They are scattered and absorbed by dust and rain. This reduces the signal strength and results in a poor quality connection over long distances.

The problems caused by the ionosphere and the dust, rain and other particles in the atmosphere limit the radio waves and microwaves that can pass all the way through it. Waves between 30 MHz and 30 GHz are able to pass through all parts of the atmosphere. This makes them very valuable for communication.

Diffraction and radio waves

You might remember that waves spread out whenever they pass through a gap or around an obstacle. This is called **diffraction**.

In general, the smaller the gap or the longer the wavelength, the stronger the diffraction. Waves with longer wavelengths passing through small gaps spread out more than waves with shorter wavelengths passing through wider gaps.

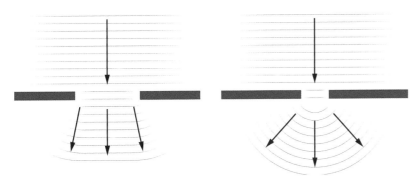

▲ The smaller the gap, the greater the diffraction

Diffraction is not always a bad thing. Radio waves diffract over hills and between buildings, allowing you to pick up signals. Longer wavelength radio signals diffract more than shorter wavelength microwaves. This allows the house in the picture above to receive a radio signal but not one for their TV.

> In general, the strongest diffraction occurs when the wavelength of the wave is the same size as the gap it passes through.

Some radio waves have such a long wavelength that they diffract around the curvature of the Earth. This allows them to be transmitted over very long distances – they diffract over the horizon. Some submarines use extremely low-frequency radio waves (between 3 and 30 Hz). This allows the submarine to send and receive signals from anywhere on the planet.

▲ Submarines can communicate using extremely long radio waves. These can diffract over the horizon and travel around the world.

A Which part of the electromagnetic spectrum has the longest wavelength?

B Radio waves below what frequency are reflected off the ionosphere?

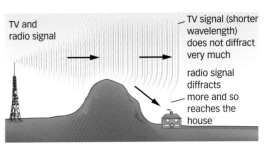

TV and radio signal

TV signal (shorter wavelength) does not diffract very much

radio signal diffracts more and so reaches the house

▲ Longer wavelength radio waves diffract more than shorter wavelength TV signals

Questions

1 Name which type of wave in the electromagnetic spectrum:
   (a) is reflected off the ionosphere
   (b) is able to pass through the ionosphere.

↓ E

2 Draw a diagram to show how waves are diffracted.

3 Explain why the house in the picture can pick up a radio signal but not a TV signal.

↓ C

4 Explain why frequencies between 30 MHz and 30 GHz are useful for longer distance communication.

↓ A*

5 Describe how the size of the gap affects the diffraction of waves.

Learning objectives

After studying this topic, you should be able to:

- ✔ describe how waves interfere
- ✔ describe some examples of interference
- ✔ explain how an interference pattern might be formed from coherent wave sources
- ✔ understand the importance of path difference, and what is needed for two wave sources to be coherent

▲ Water waves at sea can reach large heights because of constructive interference

A Two waves overlap and create a single wave with a different amplitude. What is this called?

B What is the name given to the interference where two waves cancel each other out?

Key words

Interference, constructive interference, destructive interference, coherent, monochromatic, **path difference**

When waves combine

If you stand on a pier looking at the water waves beneath you, you might notice that they are not all the same height. Some are much higher than others. This is because two or more water waves pass over one another and produce a single wave with a new amplitude. This effect is called **interference**.

Interference causes the reinforcement of some waves (also called **constructive interference).** This happens if the crests and troughs of two waves line up. This creates a wave with even greater amplitude. In the case of water waves, this would produce an even taller wave with deeper troughs.

Interference can lead to the cancellation of some waves (also called **destructive interference).** If a crest from one wave lines up with the trough of another they cancel out. If this happens to two water waves, you get a calm area.

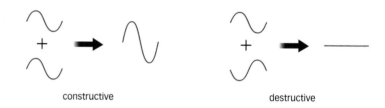

constructive   destructive

▲ Interference can be constructive or destructive

This effect happens with all types of wave, not just water waves. Interference happens with sound waves, radio waves, microwaves, and even light waves. When two waves reinforce each other you get a louder sound, stronger radio or microwave signal, or a brighter area of light. If the waves cancel out then the reverse happens. You get a darker region, a weaker signal, or a quieter sound (if the cancellation is perfect it would be silent).

Forming an interference pattern

The water waves that you see from a pier interfere in a fairly random way. However, the water waves in the ripple tank on the next page are interfering to form a stable interference pattern. This is because the dippers forming the two sets of waves are vibrating in the same way. Both dippers are fixed to the same moving beam. When two wave sources are vibrating in the same way like this, they are said to be **coherent**.

◀ A ripple tank shows an interference pattern. The two dippers are coherent wave sources, so they can produce a stable interference pattern

To get coherent sources of light waves, we need to use light of a single frequency. This is called **monochromatic** light. Lasers produce monochromatic light.

Two coherent wave sources will have the same frequency. The two sets of waves produced by the two sources will be in step with each other – they are said to be in phase. They also need to have the same amplitude to produce an interference pattern that can be seen.

Interference patterns are caused by the waves from each source travelling a different distance. This is referred to as **path difference**. If one wave travels half a wavelength further than the other one, this is a path difference of half a wavelength. For waves to produce constructive interference the path difference must be an *even* number of half wavelengths. For destructive interference the path difference must be an *odd* number of half wavelengths.

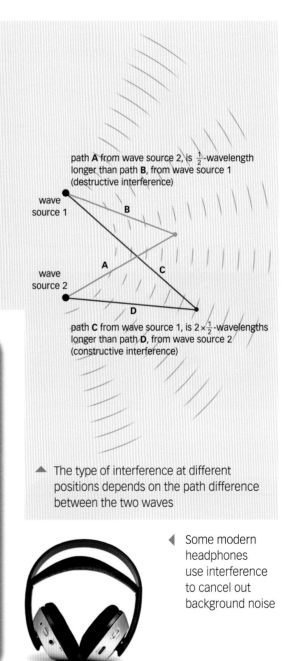

path **A** from wave source 2, is $\frac{1}{2}$-wavelength longer than path **B**, from wave source 1 (destructive interference)

path **C** from wave source 1, is $2 \times \frac{1}{2}$-wavelengths longer than path **D**, from wave source 2 (constructive interference)

▲ The type of interference at different positions depends on the path difference between the two waves

◀ Some modern headphones use interference to cancel out background noise

Questions

1 Describe the effect of interference on the volume of sound heard by an observer.

2 Draw a diagram to show how two waves can:

   (a) interfere constructively

   (b) interfere destructively.

3 Use a diagram to show how the path difference at different distances from two sources produces an interference pattern.

4 The path difference between two waves is measured at 3 cm. The wavelength of the waves is 2 cm. Explain what type of interference would be observed at this point.

Learning objectives

After studying this topic, you should be able to:

✔ understand how and why ideas about the nature of light have changed over time

✔ describe how diffraction and polarisation provide evidence for the wave nature of light

✔ understand how interference patterns of light may be formed using a double slit

✔ explain polarisation and the effect of Polaroid filters

> **A** Did Newton believe light was a stream of particles or a wave?

▲ Newton and Huygens had very different ideas about the nature of light

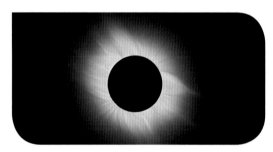

▲ The sharp shadows formed by a solar eclipse led scientists to believe that light was made up of a stream of particles

Ideas about light

Over time, ideas about the nature of light have changed. We now know that light is an electromagnetic wave, but different theories of light have caused some of the fiercest debates in the history of science. Perhaps the most well-known was between the famous English physicist, Sir Isaac Newton, and the Dutch astronomer, Christiaan Huygens.

Newton thought light was a stream of particles; Huygens thought light was a wave. There was good evidence to support both sides of the argument and there were several other scientists on both sides.

Newton stated that the evidence that light travels in straight lines was proof of its particle nature. Waves, like sound and water waves, spread out, but light doesn't. A good example of this is the formation of shadows. Each shadow has a clear edge. If light was a wave it would spread out (diffract) around the obstacle and form a blurry shadow. Newton stated that the shadows formed by a solar eclipse were indisputable proof of that light was a particle.

Evidence for light as a wave

Newton was able to explain both refraction and reflection in terms of particles. Throw a bouncing ball at the ground and it bounces back up at the same angle. Newton used a similar model to explain reflection: particles of light would bounce off surfaces.

> **B** How did Newton explain the reflection of light in terms of particles?

However, as more evidence was collected it became clear that not all phenomena could be explained using the model of light as a particle. Newton was wrong, and the model of light had to be changed.

The first key piece of evidence for light as a wave is diffraction. It had appeared that light did not diffract. However, light has such a short wavelength that the gap needed to see this effect has to be very, very small. If a tiny single slit is used, light can be diffracted. It spreads out from a narrow beam when it passes through the gap.

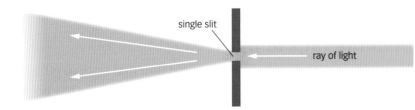

single slit

ray of light

▲ A ray of light can be diffracted through a narrow slit

If two slits are used, the light diffracts through both slits and overlaps. This forms an interference pattern. Particles do not form interference patterns. The fact that light does was the final key piece of evidence that light must be a type of wave.

For light to diffract, a tiny slit about the same size as the wavelength of light is needed.

▲ Light forms an interference pattern of light and dark bands

At different places, the light from each slit has travelled a slightly different distance. Where the path difference is an even number of wavelengths, as described on spread P5.11, the waves interfere constructively. Where it is an odd number of wavelengths, they interfere destructively. This leads to the formation of bright and dark bands on a screen.

All electromagnetic waves can be polarised. **Polarisation** only happens to transverse waves. The polarisation of light confirms that light is not only a wave but a **transverse wave**. Like all transverse waves the vibrations are at right angles to the direction of wave motion. These vibrations might take place in any plane as the wave travels forwards (eg up and down, side-to-side). Light from most sources, such as light bulbs or the Sun, is not polarised. The vibrations take place in all possible planes. Plane-polarised light has vibrations in one plane only.

A **Polaroid filter** only lets through light that is polarised in a certain plane. If you have a pair of filters and slowly rotate one in front of the other, eventually all of the light is blocked.

Key words

polarisation, transverse wave, **Polaroid filter**

Did you know...?

Some sunglasses contain Polaroid filters. Light reflected off the surface of roads, snow, and even water becomes partly polarised. Polaroid glasses block this light, reducing the glare from the surface.

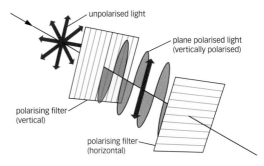

unpolarised light

plane polarised light (vertically polarised)

polarising filter (vertical)

polarising filter (horizontal)

▲ Light can be plane-polarised, confirming that it is a transverse wave

Questions

1 What evidence was there for light behaving like a stream of particles?

2 Give three examples of effects that show light must be a wave.

3 Describe how to form an interference pattern with light.

4 Explain the meaning of the term polarisation and describe the effect of a Polaroid filter.

Learning objectives

After studying this topic, you should be able to:

- ✔ describe refraction as the bending of a light wave when it travels from one medium to another
- ✔ explain the meaning of the term refractive index

Key words

refraction, medium, refractive index

▲ Refraction can lead to some strange optical effects!

> **B** What happens to the direction of light when it passes from a medium into one that has a lower density?

Bending rays of light

The **refraction** of light leads to some unusual optical effects. Mirages in deserts are caused by refraction, swimming pools look shallower than they actually are, and fish that are seen from above the surface of the water are not where they appear to be.

> **A** Give an example of an unusual optical effect caused by refraction.

As you will remember, refraction is the bending of light (or any wave) when it travels from one **medium** to another. When light moves from one medium to another its speed changes, depending on the density of the material. This speed change causes a change in the direction of the light.

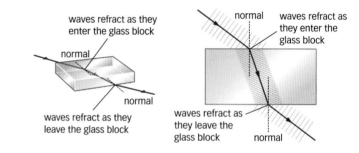

▲ Light refracts as it passes through a glass block

The direction that the light bends in depends on the relative density of the two media. If the light enters a denser material, such as travelling from air to glass, the light slows down. This makes the light bend towards the normal. The angle of incidence is greater than the angle of refraction.

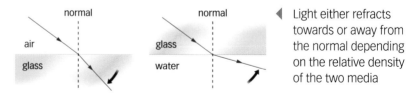

◀ Light either refracts towards or away from the normal depending on the relative density of the two media

If the light goes from a denser medium to one that is less dense, such as travelling from glass to water, the light speeds up. This makes the light bend away from the normal.

Refractive index

The **refractive index** of a material is a measure of the speed of light through the material compared with the speed of light in a vacuum. The more slowly the light travels through the material, the higher its refractive index. The denser the material, the higher its refractive index. Water has a refractive index of 1.3 and the refractive index of glass is around 1.4 (depending on the type of glass).

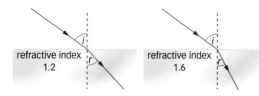

▲ The greater the refractive index, the more the light ray bends when it enters the material

Materials with a higher refractive index cause the light to slow down more and bend more towards the normal.

The refractive index of a material can be calculated using this equation:

$$\text{refractive index} = \frac{\text{speed of light in vacuum}}{\text{speed of light in the medium (material)}}$$

Worked example

Light travels at 300 000 000 m/s (3×10^8 m/s) through a vacuum. It travels at 200 000 000 m/s (2×10^8 m/s) through a piece of glass. Find the refractive index of the glass.

$$\text{refractive index} = \frac{\text{speed of light in vacuum}}{\text{speed of light in the medium (material)}}$$

speed of light in vacuum = 3×10^8 m/s = 300 000 000 m/s

speed of light in glass = 2×10^8 m/s = 200 000 000 m/s

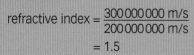

$$\text{refractive index} = \frac{300\,000\,000 \text{ m/s}}{200\,000\,000 \text{ m/s}}$$

$$= 1.5$$

When light passes into a block of material with a higher density, it slows down. This also has the effect of reducing the wavelength of the light passing through the block. When the light exits the block, both its speed and wavelength return to what they were previously.

Did you know...?

Back in 1621, the Dutch physicist Willebrord Snellius rediscovered the mathematical relationship between the refractive index and the angles at which light bent when it moved from one medium to another. It is sometimes called Snell's law in his honour. In France it is called 'Snell–Descartes' law' as Descartes derived it independently in 1637. However, maybe the honour should go to Ibn Sahl of Baghdad, who accurately described it in a manuscript called *On Burning Mirrors and Lenses* – in 984!

Questions

1 Describe what happens to the direction of light when it passes from a low density medium into one with a higher density.

2 Explain what causes a ray of light to change direction when it passes from one material to another.

3 Explain the meaning of refractive index and describe how it might be calculated.

4 Light travels at 3.0×10^8 m/s through a vacuum. It slows to 2.3×10^8 m/s when it enters water. Find the refractive index of water.

5 A piece of glass has a refractive index of 1.6. Find the speed of light through the glass.

Learning objectives

After studying this topic, you should be able to:

- ✔ describe how light is made up of different component colours
- ✔ explain how a spectrum of colours is formed when light passes through a prism
- ✔ understand that the blue end of the visible spectrum has a higher refractive index compared with the red end

Key words

dispersion, prism, visible spectrum

◀ The prism is splitting white light into the colours of the visible spectrum

Did you know...?

The English poet John Keats is believed to have felt that Newton had destroyed the poetry and beauty of the rainbow by using science to explain it. Others would argue from the opposite point of view: that learning how light is refracted inside water droplets to form a rainbow enhances the sense of wonder and beauty.

Unweaving the rainbow

White light is a mixture of all of the colours of the rainbow. When white light is refracted in a certain way it is split into its component colours. This is called **dispersion**.

> **A** What is the name given to the effect of splitting white light into its component colours?

▲ A rainbow is formed by a combination of refraction, Total Internal Reflection, and dispersion inside water droplets

A rainbow is formed by the refraction of light as it passes through tiny water droplets in the air. The light is split into the colours that we see.

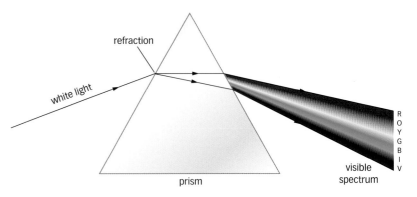

▲ The refraction of white light by a prism splits it into colours

The same effect can be seen when light passes through a **prism**. When it enters the glass, it slows down and refracts. The light bends towards the normal. However, different colours are refracted by different amounts. When the light leaves the prism it is refracted again. This causes the light to disperse far enough for us to see the separate colours.

The visible spectrum

The range of colours we can see is called the **visible spectrum**. It ranges from deep red to the blues and purples at the violet end of the spectrum.

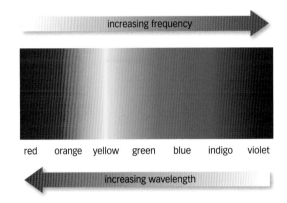

▲ The visible spectrum

The different colours have different wavelengths. Violet has the shortest wavelength, and red light has the longest. The order from longest wavelength to shortest is:

red, orange, yellow, green, blue, indigo, violet

All the colours travel at the same speed through a vacuum, but they travel at slightly different speeds when they travel through other materials (media). The shorter the wavelength, the more slowly the light travels through the medium. When light is refracted through glass, violet slows down more than red and is bent more towards the normal.

As the different colours travel at different speeds through glass, they all have different refractive indices. The shorter the wavelength, the higher the refractive index. Violet has the largest refractive index and red the smallest.

Colour	Typical refractive index in glass
red	1.520
orange	1.523
blue	1.530
violet	1.538

Exam tip OCR

✔ The shorter the wavelength, the higher the refractive index. Remember 'Blue Bends Best'. The blue/violet part of the spectrum refracts the most.

✔ You need to learn the order of the visible spectrum. From longest to shortest wavelengths: **R**ichard **O**f **Y**ork **G**ave **B**attle **I**n **V**ain.

B State the colours of the visible spectrum from longest wavelength to shortest.

Questions

1 Which part of the spectrum is refracted the most when white light is passed through a prism? ↓ E

2 Draw a diagram to show how a visible spectrum can be formed from a prism. ↓ C

3 Explain why white light splits into colours when it is dispersed through a prism.

4 Describe the relationship between the wavelength of a certain colour and its refractive index.

5 Calculate the speed of red and violet light through a piece of glass using the values given in the table. ↓ A*

Key words

Total Internal Reflection, critical angle

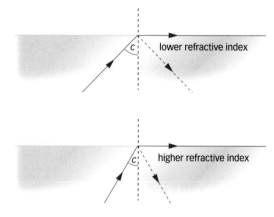

▲ Total Internal Reflection inside a glass block

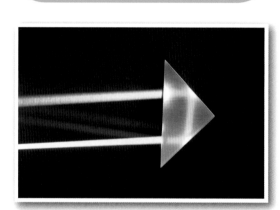

▲ The critical angle

Total Internal Reflection (TIR)

When light travels from one medium to another it refracts (bends), but there is also a small amount of internal reflection. For example, if light travels from glass to air it bends away as it leaves the glass, but a small amount is reflected back into the glass.

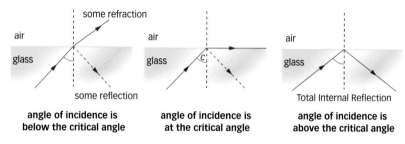

▲ Total Internal Reflection

If light hits the boundary between the glass and air at a big enough angle of incidence, all of the light stays within the glass; it is all reflected internally. This is **Total Internal Reflection**. It happens if the angle is above the **critical angle** for the material.

This effect can be seen whenever light travels from an optically dense material to a less dense one (for example, from water to air, glass to air, or Perspex to air). Two things are needed for Total Internal Reflection to happen:

• the light must be travelling in the more optically dense of the two materials

• the angle of the light must be greater than the critical angle.

Different media have different critical angles.

A What is name given to the angle above which Total Internal Reflection occurs?

The critical angle of a medium depends on its refractive index. An optically denser medium has a higher refractive index and so a lower critical angle.

Using Total Internal Reflection

You might remember how Total Internal Reflection is used in fibre optics. Optical fibres are very fine glass cables. They can be used to provide superfast broadband by sending information as pulses of light totally internally reflected along the fibre.

Optical fibres are not only used for communication. A laparoscope is a medical instrument that is inserted through a tiny keyhole incision to get an image of the inside of the body without having to cut the patient open. An endoscope also uses optical fibres, but in this case there is no incision; the long tube is often passed through the patient's mouth down to the stomach to obtain images.

Binoculars contain a pair of prisms that are specially shaped so that light is totally internally reflected. This is used to produce a magnified view of the object. The image is also turned the right way up.

An important safety use of Total Internal Reflection is in the 'cat's eyes' found in the centre of main roads. Light from the headlights of cars enters the cat's eye and is totally internally reflected. The light then exits back the way it came. This allows the driver see the path of the road in front of them over a much greater distance.

Exam tip **OCR**

✔ Remember that there are two conditions for Total Internal Reflection: the light must be travelling in the denser of the two materials, and the angle of the light from the normal must be above the critical angle of the material.

B What is an endoscope?

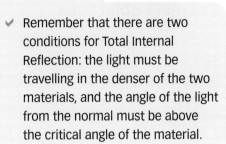

Light is totally internally reflected in prisms inside binoculars

Questions

1 State the two requirements for Total Internal Reflection. ↓E

2 Draw a diagram to show what happens to a ray of light inside a glass block when it hits the edge of the block:

   (a) below the critical angle

   (b) at the critical angle ↓C

   (c) above the critical angle.

3 Give three uses of Total Internal Reflection.

4 Describe an experiment that could be carried out to determine the critical angle of a glass block.

5 Describe the relationship between the refractive index and critical angle of a material. ↓A*

Light is totally internally reflected inside cat's eyes in the road

Learning objectives

After studying this topic, you should be able to:

✔ describe what happens to light passing through a convex lens

✔ explain that that a convex lens can bring parallel rays of light to a focus

✔ complete the path of a ray of light passing through a convex lens

Key words

converging, convex, principal axis, focus, optical centre, focal length

Life through a lens

Lenses are found in cameras, telescopes, glasses and in the eyes of most animals. There are lots of different types of lens, but they all work exactly the same way. A lens is used to refract the light that passes through it. The lens then forms an image.

◀ Like most eyes, the eyes of a shark contain a lens to focus the light

A Give two examples of where lenses can be found.

The most commonly used type of lens is a **converging** one. A **convex** lens is an example of a converging lens.

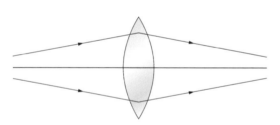

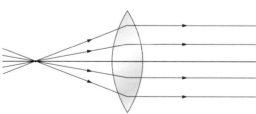

▲ A simple convex, converging lens

When rays of light parallel to the **principal axis** pass through a convex lens, they are focussed to a single point called the **focus**.

The distance from the **optical centre** of the lens to the focus is called the **focal length**. In general, the fatter the lens, the shorter the focal length.

Rays of light that are diverging (spreading out) from the focus on one side are refracted so that they come out parallel.

B What type of lens can be used to bring light to a focus?

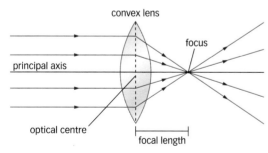

▲ A converging lens refracts the light passing through it. All rays of light passing through a convex lens are converged to some extent.

▲ The converging lens used in a magnifying glass focusses the sunlight. This can create a hot spot.

Constructing ray diagrams

We often draw (or construct) ray diagrams showing the path of light through a lens. In these examples an arrow is used to represent the object. Light is reflected from all parts of the object, but we just consider the light that is being reflected from the tip of the object.

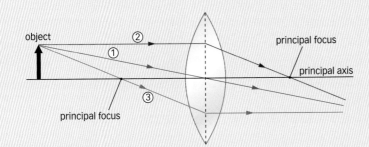

▲ The three rules for rays of light passing through a convex lens

Light is being reflected from the tip in many directions, but we can find out where the image will be by considering light that follows one of three paths.

1. *Light passing through the optical centre of the lens.* The light that passes through the centre of a lens continues through in a straight line.

2. *Light travelling parallel to the principal axis.* The light that is travelling parallel to the principal axis is refracted by the lens so that it passes through the focus.

3. *Light passing through the focus.* The light that passes through the focus is refracted by the lens so that it comes out travelling parallel to the principal axis.

Questions

1 What happens to light passing through the optical centre of a converging lens? ↓E

2 Draw a diagram to show how a converging lens can focus rays of light. Label the focal length, optical centre, and focus.

3 Describe what happens to the focal length if a fatter lens is used. ↓C

4 Draw a diagram showing the paths taken by light passing through a lens if the light:

  (a) passes through the optical centre of a lens ↓A*

  (b) is travelling parallel to the principal axis

  (c) passes through the focus.

Learning objectives

After studying this topic, you should be able to:

- ✔ state some uses of convex lenses
- ✔ calculate the magnification of an image
- ✔ describe how convex lenses can be used to produce real images
- ✔ construct ray diagrams for lenses, including one for a magnifying glass

> **A** Give two examples of optical instruments that use lenses to form images.

Forming an image

We use lenses to form images of a wide variety of objects. From looking at distant planets right down to microscopic cells, lenses are used to help us make sense of the world around us.

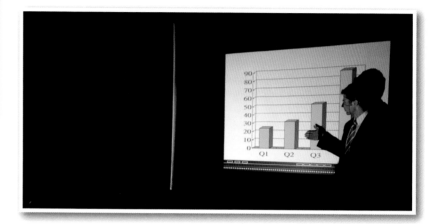

▲ A projector contains a converging lens that focuses an image on a screen

Convex lenses are used in cameras, projectors, some spectacles and in magnifying glasses. A digital projector produces an image on a big screen that is much larger than the tiny screen inside the projector. The lens inside a camera produces a smaller image on film or on a light-sensitive chip.

Images from a convex lens

A convex lens can be used to produce a **real image**. This is a type of image that can be focussed to form upon a screen or piece of film. For the image to be in focus, rather than blurry, the distances from object to lens and lens to screen must be just right. Changing the distance from the object to the lens changes the nature of the image produced.

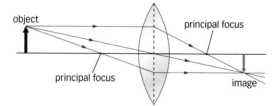

▲ Using a convex lens to form an image of an object that is far away from the lens

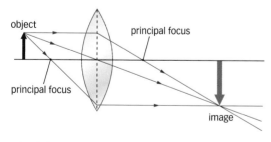

▲ If the object is closer to the lens, the image formed is very different

Using the three paths for rays of light that are shown on spread P5.16, we can construct a ray diagram showing how images are formed.

Where the rays cross shows where the image forms. If an object is far away, the image formed is smaller than the object, upside down (inverted), and a real image.

If the object is closer to the lens, then a different image is formed.

When a lens is used to magnify an object, the **magnification** can be calculated using the equation:

$$\text{magnification} = \frac{\text{image height}}{\text{object height}}$$

Any magnification greater than 1 means the image is larger than the object. A magnification of 5 would mean the image is 5× larger than the object. A 2 cm object would produce a 10 cm image.

A convex lens can be used in a magnifying glass. As the light passes through the lens, it is refracted in such a way to produce a larger image. This allows the observer to see miniscule details usually invisible to the naked eye.

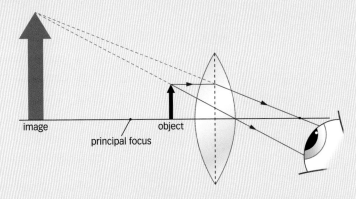

image | object | principal focus

▲ Using a convex lens as a magnifying glass produces a magnified, virtual image

Using a convex lens in this way produces a **virtual image**. This kind of image cannot be formed on a screen, but, unlike other images from a convex lens, the image is the right way up (upright). The observer must look through the lens to see the image.

◀ A magnifying glass is a single convex lens

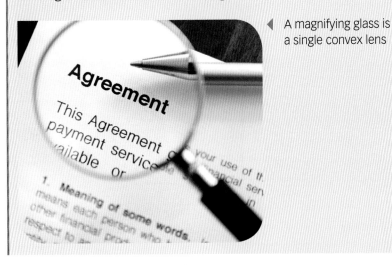

Key words

real image, magnification, virtual image

B What is meant by a magnification of 3?

Questions

1 What type of lens is used in a magnifying glass? ↓ E

2 Light from a 2.0 cm high object is projected through a lens onto a screen, producing an image 56 cm high. Calculate the magnification.

3 An image 4.8 cm high is focussed by a lens onto a piece of film. The object being photographed is 19.2 cm tall. Calculate the magnification. ↓ C

4 Describe the difference between a real and a virtual image.

5 Use graph paper to carefully produce your own lens diagrams for the three examples shown and calculate the magnification in each case. ↓ A*

Module summary

Revision checklist

- Satellites may be natural or artificial. Gravitational force (weight) causes a satellite's curved path.
- Artificial satellites are used for telecommunications, weather, GPS, and photography in low polar or geostationary orbit.
- Centripetal force keeps satellites moving in a circular orbit.
- Scalar quantities (eg mass, temperature) indicate size. Vector quantities (eg force, acceleration) indicate size and direction.
- Projectiles have a parabolic trajectory. They have a constant horizontal velocity and an increasing vertical velocity.
- Every action has an equal and opposite reaction.
- Force applied in a collision changes the momentum of an object. Action and reaction affect both objects in a collision.
- Total momentum before collision (or explosion) = total momentum after collision (or explosion).
- Higher-energy parts of the electromagnetic spectrum cannot pass through the atmosphere.
- Microwaves are used for satellite communication. Digital signals are passed from satellite to satellite as a series of microwave pulses.
- Radio waves of less than 30 MHz are reflected by the ionosphere, while higher frequency waves pass through it.
- Radio waves diffract around obstructions. Very low-frequency radio waves diffract around the curvature of the Earth.
- Wave interference can be constructive or destructive. Coherent wave sources can form interference patterns.
- Monochromatic light is light of a single frequency (eg lasers).
- Diffraction (causing interference patterns) and polarisation are evidence for the wave nature of light. Newton originally believed light was a stream of particles.
- Refraction is the bending of light as it passes from one medium into another.
- The component colours of the visible spectrum are refracted when passing through a prism, causing dispersion.
- Total Internal Reflection is used in optical fibres, endoscopes, binoculars, and cat's eyes.
- Lenses refract light. A converging (convex) lens brings rays of light parallel to the principal axis to a focus.
- Images produced by lenses may be real or virtual.

adding vectors

vectors and scalars

projectiles

motion equaliser

amplitude modulation

aerials

telecommunications

digital signals

monochromatic

lasers

visible spectrum

dispersion

refractive index

speed in vacuum/ speed in medium

NOW USE THE P5 GRADE CHECKER ON PAGE 248

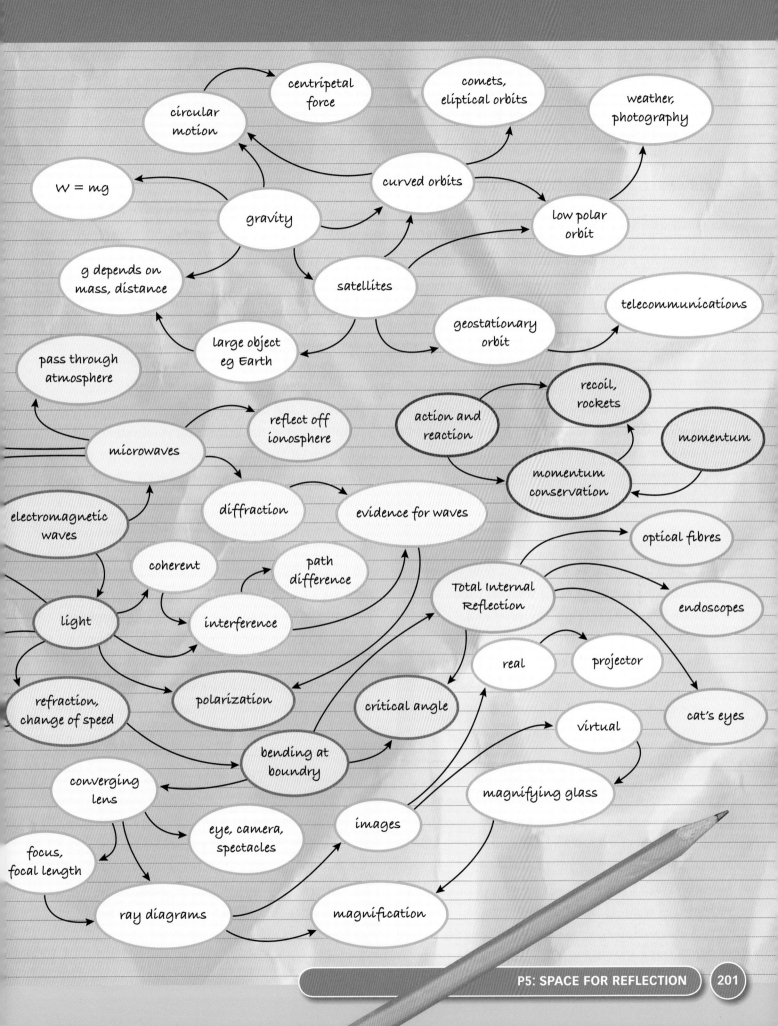

centripetal force

circular motion

comets, eliptical orbits

weather, photography

W = mg

curved orbits

gravity

low polar orbit

g depends on mass, distance

satellites

telecommunications

large object eg Earth

geostationary orbit

pass through atmosphere

reflect off ionosphere

action and reaction

recoil, rockets

momentum

microwaves

momentum conservation

diffraction

evidence for waves

electromagnetic waves

optical fibres

coherent

path difference

Total Internal Reflection

light

endoscopes

interference

real

projector

refraction, change of speed

polarization

critical angle

cat's eyes

converging lens

bending at boundry

virtual

magnifying glass

focus, focal length

eye, camera, spectacles

images

ray diagrams

magnification

Answering Extended Writing questions

The diagram illustrates a satellite in a circular orbit round the Earth.

Explain why the satellite keeps moving in its circular path.

The quality of written communication will be assessed in your answer to this question.

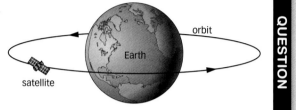

QUESTION

The path curves because of gravity. if gravity was swixchd off centrifugl force (which dosnt realy exist would make the satelite fly off sideways. the satelite carries on because of the rokket that fired it at the lornch.

↓ E

Examiner: This answer demonstrates only vague understanding of the physics. Some ideas have been half-remembered, but the reasoning is muddled and misunderstood. Of the physics words needed for a full explanation, only gravity is used correctly. Spelling, punctuation, and grammar are not good.

The path is curved, so a sideways force is needed. The earth's gravity provides this, which is called centripetle force. If this wasn't there the satelite would fly off into space and go on for ever. Its like a conker on the end of a string being whirled round, the string pulls it towards the middle.

↓ C

Examiner: Most of the physics is correct, but there are ideas missing. There is no mention of changing velocity, acceleration, or unchanging forward speed and KE. The sequence of ideas is not structured well. The second half, though true, is not relevant. There are occasional errors in spelling, punctuation, and grammar.

The direction of movement of the satellite is continuously changing. That means its velocity is changing, so it is accelerating. The direction of its acceleration is towards the centre of the Earth. This requires a force, called centripetal force. This is provided by the Earth's gravity, pulling on the satellite towards the centre of the Earth. There is no air resistance; so the KE of the satellite, originally provided by the rocket, is not reduced.

↓ A*

Examiner: This answer is well ordered and accurate. It gives an account of why the speed of the satellite doesn't change, as well as why the path is curved. The word vector isn't used, but the concepts of velocity, acceleration, and force as vectors are well expressed. The physics explanations and the use of technical terms are all correct. Spelling, punctuation, and grammar are all good.

Exam-style questions

1 a Draw a diagram showing a beam of white light entering a prism, passing through it, then leaving again after it has been split into its colours.
   b Label the seven colours correctly.
   c What is this splitting of the light into its colours by the prism called?

2 a Explain how a converging lens affects light.
   b Explain the meaning of focal length for a converging lens.
   c Explain the meaning of real image.
   d Using a particular projector, a transparency of width 15 cm produces an image 1.8 m wide on a screen. Calculate the magnification achieved.
   e What is a virtual image?

3 a An object 4 cm tall is 8 cm from a converging lens with focal length 5 cm. Draw a ray diagram at actual size on a sheet of A4 graph paper to find the size and nature of the image. Show all three possible construction rays. (Hint: use the paper in landscape orientation, and put the lens about 10 cm from the left edge of the paper.)
   b Describe how the image changes if the object is brought gradually closer to the lens.

4 A stuntman takes a running jump off the roof of a building, to be caught in a net at ground level. He leaves the roof horizontally at 8 m/s. The roof is 10 m above ground level.
   a Calculate the time taken by the man to reach the ground.
   b Calculate how far from the base of the building he lands.
   c Calculate the man's resultant velocity when he lands.

Extended Writing

5 Describe two examples of artificial satellites. For each of your examples, explain how the use of the satellite dictates what orbit is chosen for it.

6 Explain how Total Internal Reflection (TIR) occurs. Why is TIR not possible if light is travelling in air towards a glass surface?

7 Explain what is meant by interference when discussing waves. What evidence does interference give about the nature of light?

A01 Recall the science
A02 Apply your knowledge
A03 Evaluate and analyse the evidence

P5: SPACE FOR REFLECTION   203

P6

Electricity for gadgets

Why study this module?

Electricity is a fundamental part of our lives. We use many electronic devices that need a supply of electrical energy to operate. We can control these devices, and many of them store information. Electronic devices are also used to control things automatically – for example a cooling fan in a computer switching on automatically when the computer gets too hot, or turning on central heating when it gets too cold. Engineers need to understand the physics behind these devices so that they can design new ones and repair existing ones when they go wrong.

In this module you will learn about other components of electronic circuits such as resistors, thermistors, transistors, diodes, and capacitors. You will also learn about how transistors can be combined to form logic gates, and how logic gates can be used to control devices. You will learn about motors and dynamos. You will also learn about how transformers are used to increase and decrease voltages to minimise power losses in transmission lines.

You should remember

1 That the power used by an electrical device depends on the potential difference across it and the current flowing through it.

2 How electricity is conducted through a metal.

3 How the electrical resistance of a component is connected to the potential difference across the component and the current flowing through it.

4 How electricity is generated and that it is transmitted around the country by the National Grid.

5 What a transformer is.

The capacity of silicon chips has been getting greater and greater as the transistors on them have been getting smaller and smaller. The number of transistors that can be put on a single silicon chip has been doubling approximately every 18 months. In the 1960s, manufacturers were able to get a few hundred transistors on a silicon chip. Manufacturers can now get up to 500 million transistors on a single chip with an area of 350 mm^2!

Learning objectives

After studying this topic, you should be able to:

- ✔ use standard circuit symbols
- ✔ calculate resistance from voltage and current
- ✔ use a voltage–current graph

Key words

switch, cell, battery, resistor, variable resistor, power supply, resistance

Did you know...?

Circuit symbols are an almost universal language. This means that when you draw a circuit diagram, most electricians around the world could understand it.

Circuit symbols

Symbols for some components of circuits are shown in the table.

Symbol	Name	Photo
	open **switch** closed switch	
	cell	
	battery	
	resistor	
	variable resistor (rheostat)	
	bulb	
	power supply	

Resistance, voltage, and current

You may remember that you can calculate **resistance** using the equation:

$$\text{resistance (ohms, } \Omega) = \frac{\text{voltage (volts, V)}}{\text{current (amperes, A)}}$$

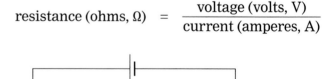
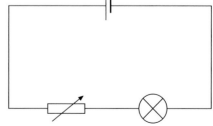

▲ Circuit with a variable resistor

A Draw the symbols for a variable resistor and a cell.

B A variable resistor is connected in series with a bulb and a cell. How could you use the variable resistor to change the brightness of the bulb?

C How could you use the variable resistor to change the speed of a motor in a circuit?

How a variable resistor works

The resistance of a length of wire depends on its length. The longer the piece of wire, the higher its resistance is. A variable resistor consists of a long piece of wire that is often in a coil. Its resistance is changed by altering the length of the resistance wire in the circuit.

Voltage–current graphs

The diagram below shows voltage–current graphs for three different resistors. Resistor C has the lowest current for a particular voltage. Therefore it has the highest resistance of the three resistors.

Remember that when the resistance goes up, the current comes down.

These resistors are ohmic resistors: their voltage–current graphs are straight lines.

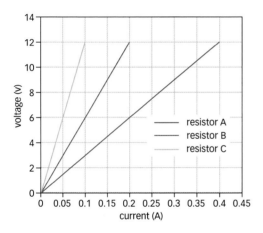

▲ Voltage–current graphs for three resistors

> **D** How do you know that resistor C has the highest resistance?

Finding the resistance from a voltage–current graph

You can calculate the resistance from a voltage–current graph by reading off the values of voltage and current at a point and substituting them into the equation for resistance.

Exam tip

✔ Take care with the units of current and resistance when using them in calculations. Always make sure you convert kilo-ohms (kΩ) and milliamps (mA) to ohms and amps.

Questions

1 Name each of the components shown in the circuit diagram.

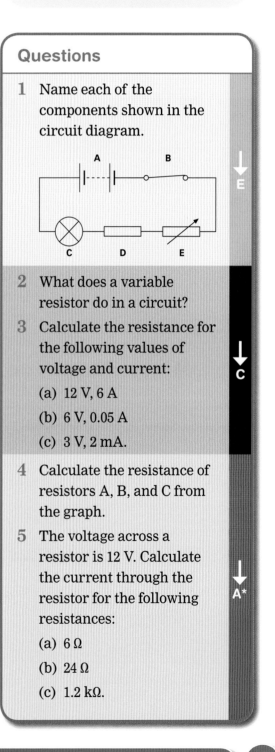

2 What does a variable resistor do in a circuit?

3 Calculate the resistance for the following values of voltage and current:
   (a) 12 V, 6 A
   (b) 6 V, 0.05 A
   (c) 3 V, 2 mA.

4 Calculate the resistance of resistors A, B, and C from the graph.

5 The voltage across a resistor is 12 V. Calculate the current through the resistor for the following resistances:
   (a) 6 Ω
   (b) 24 Ω
   (c) 1.2 kΩ.

Resistance in a wire

The current in a wire conductor is a flow of free electrons that carry charge. These electrons collide with the atoms of the conductor. This makes the flow of charge more difficult, and is called the resistance of the conductor

When there are fewer collisions with atoms (lower resistance), the electrons flow more easily through the conductor, and the current is higher. When there are more collisions (higher resistance) it is more difficult for the electrons to flow, and the current is lower.

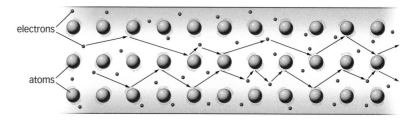

electrons

atoms

▲ Electrons moving through a metal conductor

A What is happening to electrons in a wire when the resistance is higher?

Why do resistance and temperature increase?

The atoms in a conductor are vibrating. When the electrons moving through the conductor collide with the atoms, some energy is transferred to the atoms. The atoms vibrate more, and the number of collisions increases. This means that the resistance increases – it becomes more difficult for the electrons to move through the metal. The increased vibration of the atoms also means that the temperature of the conductor increases.

Did you know...?

The relationship between voltage, current, and resistance is known as Ohm's law, after Georg Ohm (1789–1854) who first described it.

Conductors whose resistance changes

A bulb has a thin coil of wire that is usually made of a metal with a high melting point such as tungsten. When a current flows through the wire, it glows brightly and becomes hot.

When you plot a graph of current against voltage for the bulb, you find that it is not a straight line. It is a curve.

As the graph is not a straight line, this shows that the resistance is not constant. As the current increases, the resistance is also increasing.

Devices that have a voltage–current graph that is not a straight line are called **non-ohmic**.

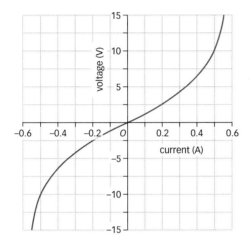

▲ Voltage–current graph for a filament lamp

> **B** What happens to the resistance of a bulb as the temperature increases?
>
> **C** What does non-ohmic mean?

Why the voltage–current graph curves

When the voltage increases, this means that the electrons are carrying more energy. So when they collide with the atoms they transfer more energy, making the atoms vibrate even more. The greater vibration of the atoms means that the temperature and the resistance increase. So as the voltage goes up, so does the resistance. The current still increases for a while, but not as much as at lower voltages.

▲ A filament lamp

Questions

1 What is the current in a wire?

2 What happens to resistance when a wire gets hot?

3 Why is the voltage–current graph for a bulb not a straight line?

4 Describe how a voltage–current graph shows the changing resistance in a non-ohmic device.

5 Explain what happens to the charge carriers in a metal conductor as the voltage increases.

Learning objectives

After studying this topic, you should be able to:

✔ calculate the total resistance for resistors connected in series

✔ explain what a potential divider does

✔ explain how the output of a potential divider can be varied

Key words

series, potential divider

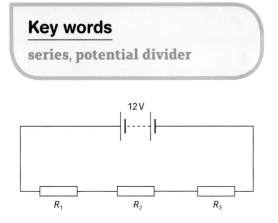

▲ Three resistors connected in series

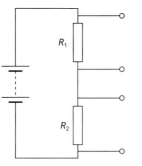

▲ Simple potential divider circuit

B What is a potential divider?

In electronic circuits, the supply voltage usually needs to be varied. This is done by splitting the voltage across two resistors connected in series.

Resistors in series

When resistors are connected in **series**, they increase the total resistance of the circuit. The total resistance is given by:

$$R_T = R_1 + R_2 + R_3$$

This equation is true for any number of resistors connected in series.

Worked example 1

Three resistors are connected in series. Their resistances are 5 Ω, 11 Ω and 8 Ω. What is the total resistance?

$$R_T = R_1 + R_2 + R_3 = 5\ \Omega + 11\ \Omega + 8\ \Omega = 24\ \Omega$$

A What is the total resistance of three resistors with values 8 Ω, 10 Ω, and 7 Ω when they are connected in series?

Potential divider

In a series circuit, the current flowing in the circuit is the same everywhere. The total voltage is shared between all the components, in proportion to their resistances. The voltage across a component is also known as the potential difference.

A **potential divider** circuit is shown in the diagram on the left. The same current flows through both resistors, R_1 and R_2. When the two resistors have the same value, the voltage across each resistor is the same – it is divided between the two resistors. If the resistance of R_2 is double that of R_1, the voltage across R_2 will be double the voltage across R_1.

The voltage across either resistor can be used as an output for other circuits.

If R_2 is replaced with a variable resistor, the output voltage, V_{out}, can be easily changed as required.

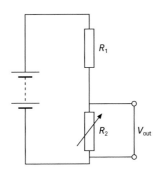

▲ Potential divider circuit where V_{out} can be varied

Exam tip

✔ You need to be able to recognise and name a potential divider circuit.

Output from a potential divider

The circuit for a potential divider is often drawn as shown in the diagram. The power supply is not shown. There is a line that is shown as 0 V and the voltages are shown relative to this.

You can calculate V_{out} using ratios. If the resistance of R_2 is twice the resistance of R_1 then the voltage across R_2 (V_{out}) will be double that across R_1. For example if V_{in} = 30 V and R_1 = 4 Ω and R_2 8 Ω, V_{out} will be 20 V.

When R_2 is smaller than R_1, V_{out} will be smaller than the voltage across R_1. For example, if R_2 is ten times smaller than R_2 then V_{out} will be ten times smaller than the voltage across R_1.

The larger R_2 gets compared with R_1, the higher V_{out} becomes. When R_2 is much greater than R_1, the value of V_{out} is approximately equal to V_{in}. When R_2 is much less than R_1, the value of V_{out} is approximately zero.

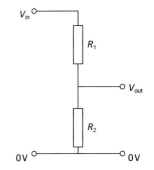

▲ How a potential divider circuit is usually shown

C Calculate V_{out} when V_{in} is 24 V, R_1 is 600 Ω, and R_2 is 2 Ω.

Worked example 2

Calculate V_{out} when V_{in} is 12 V, R_1 is 6 Ω and R_2 is 18 Ω.

The resistance of R_2 is 18/6 = 3 times larger than the resistance of R_1, so V_{out} will be 3 times bigger than the voltage across R_1.

So V_{out} = 9 V (and the voltage across R_1 is 3 V).

R_1 and R_2 can be replaced with two variable resistors. This means that you can change the threshold of the output voltage. This is the point at which V_{out} becomes significantly higher than zero, high enough to perform a specific task (eg sound an alarm).

Questions

1 Three resistors with resistances of 20 Ω, 6 Ω, and 9 Ω are connected in series. What is the total resistance? ↓E

2 Explain how the output voltage can be varied using a variable resistor in a potential divider circuit. ↓C

3 What values of R_1 and R_2 could you use so that V_{out} is approximately equal to V_{in}?

4 Calculate V_{out} when V_{in} is 18 V, R_1 is 1.2 kΩ, and R_2 is 300 Ω. ↓A*

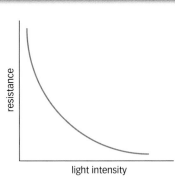

▲ How the resistance of an LDR (light-dependent resistor) changes with intensity of light

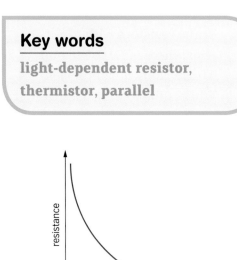

▲ How the resistance of a thermistor varies with temperature

Light-dependent resistors

A **light-dependent resistor** (LDR) is a special type of resistor. Its resistance changes as the intensity of the light falling on it changes.

When light levels are low, the resistance of an LDR is high. When bright light shines on an LDR, the resistance is much lower.

This change in resistance according to the intensity of light means that LDRs can be used as switches. For example, they can be used to switch on security lights when it gets dark.

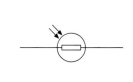

▲ An LDR (light-dependent resistor) and its circuit symbol

Thermistors

A **thermistor** is another special type of resistor. Its resistance changes as its temperature changes.

When the temperature of the thermistor is low, its resistance is high. As the temperature increases, the resistance of the thermistor decreases. (Thermistors are not made of metal and don't behave like the wire filaments we met earlier.)

▲ A thermistor and its circuit symbol

A What happens to the resistance of a thermistor as the temperature increases?

LDRs and thermistors in potential dividers

You can replace R_2 in the potential divider circuit with an LDR or a thermistor. This provides an output signal that depends on light or temperature conditions.

In low light the resistance of the LDR is higher in comparison with R_1, and the voltage across it is higher. The output voltage is higher. As light gets brighter, the resistance of the LDR goes down compared with R_1 and the output voltage from it also goes down.

For a thermistor, when the temperature is low, its resistance is higher and the output voltage across it is higher. As the temperature increases, the resistance of the thermistor decreases compared with R_1, and the output voltage goes down.

Resistors in parallel

Components can be connected in **parallel** in a circuit. This means that there is more than one way for the current to flow round the circuit, as shown in the diagram.

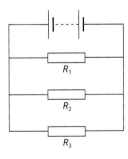

◀ Resistors connected in parallel

Connecting resistors in parallel reduces the total resistance of a circuit.

Calculating total resistance for resistors in parallel

You can calculate the total resistance, R_T for three resistors in parallel with resistances of R_1, R_2, and R_3, using the equation:

$$\frac{1}{R_T} = \frac{1}{R_1} + \frac{1}{R_2} + \frac{1}{R_3}$$

This equation is true for any number of resistors connected in parallel.

Worked example

Three resistors are connected in parallel. Their resistances are 2 Ω, 2 Ω, and 6 Ω. What is the total resistance? Use the equation above.

$$\frac{1}{R_T} = \frac{1}{2\,\Omega} + \frac{1}{2\,\Omega} + \frac{1}{6\,\Omega}$$

$$= \frac{3 + 3 + 1}{6\,\Omega}$$

$$= \frac{7}{6\,\Omega}$$

$$R_T = \frac{6}{7}\ \Omega \text{ or } 0.86\ \Omega.$$

Questions

1 (a) What is a thermistor?   (b) What is an LDR?

2 What happens to the total resistance when resistors are connected in parallel?

3 Three resistors of values 3 Ω, 9 Ω, and 15 Ω are connected in parallel. What is their total resistance?

4 Explain how you would design a potential divider circuit so that it provided an output when the temperature dropped below a certain level.

Learning objectives

After studying this topic, you should be able to:

- ✔ explain what a transistor is
- ✔ describe base, emitter, and collector currents
- ✔ explain how a transistor can be used as a switch for an LED

Key words

transistor, base, collector, emitter, light-emitting diode

collector

base

emitter

◀ The circuit symbol for an npn transistor

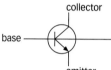

◀ Types of transistor. Each has three terminals.

Did you know...?

As transistors get smaller and smaller, issues arise about the possible dangers of new technologies. Should scientists develop machines with greater artificial intelligence? Are our personal freedoms under threat with increasing facial recognition and tracking? Who owns information (especially biometric data) about you?

How a transistor works

Transistors are the main building block of electronic components. There are probably billions of them in your school or house. A computer will have millions of transistors.

The circuit symbol for an npn transistor is shown in the diagram. There are three terminals – the **base**, the **collector** and the **emitter**.

Advantages of miniaturisation	Disadvantages of miniaturisation
Computer chips can contain more transistors, making them more powerful.	Smaller components are more complex to manufacture, making them initially more expensive.
Smaller components are more energy efficient.	
Smaller components have a wider range of applications.	
Smaller components mean that the products containing them can be made smaller.	

A transistor is an electronic switch – it is either on or off. In the circuit shown below, when the voltage between the base and the emitter is low, or zero, no current flows in the base and emitter part of the circuit. In a transistor, when no current flows through the base–emitter circuit, no current can flow between the collector and emitter either. So the lamp in the circuit will not light up.

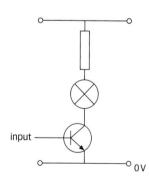

input

0V

◀ A small current between the base and the emitter 'switches on' a much bigger current between the collector and emitter

When the voltage between the base and the emitter is high, a small current flows through the base, and this allows a much larger current to flow between the collector and emitter. The lamp lights up.

The very small current in the base–emitter part acts like a switch that turns on the much bigger current in the collector–emitter part of the circuit.

In the npn transistor, the current at the emitter is the sum of the currents from the base and the collector:
current through emitter = current through base + current through collector

$$I_e = I_b + I_c$$

Worked example

The current through the base of a transistor is 0.5 mA, and the current through the emitter is 0.2 A. What is the current through the collector?

$$I_e = I_b + I_c$$
$$0.2\,A = 0.5\,mA + I_c$$
$$\text{Rearranging, } I_c = 0.2\,A - 0.5\,mA$$
$$= 200\,mA - 0.5\,mA$$
$$= 199.5\,mA.$$

An npn transistor can be used as a switch for a **light-emitting diode (LED)**, as shown in the diagram.

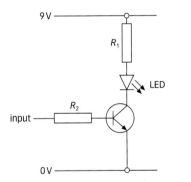

◀ Circuit to control an LED

A What is the main function of a transistor?

B The current through the collector of a transistor is 0.1896 A and the current through the emitter is 0.19 A. What is the current (in milliamperes, mA) through the base?

Using a transistor as a switch for an LED

When there is a current into the base the transistor is turned on. This allows a current to pass through R_1 and the LED, turning it on. If there is no current into the base the LED remains off.

The base of the transistor would be damaged if a large current flowed through it, so a resistor, R_2, is connected in series with it to limit the size of any current in the base–emitter circuit.

Questions

1 Draw the circuit symbol for an npn transistor and label its terminals.

2 What happens when a small current flows through the base of a transistor?

3 What are the two states of a transistor?

4 Look at the LED switch circuit. Explain why R_2 has a high resistance.

5 What do you think the resistor R_3 does in the LED circuit?

Inputs		Output
A	B	
low	low	low
low	high	low
high	low	low
high	high	high

▲ Truth table for an AND gate

A What do logic gates do?

B An AND gate has a low input at A and the input at B is high. What is the output?

C An OR gate has inputs A and B. The input at A is low and the input at B is low. What is the output?

Inputs		Output
A	B	
low	low	low
low	high	high
high	low	high
high	high	high

▲ Truth table for an OR gate

An industrial heating boiler must only start up if its pilot light is lit AND if its chimney (flue) is not blocked. It should start if the timer is on OR if someone presses the 'override' button OR if the temperature of the building falls to near freezing.

The boiler is attached to electronic circuits that use logic gates to control how it works. The output (turning the heating on or off) depends on the inputs, for example from sensors such as thermistors, or from other circuits. **Logic gates** are the basis of electronic circuits.

The AND gate

Transistors can be connected together to make logic gates. Here two transistors are used to make an **AND gate**. Each input is connected to the base of one transistor. The input signal for a logic gate is either low (about 0 V) or high. When the input is 0 V, no base current will flow and the transistor is switched off. When the input is high, there is a base current and the transistor is switched on. In an AND gate, both inputs have to be high for the output to be high.

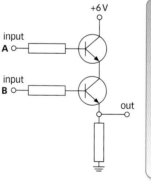 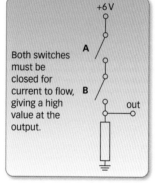

◀ The circuit for an AND gate. The inputs at A AND at B must be high for a high output. (You might think of the two transistors acting like two switches in series.)

A **truth table** for a logic gate (see margin) shows the outputs for all the possible different combinations of inputs.

The OR gate

In an **OR gate**, the output is high when either or both of the inputs are high.

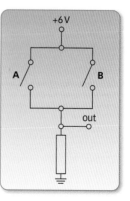

◀ You can think of an OR gate as like two switches connected in parallel. If either A OR B is closed, a current will flow. If both are closed, a current will flow too.

The NOT gate

A **NOT gate** has only one input. The output is the opposite of the input, so the truth table is very simple.

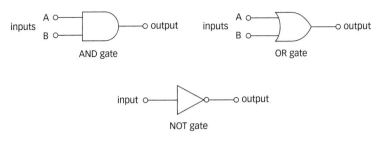

AND gate

OR gate

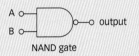

NOT gate

▲ Circuit symbols for the AND, OR, and NOT logic gates

Input	Output
low	high
high	low

▲ Truth table for a NOT gate

NAND and NOR logic gates

Logic gates can be combined. A **NAND gate** is an AND gate with a NOT gate connected to the output. Its outputs are the opposite to those of an AND gate.

An OR gate combined with a NOT gate makes a **NOR gate**. Its outputs are the opposite of those of an OR gate.

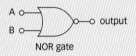

NAND gate

NOR gate

▲ Circuit symbols for NAND and NOR gates

Inputs		Output
A	B	
low	low	high
low	high	high
high	low	high
high	high	low

▲ Truth table for a NAND gate

Inputs		Output
A	B	
low	low	high
low	high	low
high	low	low
high	high	low

▲ Truth table for a NOR gate

Questions

1 Explain what a NOT gate does in terms of its inputs and outputs.

2 Explain what an OR gate does in terms of its inputs and outputs.

3 For a new car to start, the key card should be in its slot and the brake pedal needs to be pressed. What type of logic gate should be used?

4 The sensors in a greenhouse give a high output when the greenhouse is hot and the windows are open. A heater should switch on when it is cold and the windows are closed. Explain why a NOR gate could be used.

Key words

logic gate, AND gate, truth table, OR gate, NOT gate, NAND gate, NOR gate

Learning objectives

After studying this topic, you should be able to:

✔ complete a truth table with inputs from three logic gates

✔ complete a truth table with inputs from four logic gates

A What are the types of gates shown in the diagram?

B What is the output of an OR gate when one input is high and the other is low?

C What inputs to an AND gate will give a low output?

Exam tip OCR

✔ In an exam, you will be given the truth table to complete – you will not have to draw one up yourself.

When you open a car door, a courtesy light comes on inside the car. The light comes on when you open the driver's door OR the passenger's door OR when you switch the light on.

You can use a logic gate diagram to show this and to show how to provide the output to turn the light on. Two OR gates are needed as shown in the diagram below.

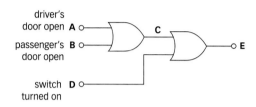

▲ Logic circuit for courtesy light in car

The truth table for this circuit looks like this:

A	B	C	D	E
low	low	low	low	low
low	low	low	high	high
low	high	high	low	high
low	high	high	high	high
high	low	high	low	high
high	low	high	high	high
high	high	high	low	high
high	high	high	high	high

Worked example

Complete the truth table for the logic system shown in the diagram.

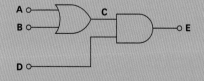

Step 1. Identify the logic gates. A and B are inputs to an OR gate. This gives an output at C. This signal at C and the input at D are inputs to an AND gate, giving an output at E.

Input A	Input B	C	Input D	Output E

Step 2. Find all of the possible combinations of inputs. The inputs from outside the circuit are at A, B, and D.

A	B	C	D	E
low	low		low	
low	low		high	
low	high		low	
low	high		high	
high	low		low	
high	low		high	
high	high		low	
high	high		high	

In the first row, start with all the inputs as low.

In the next row, change input D to high.

Next, change input B to high. This means two new rows. Can you see why?

Next, change input A to high. This means four new rows, to cover all the combinations of B and D that you have already.

Now you have all the possible combinations of inputs at A, B, and D.

Step 3. Work out the outputs. For example, looking at the first row, the output at C will be low, and the output at E will also be low. Looking at the sixth row, the OR gate for inputs A and B will give an output of high at C; the input to the AND gate is high from C and high from D, so the output at E is high. The completed truth table looks like this:

A	B	C	D	E
low	low	low	low	low
low	low	low	high	low
low	high	high	low	low
low	high	high	high	high
high	low	high	low	low
high	low	high	high	high
high	high	high	low	low
high	high	high	high	high

Questions

1 What is the output of a NOT gate when the input is low?

2 For a fire alarm to go off, both the smoke detector and the heat detector need to have high inputs. In addition, there is a button that can be pressed to test the fire alarm. The logic circuit is shown in the diagram.
   (a) Identify each of the gates in the diagram.
   (b) Copy and complete the truth table. You will need 12 rows in your table.

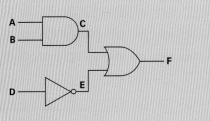

A	B	C	D	E	F
low	low		low		

3 (a) Identify each of the gates in the diagram.
   (b) Copy and complete the truth table. You will need 16 rows in your table.

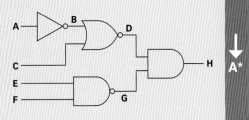

A	B	C	D	E	F	G	H
low		low		low	low		

8: Using logic gates

A What can be used as inputs for logic gates?

Logic gate inputs

Input signals for logic gates can be provided by switches, LDRs, and thermistors. A fixed resistor is connected in series with the switch, thermistor, or LDR, as shown in the diagram. The two components work as a potential divider.

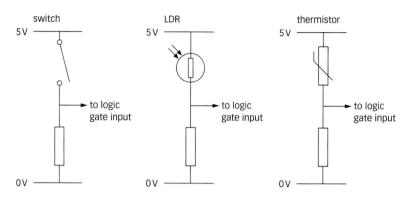

▲ Using different inputs for a logic gate

Controlling the input

By using a thermistor with a fixed resistor, you can generate an input for a logic gate that depends on temperature. As the temperature increases, the resistance of the thermistor drops. So the voltage across the thermistor decreases and the voltage across the resistor increases. When the temperature goes above a certain level, the thermistor resistance becomes so small that the voltage across the resistor provides a high enough input for the logic gate.

With an LDR, as light levels increase, its resistance decreases and the voltage across the resistor increases. When the light increases above a certain level, the resistance of the LDR will have dropped sufficiently to provide a voltage across the resistor that is a high input to the logic gate.

If you use a variable resistor in place of the fixed resistor, you can change the point at which the resistance of the LDR or thermistor has decreased enough to provide a high input. This means that for a thermistor, you could change the temperature at which you get a high input. For an LDR you could change the light level.

Logic gate outputs

LEDs can be connected to the output of a logic gate, as shown in the diagram. When the output is high, the LED will emit light. When the output is low, the LED will not emit any light. LEDs are often used like this to show that something is switched on.

> When the output of the logic gate is high, there is a voltage across the LED and resistor, so a current will flow through them. The resistor limits the size of the current that can flow through the LED. Without the resistor, the current flowing through the LED would be too high and it would burn out.

Relays

A **relay** is a device that uses a small current flowing through a coil to switch on a circuit where a much bigger current is flowing. Typically, these are used where there is an output from a logic gate that is used to switch something on. For example, an LDR may be used to switch security lights on when the light level drops below a certain level. The high output from the logic gate causes a current to flow through the coil of wire, producing a magnetic field. The iron switch in the main circuit is attracted towards the coil, closing the switch and completing the circuit with the security light in it. The light switches on.

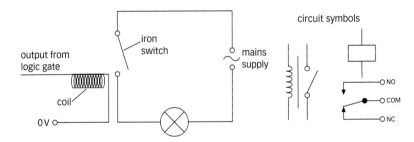

▲ A relay circuit and symbol

Why use relays?

Logic gates are low-power devices. The mains circuit uses a much larger voltage that would damage the logic gate. The relay isolates the logic gate from the mains power. Similarly it isolates the low-voltage sensor circuit of say, a thermistor or LDR, from the mains supply.

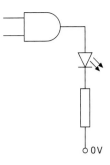

▲ Using an LED to show that the output of a logic gate is high

> **B** How is an LED used in a logic gate circuit?
>
> **C** What is a relay?

Questions

1 Draw the circuit symbol for a relay. ↓ E

2 How is a thermistor used to provide an input for a logic gate?

3 Describe what happens in the relay circuit shown on the left when the output from the logic gate is high. ↓ C

4 (a) Explain how you could use a thermistor as part of the logic gate input to adjust the temperature at which a central heating systems switches on.

   (b) How could you show that the central heating system is switched on? ↓ A*

5 Explain why relays are needed to switch circuits on and off.

Learning objectives

After studying this topic, you should be able to:

- ✔ describe the magnetic fields around a current-carrying wire and a solenoid
- ✔ understand why a current-carrying wire experiences a force when placed inside a magnetic field, and describe the effect of reversing the current
- ✔ use Fleming's left-hand rule to determine the direction of the force on a current-carrying wire inside a magnetic field

Key words

magnetic field, motor effect, Fleming's left-hand rule

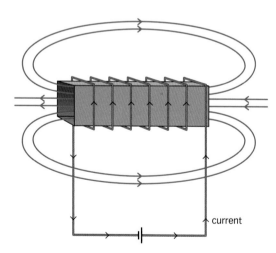

▲ The magnetic field around a rectangular coil carrying a current is the same shape as the field around a cylindrical solenoid and a simple bar magnet

Current and magnetic fields

When an electric current flows in a wire it creates a **magnetic field** around the wire. This magnetic field is only there when there is a current. If the current stops, the magnetic field collapses. It is a bit like the wake from a moving boat. When the boat is moving, a wake is created behind it. When the boat is not moving, there is no wake.

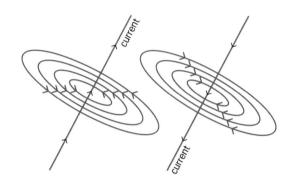

▲ The magnetic field lines around a wire that is carrying a current are shaped like concentric circles. Reversing the direction of the current reverses the direction of the field.

The shape of the magnetic field around a single wire is a series of concentric circles. However, if the wire is looped into a coil (or solenoid) the shape resembles a bar magnet.

> **A** Describe the shape of the magnetic field around a coil of wire.

If the current is reversed then the direction of the magnetic fields is also reversed, but in both cases it stays the same shape.

> **B** What happens to the magnetic field around a current-carrying wire if the current reverses direction?

The motor effect

If a current-carrying wire is placed inside another magnetic field (for example in between the poles of two other magnets), the two magnetic fields interact. The magnetic field from the current and the magnetic field from the magnets push on each other, creating a force on the wire. This often makes the wire kick or move.

This is called the **motor effect**. The force on the wire is always at right angles to the magnetic field.

> C What will happen to a current-carrying wire placed inside a magnetic field?

If you reverse the direction of the current, the wire kicks in the opposite direction. Changing the direction of the magnetic field, by swapping the poles of the magnets around, also reverses the direction of the force on the wire.

Predicting the force direction

The direction of the force acting on the wire can be predicted by using **Fleming's left-hand rule**:
If the **F**orefinger points in the direction of the **F**ield and the se**C**ond finger points in the direction of the **C**urrent, then the thu**M**b points in the direction of the **M**ovement.

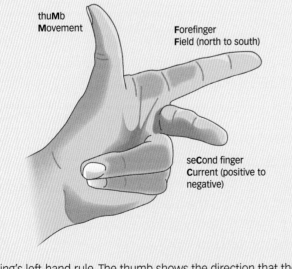

thu**M**b
Movement

Forefinger
Field (north to south)

se**C**ond finger
Current (positive to negative)

▲ Fleming's left-hand rule. The thumb shows the direction that the wire moves in (and therefore the direction of the force).

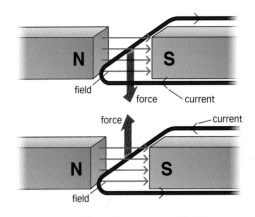

▲ The motor effect. The magnetic field from the current in the wire interacts with the field from the magnets, making a force that pushes the wire, making it move. Reversing the direction of the current flips the direction of the force.

Questions

1 What must pass through a wire in order to create a magnetic field around it?

2 Describe how the motor effect happens.

3 State Fleming's left-hand rule and draw a diagram showing how it might be used.

4 Explain what would happen to the direction of the force acting on a current-carrying wire placed inside a magnetic field if first the current was reversed, and then the poles of the magnets were swapped.

5 In terms of magnetic fields, suggest why reversing the direction of the current reverses the direction of the force on the wire.

Learning objectives

After studying this topic, you should be able to:

- ✔ state some examples of uses of electric motors
- ✔ describe the energy changes in an electric motor
- ✔ explain how an electric motor works and state the factors affecting how fast it turns
- ✔ describe how the current through an electric motor is changed to keep the motor spinning

Key words

electric motor, split-ring commutator, radial field

▲ Electric motors are not just found in small devices. They can be used in large machines, including trains and cars.

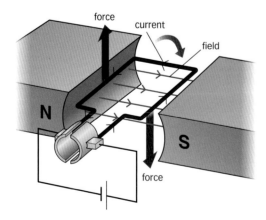

▲ A simple motor spins due to the motor effect

Electric motors

Electric motors are found in a range of things, from washing machines and CD players to food processors and electric drills. They are used to move windscreen wipers on cars, they provide the tiny vibrations in some mobile phones, and they power hybrid cars and even some high-speed trains.

◀ There is a small motor inside an electric drill

Electric motors use the motor effect to transfer electrical energy into kinetic energy. When the motor spins, energy is transferred to a moving load. This results in useful work being done. For example, a motor can be used to lift heavy weights or pull objects along the ground.

No electric motor is 100% efficient. Whenever a motor spins, some energy is transferred to the surroundings. This is usually in the form of waste heat.

> **A** Give one example of a use of an electric motor.
> **B** Describe the useful energy changes inside an electric motor.

How motors spin

A simple electric motor consists of a coil of wire inside the magnetic field between two magnets. When there is a current in the wire, the magnetic fields interact. One side of the coil is pushed down and the other side is pushed up. This makes the motor spin.

The size of the current, the strength of the magnetic field from the magnets, and the number of turns in the coil all affect the speed of a motor.

The motor's speed can be increased by:
- increasing the size of the current in the coil
- increasing the number of turns on the coil
- increasing the strength of magnetic field by using stronger magnets

For the motor to continue to spin in the same direction, the current needs to be reversed every half-turn of the coil. This is done using a special switch called a **split-ring commutator**. Each time the coil is vertical, the current inside it reverses. The side of the loop that was pushed up is now pushed down. This allows the motor to continue to spin.

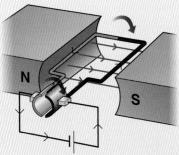

① The blue part of this coil is pushed upwards and the red half downwards. (Check with Fleming's left-hand rule.)

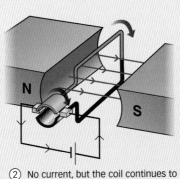

② No current, but the coil continues to turn because of its own momentum.

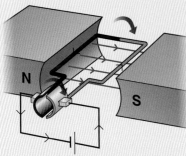

③ The direction of the current in the coil and commutator is reversed. Now the blue part is pushed downwards and the red half upwards.

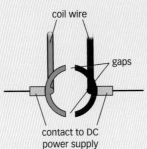

coil wire

gaps

contact to DC power supply

▲ Reversing the current in the wire coil. Look at the direction of the current in the part of the commutator and coil that is shaded blue. The direction of the current changes with each half-turn of the commutator. The same applies to the part shaded red.

Most practical electric motors use curved magnets. This produces a **radial field** so the current remains at right angles to the magnetic field for longer. This provides a more consistent force for longer.

▲ Most motors use curved magnets to create a radial field

Questions

1. What happens to the wasted energy from most electric motors? ↓E

2. Describe how the speed of a motor can be increased.

3. Explain why the coil inside a simple motor begins to rotate. ↓C

4. Use Fleming's left-hand rule to explain why, inside a simple motor, one side of the coil of wire is pushed down while the other side is pushed up. ↓A*

5. Describe the purpose of the split-ring commutator found in most simple motors, and explain how it works.

Learning objectives

After studying this topic, you should be able to:

✔ describe the dynamo effect

✔ describe the key parts of a simple generator

✔ describe how to increase the voltage generated

✔ explain the role of slip rings and brushes inside a generator

Key words

dynamo effect, generator, slip rings

▲ Small generators are found in wind-up torches

Did you know...?

You may remember that the mains electricity supply is ac and it has a frequency of 50 Hz. This means the voltage reverses direction 50 times every second (or once every 0.02 s). In the US the frequency of the supply is 60 Hz. Most modern electronic devices such as laptops or mp3 players can run on either 50 Hz or 60 Hz.

The dynamo effect

You might remember that electricity can be generated by:

- moving a wire near a magnet
- moving a magnet near a wire.

This is called the **dynamo effect**. When a wire moves through a magnetic field, a voltage is induced. The same thing happens when a wire is inside a changing magnetic field. As long as the field is changing, a voltage is induced across the wire, and this causes a current to flow.

> **A** State two ways in which a voltage can be induced in a wire.

▲ Large industrial generators are used to supply electricity in the event of a power cut

There are many different types of **generator**, but they are all essentially just motors in reverse:

motor: electrical energy → kinetic energy
generator: kinetic energy → electrical energy

> **B** Describe the energy changes inside a generator.

Generating alternating current (AC)

Generating AC rather than DC (direct current) allows energy to be transmitted over long distances. All generators found inside power stations generate alternating current. They use a rotating electromagnet inside a coil of wire. This creates a changing magnetic field inside the coil, inducing a voltage. If the magnetic field is reversed, the voltage is also reversed. Whenever a magnet rotates inside a coil of wire, it induces an alternating voltage and generates alternating current.

The number of turns on the coil of wire inside a generator affects the size of the induced voltage. The greater the number of turns, the higher the voltage. Double the number of turns means the induced voltage is twice as great.

The speed of rotation also affects the induced voltage. Spinnng the coil or electromagnet faster has two effects.

- Spinning the coil faster increases the size of the induced voltage. Spinning it twice as fast will double the size of the voltage.
- Increasing the speed of the coil also affects the frequency of the alternating voltage. Spinning twice as fast doubles the number of rotations each second, doubling the frequency.

If a voltage is induced by a changing magnetic field, the size of this induced voltage depends on the rate at which the magnetic field changes. The faster the field changes, the higher the voltage.

If a voltage is induced by rotating a coil of wire inside a magnetic field, the faster the coil rotates, the greater the size of the induced voltage and the higher the frequency.

If a coil is made to rotate, special connectors called **slip rings** allow the coil to spin without tangling the wires. These slip rings are connected to the circuit through brushes. These provide a good electric electrical contact whilst allowing the coil to rotate.

▲ This generator is in a power station

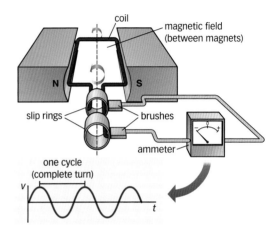

▲ An AC generator and its output

Questions

1 What is the frequency of the main AC supply in the UK? ↓ E

2 What type of electricity is generated when a magnet rotates inside a coil of wire?

3 Describe the effect on the induced voltage of: ↓ C

  (a) increasing the number of coils inside the generator

  (b) spinning the magnet faster.

4 Explain the role of slip rings and brushes in a simple AC generator. ↓ A*

Learning objectives

After studying this topic, you should be able to:

✔ describe how transformers change the size of an alternating voltage

✔ describe the structure of step-up and step-down transformers

✔ explain how a transformer works

✔ use the equation linking voltage across the coils and number of turns in the coils

Key words

iron core, primary coil, secondary coil, step-up transformer, number of turns, step-down transformer

A Why does a current not flow from the primary coil to the secondary coil?

B In a step-up transformer which coil has the greater voltage?

C In a step-down transformer which coil has the greater number of turns?

Structure of a transformer

Transformers are used to change the size of an alternating voltage, they do not change alternating current to direct current.

A transformer consists of an **iron core** with two coils of wire wound around it – the **primary coil** and the **secondary coil**. The primary coil is connected to a power supply.

The two coils of wire are separate – they are not connected, so current cannot flow from the primary coil to the secondary coil.

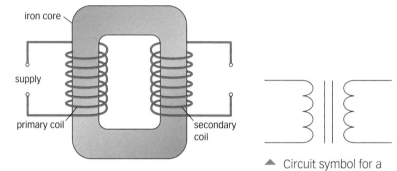

▲ The main parts of a transformer

▲ Circuit symbol for a transformer

A transformer only works with an alternating current – it does not work with direct current.

In a **step-up transformer**, the voltage across the secondary coil is greater than the voltage across the primary coil. The **number of turns** on the secondary coil is greater than the number of turns on the primary coil.

In a **step-down transformer** the voltage across the secondary coil is less than the voltage across the primary coil. The number of turns on the secondary coil is less than the number of turns on the primary coil.

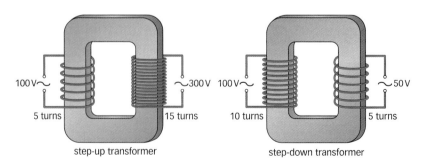

▲ A step-up transformer and a step-down transformer

▲ The inside of a transformer

How a transformer works

When there is an alternating current in the primary coil a constantly changing magnetic field is created. The iron core concentrates the changing magnetic field and this field is transferred throughout the core.

As the current in the primary coil changes direction the magnetic field it creates is reversed. This changing magnetic field continuously magnetises the iron, demagnetises it and then re-magnetises it in the opposite direction.

As the secondary coil is wrapped around the core the changing magnetic field inside the coil acts like a magnet being pushed into and out of the coil. An alternating voltage is induced in the secondary coil. The magnetic field must be changing to induce the voltage, just like a magnet must be moving through a coil to produce a voltage. Using direct current does not create a changing magnetic field and so no voltage would be induced in the secondary coil.

The voltages across the primary and secondary coils of a transformer are related by the equation:

$$\frac{\text{voltage across primary coil}}{\text{voltage across secondary coil}} = \frac{\text{number of turns on primary coil}}{\text{number of turns of secondary coil}}$$

If V_p is the voltage across the primary coil in volts, V, V_s is the voltage across the secondary coil in volts, n_p is the number of turns on the primary coil, and n_s is the number of turns on the secondary coil, then:

$$\frac{V_p}{V_s} = \frac{n_p}{n_s}$$

✔ Remember all the parts of a transformer – you may need to identify them in the exam.

✔ No current flows between the primary and secondary coils – they are not connected electrically.

✔ Transformers do not change alternating current to direct current.

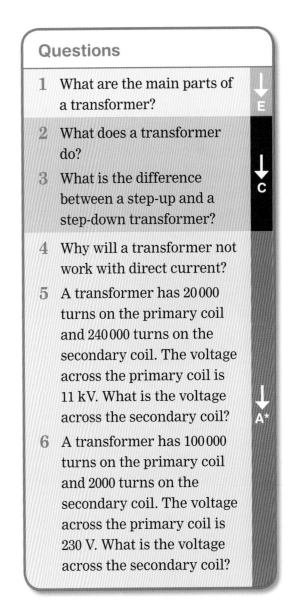

Questions

1 What are the main parts of a transformer?

2 What does a transformer do?

3 What is the difference between a step-up and a step-down transformer?

4 Why will a transformer not work with direct current?

5 A transformer has 20 000 turns on the primary coil and 240 000 turns on the secondary coil. The voltage across the primary coil is 11 kV. What is the voltage across the secondary coil?

6 A transformer has 100 000 turns on the primary coil and 2000 turns on the secondary coil. The voltage across the primary coil is 230 V. What is the voltage across the secondary coil?

Worked example

A computer runs off the mains supply, but only needs a voltage of 11.5 V. There are 1000 turns on the secondary coil. How many turns are there on the primary coil?

$$\frac{V_p}{V_s} = \frac{n_p}{n_s}$$

V_p = 230 V (mains voltage), V_s = 11.5 V and n_s = 1000

$$\frac{230\,\text{V}}{11.5\,\text{V}} = \frac{n_p}{1000} \quad n_p = 1000 \times \frac{230\,\text{V}}{11.5\,\text{V}} = 1000 \times 20 = 20\,000 \text{ turns}$$

Learning objectives

After studying this topic, you should be able to:

- ✔ give some applications of transformers
- ✔ explain why isolating transformers are used
- ✔ describe how transformers are used in the National Grid
- ✔ use the transformer power equation

Key words

isolating transformer

◀ A shaver socket contains an isolating transformer

◀ An industrial transformer that steps voltage down from 11 kV to 433 V

Applications of transformers

Some electrical devices need a much lower voltage than the 230 V mains supply. Step-down transformers are used in their power supplies to reduce the voltage to what is needed.

▲ The power supplies for all of these devices include a transformer. The laptop needs 19 V, the phone 6.5 V, and the battery charger 4.2 V.

Some electricity circuits use an **isolating transformer**. This means that there is no direct link between the current that flows through the device and the mains supply, so they are safer. They are used for bathroom shaver sockets, because there is an increased chance that water could get into the socket.

> Isolating transformers have equal numbers of turns in the primary and secondary coils. As the link is through the changing magnetic field, it is safer because there is less chance of an earth wire touching live parts.

Transformers in the National Grid

Step-up transformers are used to increase the voltage from the generators at a power station. The power is transmitted at a high voltage over the National Grid.

At electricity substations the voltage is then reduced by step-down transformers for use in homes, shops, and offices.

Some power is wasted as heat. The current flowing through the cables has a heating effect, and the transformers also heat up slightly.

> A Give three examples of devices that use step-down transformers?
>
> B What are step-down transformers used for in the National Grid?

Why power is transmitted at high voltages

The power loss when electrical energy is transmitted is related to the square of the current in the transmission lines:

$$\text{power loss, } P \ = \ (\text{current, } I)^2 \ \times \ \text{resistance}$$
$$\text{(watts, W)} \qquad \text{(amperes, A)} \qquad \text{(ohms, } \Omega)$$

Transformers are very efficient. If a transformer is assumed to have an efficiency of 100%, the power input to the primary coil is equal to the power output from the secondary coil. Power is voltage × current.

So we can say:

$$V_p \ \times \ I_p \ = \ V_s \ \times \ I_s$$

If V_p is the voltage across the primary coil in volts (V), I_p is the current in the primary coil in amperes (A), V_s is the voltage across the secondary coil in volts (V), and I_s is the current in the secondary coil in amperes (A).

Worked example

The voltage across the primary coil of a transformer is 11 000 V. The voltage across the secondary coil is 230 V, and the current through the secondary coil is 13 A. What is the current through the primary coil?

$$V_p \times I_p = V_s \times I_s$$

$V_p = 11\,000\,V, V_s = 230\,V, I_s = 13\,A$

$$11\,000\,V \times I_p = 230\,V \times 13\,A$$

Rearranging the equation:

$$I_p = \frac{230\,V}{11\,000\,V} \times 13\,A$$

$$= 0.27\,A$$

When the voltage is increased, the current decreases for transmitting the same power. For example, increasing the voltage from 230 V to 11 000 V would reduce the current from 13 A to 0.27 A. The power losses depend on the square of the current.

Questions

1 What are step-up transformers used for in the National Grid? ↓E

2 Why is some power lost when electrical energy is transmitted?

3 Why are isolating transformers used for bathroom shaver sockets? ↓C

4 Calculate the voltage across the primary coil of a transformer when the current through the primary coil is 0.25 A, the voltage across the secondary coil is 230 V, and the current through the secondary coil is 13 A.

5 Calculate the current in the secondary coil of a transformer when the voltage across the secondary coil is 132 kV, the voltage across the primary coil is 11 kV, and the current in the primary coil is 100 A. ↓A*

6 How much less is the energy loss when power is transmitted at 230 V rather than 11 000 V?

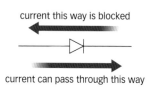

current this way is blocked

current can pass through this way

▲ The symbol for a diode shows which way current can pass through it

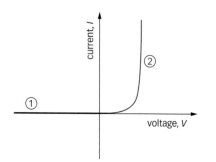

▲ The current–voltage graph (characteristic) for a diode

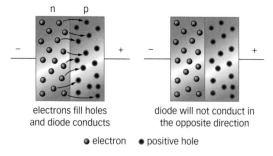

electrons fill holes and diode conducts

diode will not conduct in the opposite direction

● electron ● positive hole

▲ The diode will only conduct if the electrons are pulled across to fill the positive holes

What is a diode?

Diodes are tiny electronic components. They are an essential part of modern technology. There are hundreds of diodes in most PCs, mobile phones, TVs, and games consoles. Diodes contain two layers of material sandwiched together. These layers have special properties that only allow electric current to pass through the diode in one direction.

The symbol for a diode shows the direction of current through it. Any current in the opposite direction will not pass through the diode.

Plotting the graph of current against voltage for a diode produces an unusual shape (see left). As the current is only allowed through the diode in one direction, any current in the negative (or reverse) direction is blocked by the very high resistance of the diode (this is the part labelled '1' on the graph). When the current is in the positive (or forward) direction, the diode has a low resistance and the current easily passes through the diode (the part labelled '2' on the graph).

The resistance of the diode is different for opposite directions of current because of the materials in the diode. One of the two special layers inside the diode has many extra electrons; this layer is called the 'n' (for 'negative') layer. The other layer (called 'p' for 'positive') is missing electrons; instead there are a series of **positive holes** where the electrons should be.

If the current is in the positive direction through the diode, the extra electrons in the n layer are pulled into the holes in the p layer, allowing a current to pass through the diode. The resistance is very low. However, if the current is in the negative direction, there are no free electrons in the holes and so the diode does not conduct. The resistance is very high.

Converting AC to DC

Nearly all electronic devices use direct current, but the electricity transmitted to homes is alternating current. Conversion of AC to DC is called **rectification**.

There are two types of rectification, and both use diodes to convert the AC into DC. In **half-wave rectification,** a single diode blocks the current in one direction.

Half-wave rectification produces a series of peaks in the current, with gaps in between. The current is always positive, always in the same direction.

Key words

diode, **positive hole**, rectification, **half-wave** rectification, **full-wave** rectification, **bridge circuit**

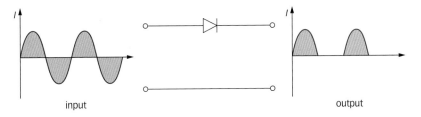

input   output

▲ Half-wave rectification can be achieved using a single diode

Combining four diodes in a bridge circuit produces **full-wave rectification**. Here the diodes are cleverly arranged to convert the negative current (the current in the reverse direction) into a positive one. This produces a series of positive pulses of current. As this output current is only ever in one direction, it is DC. However, as it is a series of pulses it is not very smooth, and further processing is needed before it can be used by some electronic devices.

The **bridge circuit** ensures that current is only allowed through in one direction. As the input is AC, the inputs switch between positive and negative values. If the top input is positive, the current can ony pass through diode A and is blocked by diode C. When the input switches and the bottom input becomes positive, the current is blocked by diode D but it passes through diode B. This ensures the top output is always positive and the bottom is always negative, so the output current is only in one direction.

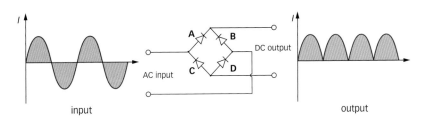

input   output

▲ A four-diode bridge produces full-wave rectification

Questions

1 Draw the circuit symbol for a diode and explain how it shows whether current will pass through it.

2 Draw the voltage–current graph for a diode and explain its key features.

3 Describe the differences between half-wave and full-wave rectification.

4 Explain why diodes only allow current through in one direction.

5 Explain how diodes are used in full-wave rectification.

E

C

A*

▲ The circuit symbol for a capacitor

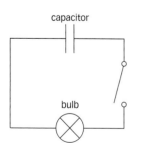

▲ Capacitors are an essential component in modern electronic devices

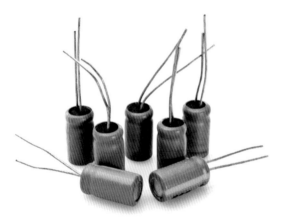

▲ When a capacitor is discharged through a bulb, the bulb lights up

What is a capacitor?

Like a diode, a **capacitor** is a simple electronic component that plays an important role in every electronic device. Without capacitors we would not be able to tune into radios or TV signals, most electronic clocks wouldn't work, and computers would not be possible.

A capacitor is an electrical component that temporarily stores charge. This charge can be discharged later. The simplest capacitor consists of a pair of parallel plates separated by an insulator.

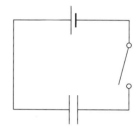

▲ A cell can be used to charge a capacitor

The circuit shown above has an uncharged capacitor. When the switch is closed, charge begins to build up on the plates of the capacitor. The voltage across the capacitor increases.

When the capacitor is fully charged, the voltage across the plates is the same as the voltage from the power supply or cell. The capacitor can now be disconnected and the charge stays on the plates. The capacitor remains charged.

> A Draw the circuit symbol for a capacitor.
>
> B Name two devices that use capacitors.
>
> C What happens to the charge on a charged capacitor when it is disconnected from a circuit?

Discharging a capacitor

If you connect a component like a resistor or a bulb across a charged capacitor, then it discharges, providing a current in the circuit.

As the capacitor discharges, the voltage across the plates falls. This has the effect of reducing the current in the circuit.

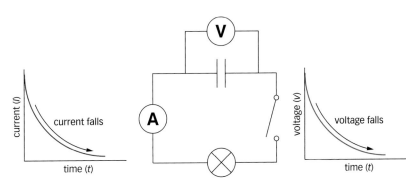

▲ When capacitor discharges through a component, the current and the voltage fall with time

The lower the resistance of the circuit, the faster the capacitor discharges, so the current and voltage fall away much more quickly.

Using capacitors

Capacitors have a number of important uses. They can be used as part of timing circuits and to store small amounts of energy.

One of the most common uses of a capacitor is to help provide a smoother voltage supply. Most electronic devices use DC. A diode is often used to rectify the AC supply, but as we have seen this does not produce a smooth supply – it fluctuates a lot. A constant supply is essential for some electronic devices. A capacitor is used to smooth out the supply.

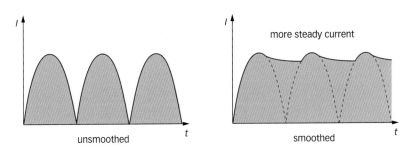

▲ Using a capacitor after full-wave rectification produces a much smoother DC supply

The capacitor is connected as part of the rectification circuit. When the voltage is increasing, the capacitor stores charge. As the voltage begins to fall, the capacitor discharges some of its charge and so keeps the supply more constant. As the voltage begins to rise again, the process is repeated.

Key words

capacitor

Did you know...?

Most large speakers have several different drivers (or speaker cones). They are designed to play different sounds, rather than just having one speaker playing all the frequencies. Capacitors are used to filter the different frequencies of sounds sent to different speakers. Higher frequencies are filtered out of the signal sent to the large bass speaker. The tweeter receives a signal with the lower frequency sounds removed; it just plays the higher frequency notes. This provides a much clearer, much more natural sound.

Questions

1 Describe how a capacitor can be charged. ↓ E

2 Describe what happens to the current in a circuit and the voltage across the capacitor when a capacitor is discharged. ↓ C

3 Explain how a capacitor is used to produce a smoother DC supply.

4 Suggest why a charged capacitor takes longer to discharge through a circuit with a higher resistance. ↓ A*

Module summary

Revision checklist

- Resistance (ohms, Ω) $= \dfrac{\text{voltage (volts, V)}}{\text{current (amperes, A)}}$.

- Variable resistors control current. Voltage–current graphs show constant resistance as a straight line. A curved graph shows that resistance is not constant (non-ohmic).

- Resistance in a metal conductor is caused by collision of free electrons in the current with the atoms of the conductor.

- Total resistance in resistors connected in series is cumulative.

- A potential divider shares voltage across components in a circuit. Its output can be varied using a variable resistor.

- The resistance of a light-dependent resistor (LDR) is lower when light levels are high. The resistance of a thermistor is lower when temperature is high.

- Connecting resistors in parallel reduces total resistance.

- Logic gates control how an electrical circuit works. A truth table shows the outputs for all possible input combinations.

- An LED can be used to show that the output of a logic gate is high. A relay is used where an output from a logic gate is used to switch something on.

- The magnetic field around a single wire is a series of concentric circles. The field around a coil of wire (solenoid) is the same as that of a bar magnet.

- The magnetic field from a current-carrying wire placed between two magnets opposes the field from the magnets, creating a force on the wire. This is the motor effect. Fleming's left hand rule predicts the direction of motion.

- Electric motors use the motor effect to convert electrical energy into kinetic energy (some energy is wasted as heat).

- A split ring commutator reverses the current at every half-turn of the coil so the motor continues to spin.

- Electricity is generated by the dynamo effect.

- A transformer is an iron core with two coils of wire around it. Step-down transformers step down voltage supplied to devices that need less than 230 V. Step-up transformers step up voltage from generators at power stations for transmission across the National Grid. Isolating transformers isolate current for safety (eg in bathrooms).

- Diodes allow current through in one direction only.

- Capacitors are used and to smooth DC supply.

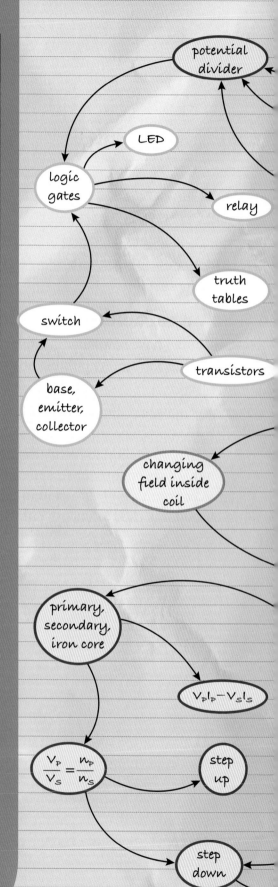

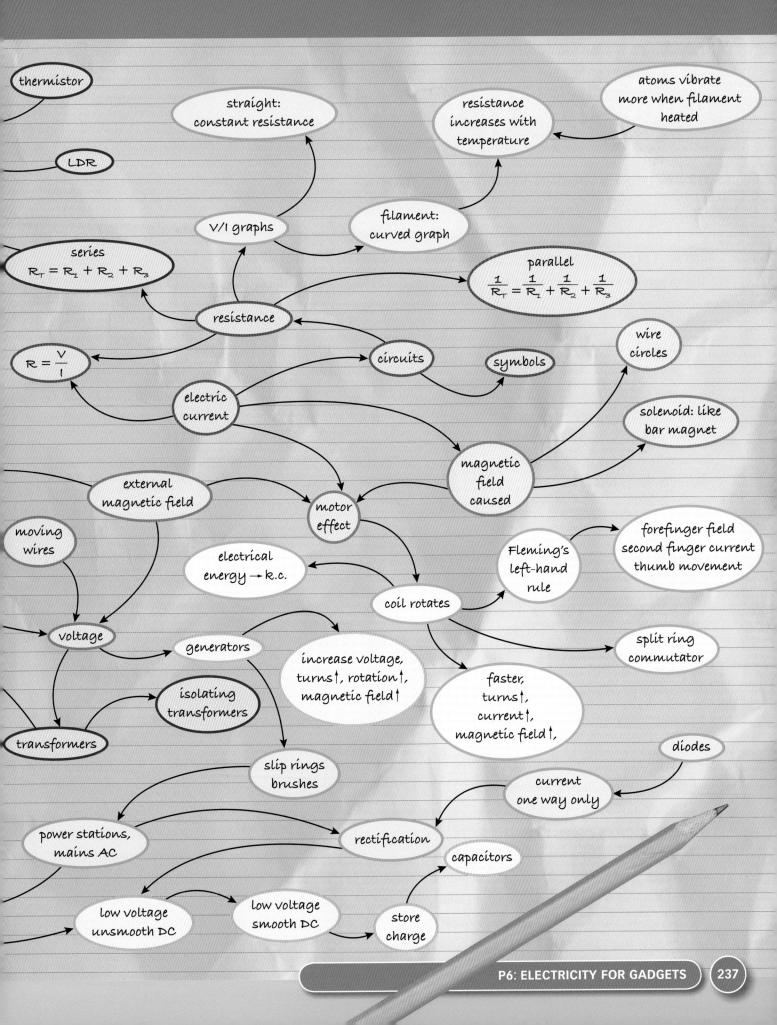

thermistor

LDR

straight:
constant resistance

resistance
increases with
temperature

atoms vibrate
more when filament
heated

V/I graphs

filament:
curved graph

series
$R_T = R_1 + R_2 + R_3$

parallel
$\frac{1}{R_T} = \frac{1}{R_1} + \frac{1}{R_2} + \frac{1}{R_3}$

resistance

$R = \frac{V}{I}$

circuits

symbols

wire
circles

electric
current

solenoid: like
bar magnet

external
magnetic field

magnetic
field
caused

moving
wires

motor
effect

electrical
energy → k.c.

Fleming's
left-hand
rule

forefinger field
second finger current
thumb movement

coil rotates

split ring
commutator

voltage

generators

increase voltage,
turns↑, rotation↑,
magnetic field↑

faster,
turns↑,
current↑,
magnetic field↑,

isolating
transformers

diodes

transformers

slip rings
brushes

current
one way only

power stations,
mains AC

rectification

capacitors

low voltage
unsmooth DC

low voltage
smooth DC

store
charge

Answering Extended Writing questions

QUESTION

Many household appliances include a simple step-down transformer.

Explain how a step-down transformer works, and why one might be used.

The quality of written communication will be assessed in your answer to this question.

A step-down transformer changes the curent so it is safe cos it can kill you the current come into the primary and less current comes out of the secondry it comes in at 230 V and to get less out there must be fewer coils.

↓ E

Examiner: This answer shows only vague understanding of the physics. Some ideas have been half-remembered, but the answer is rambling. Current and voltage are used interchangeably. There is no mention of AC, iron core, or magnetic field; and no explanation of coils or turns ratio. Spelling, punctuation, and grammar are erratic.

There are transformers everywhere, a step-down transformer reduces the voltage, which comes to a house at 230 V and is quite dangrous. There is a primery, a core, and a secondery. Current flows in the primary, and makes a magnetic field, this causes a current in the secondary, for step-down there must be fewer coils on the secondary.

↓ C

Examiner: Most of the described physics is correct. However, the sequence of ideas is not structured well, and there is some rambling and digression. Key points or words are missing: coil, iron, turns, the idea of AC, and changing field. There are occasional errors in spelling, punctuation, and grammar.

A step-down transformer alters the voltage of an electricity supply. In a house the mains comes in at 230 V; an appliance may need a lower voltage, say 12 V. There is a primary coil, an iron core, and a secondary coil. Current in the primary causes a magnetic field in the core; it is AC, so the field changes continuously. This causes AC voltage in the secondary. For step-down there must be fewer turns on the secondary – the same turns ratio as the voltage ratio.

↓ A*

Examiner: This answer is well ordered and accurate. The physics explanations and the use of technical terms are all correct. The sequence explaining how a transformer works is concise and logical. This is a difficult question to answer in a short space, and all the key ideas are there. Spelling, punctuation, and grammar are all good.

Exam-style questions

1 Draw a complete circuit with one battery, two bulbs, and a variable resistor. The two bulbs are in parallel with each other. The battery is in series with the two bulbs, and the variable resistor controls the current to them.

A02

2 State which of the following statements are false, and which are true. Rewrite each false statement to make it true.

A02 **a** For resistors in parallel, the total resistance is given by $R_T = R_1 + R_2 + R_3$.

A02 **b** Increasing the light shining on an LDR makes its resistance decrease.

A02 **c** The output of an AND gate is 1 only when both inputs are 1.

A02 **d** If resistors of $1\,\Omega$ and $100\,\Omega$ are in parallel, the total resistance is just less than $100\,\Omega$.

A01 **e** LED stands for Low Electricity Demand.

A02 **f** The output of a NOT gate is always 0.

3 The diagram below shows the main parts of a simple electric motor.

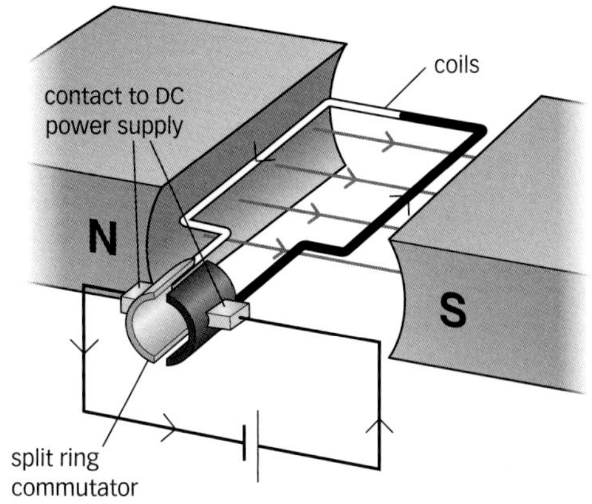

contact to DC power supply

coils

N

S

split ring commutator

A01 **a** Explain why there is a force on the white part of the coil.

A02 **b** Use Fleming's left-hand rule to work out the direction of the force.

A02 **c** What is the direction of the force on the black part of the coil?

A02 **d** What is the combined effect of the forces on the two parts of the coil?

A01 **e** Explain how the split ring commutator allows the motor to work as required.

Extended Writing

4 Draw voltage–current graphs for a fixed resistor, a diode, and a filament lamp. Explain what each graph tells you about the component.

A01

5 Why do all metals have electrical resistance? Explain what happens to the resistance of a metal wire as it gets hotter.

A01

6 Explain the physics of an electricity generator. What changes can be made to the design of a generator to increase the voltage output?

A01

↓ E

↓ A*

↓ C

↓ A*

↓ E

↓ C

↓ A*

A01 Recall the science
A02 Apply your knowledge
A03 Evaluate and analyse the evidence

P6: ELECTRICITY FOR GADGETS · 239

Revising module P1

To help you start your revision, the specification for module P1 has been summarised in the checklist below. Work your way along each row and make sure that you are happy with all the statements for your target grade.

If you are not sure of any of the statements for your target grade, make a note of them as part of your revision plan. You can then work back through the relevant parts of pages 14–47 to fill gaps in your knowledge as a start to your revision.

To aim for a grade G–E	To aim for a grade D–C	To aim for a grade B–A*
P1a **Understand** that for warm bodies the rate of cooling depends on the temperature difference compared to the surroundings. **Understand** that colour in a thermogram indicates temperature. **Recall** that heat is a measurement of energy and is measured in Joules (J). **Describe** the factors affecting the energy needed to change the temperature of a body. **Describe** an experiment to measure the energy required to change the temperature of a body.	**Recognise** and understand the consequences of the direction of energy flow between bodies of different temperatures. **Understand** that temperatures can be represented by a range of colours in a thermogram. **Understand** the concepts of specific heat capacity and specific latent heat. **Use** the specific heat capacity equation. **Use** the specific latent heat equation. **Describe** how there is no temperature change when materials are boiling, melting, or freezing.	**Describe** temperature as a measure of hotness on an arbitrary scale. **Understand** that temperature is dependent on kinetic energy. **Explain** that the hottest parts of a thermogram are white/yellow/red, and the coldest parts are black/dark blue/purple. **Describe** heat as a measurement of energy on an absolute scale. **Use** specific heat capacity and specific latent heat equations, including a change of subject. **Explain** why temperature does not change during a change of state.
P1b **Explain** why trapped air in materials is a good insulator. **Recall** that infrared radiation is reflected or absorbed by different surfaces. **Understand** how absorption and reflection of infrared radiation can be applied in everyday situations. **Describe** examples of energy saving methods in the home. **Explain** how the fact that air is a good insulator is used to keep homes warm. **Describe** other domestic energy saving methods. **Use** the energy efficiency equation.	**Explain** how energy is transferred. **Explain** how losses by energy transfer can be reduced by domestic energy saving measures. **Explain** that energy is lost from houses to the atmosphere. **Understand** that energy is conserved.	**Describe** how energy is transferred by conduction, convection, and radiation. **Explain** energy loss in a cavity wall and what measures can be taken to minimise it. **Explain** conduction, convection, and radiation in terms of home and appliance design, and energy saving strategies.
P1c **Identify** and name the main features of a transverse wave. **Recall** that all electromagnetic waves travel at the same high speed in space or in a vacuum. **Use** the wave equation. **Recall** that electromagnetic waves travel in straight lines. **Use** ray diagrams to describe reflection at single plane boundaries. **Describe** a communications use for radio, microwave, infrared, and visible light.	**Describe** the main features of a transverse wave. **Determine** the wavelength or frequency of a wave from a diagram and use this in the wave equation. **Use** ray diagrams to describe reflection at multiple plane boundaries. **Understand** that refraction occurs due to change in wave speed. **Describe** diffraction of waves at an opening. **Identify** and order the seven types of electromagnetic wave in the spectrum. **Relate** the size of a communications receiver to the wavelength of the type of signal received.	**Use** the wave equation, including a change of subject and use of standard form. **Describe** a diffraction pattern for waves, including the significance of the size of opening/ barrier and wavelength. **Describe** and **explain** the limiting effects of diffraction on telescopes and optical microscopes.

To aim for a grade G–E	To aim for a grade D–C	To aim for a grade B–A*	
Describe the historic use of light for communication in the form of code. **Recognise** where Total Internal Reflection happens. **Understand** how light and infrared radiation travel along an optical fibre by reflection. **Understand** the type of light produced by lasers, and what this makes them useful for.	**Describe** Morse code as a use of light for communication. **Recognise** that Morse code is a type of digital signal. **Describe** what happens to light at a boundary, below, at, and above the critical angle. **Understand** how light and infrared radiation travel along an optical fibre by Total Internal Reflection. **Understand** that a laser produces a narrow beam of light of a single colour.	**Explain** the advantages and disadvantages of different communication systems. **Describe** why Morse code is a digital signal. **Describe** applications of Total Internal Reflection in fibre optics. **Explain** why lasers produce an intense, coherent beam of light. **Explain** how a laser beam is used in a CD player.	P1d
Recall that warm and hot objects emit infrared radiation. **Understand** that infrared radiation is absorbed by different surfaces, causing temperature increase. **Recognise** that microwaves cause heating when absorbed by water or fat. **Recall** that mobile phones use microwave signals. **Describe** concerns about children using mobile phones. **Recall** that different studies into the effects of mobile phone use have reached conflicting conclusions.	**Describe** properties of infrared radiation. **Describe** properties of microwaves. **Understand** and **describe** the use of microwaves to transmit information over large distances. **Describe** why mobile phones and masts may or may not be dangerous. **Describe** how potential dangers may be increased by frequent use. **Explain** how publishing studies into mobile phone radiation enables results to be checked.	**Explain** how microwaves and infrared transfer energy to materials. **Describe** how energy associated with microwaves and infrared depends on their frequency. **Relate** the energy of microwaves and infrared to their potential dangers. **Explain** how microwave signal loss happens. **Describe** how signal loss problems are reduced. **Understand** that individuals and society must balance the risks and benefits of mobile phone use.	P1e
Describe everyday uses of infrared radiation. **Understand** how passive infrared sensors and thermal imaging cameras work. **Describe** the differences between analogue and digital signals.	**Describe** how infrared signals can carry information to control devices. **Recall** that the properties of digital signals contributed to the switch to digital TV and radio broadcasts. **Describe** the transmission of light in optical fibres.	**Explain** how signal from an infrared remote control uses digital signals. **Describe** the advantages of digital signals. **Describe** the advantages of optical fibres.	P1f
Describe reflection of radiation used for communication. **Recognise** that wireless technology uses electromagnetic radiation. **Describe** the advantages of wireless technology.	**Recall** refraction and reflection of radiation used for communication, and how this can be an advantage or a disadvantage for signal reception. **Describe** common uses of wireless technology. **Understand** interference between radio stations with similar frequencies. **Describe** advantages and disadvantages of DAB broadcasts.	**Explain** the dependencies involved in long-distance communication. **Recall** that refraction and reflection in the atmosphere is similar to Total Internal Reflection of light. **Explain** how refraction and diffraction of radiation affects communications. **Explain** the advantage of digital radio in terms of interference.	P1g
Describe the effects of shock waves from an earthquake. **Recall** the effects of exposure to ultraviolet radiation. **Recognise** that sunscreens can reduce damage from ultraviolet radiation. **Recall** the unexpected discovery of the ozone hole. **Describe** how scientists used scientific ideas to explain their measurements.	**Understand** that shock waves from earthquakes can travel inside the Earth. **Recall** the two types of seismic wave. **Explain** how cancer risk is reduced by darker skin. **Calculate** how long a person can spend in the sun without burning. **Describe** how the dangers of exposure to ultraviolet radiation have been publicised. **Describe** how ozone reduction measurements were verified.	**Describe** how seismic waves can provide evidence for the structure of the Earth. **Describe** how the ozone layer protects the Earth from ultraviolet radiation. **Describe** the effects of environmental pollution by CFCs. **Describe** how discovery of the ozone hole has changed behaviour.	P1h

Revising module P2

To help you start your revision, the specification for module P2 has been summarised in the checklist below. Work your way along each row and make sure that you are happy with all the statements for your target grade.

If you are not sure of any of the statements for your target grade, make a note of them as part of your revision plan. You can then work back through the relevant parts of pages 54–83 to fill gaps in your knowledge as a start to your revision.

To aim for a grade G–E	To aim for a grade D–C	To aim for a grade B–A*
P2a **Understand** the properties of photocells. **Recall** that DC electricity is current in the same direction all the time. **Describe** how the Sun's energy can be harnessed.	**Describe** advantages and disadvantages of photocells. **Describe** advantages and disadvantages of wind turbines.	**Describe** how light produces electricity in a photocell. **Describe** the factors determining the current and power produced in a photocell. **Explain** why passive solar heating works. **Recall** that an efficient solar collector must track the Sun across the sky.
P2b **Describe** how movement of a coil or magnet generates electricity by means of the dynamo effect. **Recall** that a generator produces alternating current (AC). **Recall** that a battery produces direct current (DC). **Describe** the main stages in the production and distribution of electricity. **Recognise** energy waste in a conventional power station. **Use** the energy efficiency equation in the context of a power station.	**Describe** and recognise ways to increase the dynamo effect. **Describe** and interpret AC using a voltage-time graph. **Describe** how simple AC generators work. **Describe** how electricity is generated at a conventional power station.	**Use** the energy efficiency calculation to calculate useful energy output, total energy input, or wasted energy.
P2c **Understand** that gases in the atmosphere prevent heat radiating into space. **Recall** and **recognise** this as the greenhouse effect. **Recall** and **identify** greenhouse gases. **Describe** reasons for climate change caused by global warming. **Describe** the difficulties of measuring global warming. **Explain** why climate scientists should share data.	**Describe** how certain electromagnetic wavelengths are absorbed by gases in the atmosphere. **Recall** and **identify** natural and man-made sources of greenhouse gases. **Explain** the impact of human activity and natural phenomena on weather patterns. **Describe** scientific evidence for and against the idea of man-made global warming. **Distinguish** between opinion and evidence-based statements about global warming.	**Explain** the greenhouse effect. **Explain** how scientists can agree about the greenhouse effect, but disagree about whether human activity is affecting global warming.
P2d **Recall** that the unit of power is the watt or kilowatt. **Understand** that the cost of using electrical appliances depends on their power and the time they are used for. **Use** the power equation to calculate the power of an appliance. **Recall** the use of transformers to increase or decrease voltage.	**Use** the power equation to calculate the power of an appliance, including conversion of units of power. **State** that the unit of electrical energy supplied is the kilowatt hour. **Calculate** the number of kilowatt hours given power and time used. **Use** the energy supply equation to calculate energy supplied. **Calculate** the cost of energy supplied.	**Use** and manipulate the power equation. **Use** the kilowatt hour as a measure of energy supplied. **Describe** the advantages and disadvantages of using off-peak electricity in the home. **Explain** how an increased voltage reduces current, decreasing energy lost from cables as heat.

To aim for a grade G–E	To aim for a grade D–C	To aim for a grade B–A*	
Recognise beneficial and harmful effects of radiation. **Recall** the three types of nuclear radiation. **Understand** that nuclear radiation causes potentially harmful ionisation. **Describe** how to handle radioactive materials safely. **Describe** nuclear waste as radioactive and harmful, but not responsible for global warming.	**Describe** examples of beneficial uses of radiation. **Understand** that radioactive materials give out radiation over time. **Describe** the relative penetrating power of alpha, beta, and gamma radiation. **Understand** that nuclear radiation can form positive ions when atoms lose electrons. **Understand** that nuclear radiation can form negative ions when atoms gain electrons. **Recall** that uranium is a non-renewable resource. **Recall** that plutonium is a nuclear waste product and can be used to make nuclear bombs. **Describe** methods of disposing of radioactive waste.	**Explain** how ionisation can damage the DNA in human cells. **Describe** the advantages and disadvantages of nuclear power. **Explain** the problems of dealing with radioactive waste.	**P2e**
Identify the relative positions of the Earth, Sun, and planets. **Recall** the make-up of the Universe. **Explain** why stars give off light and can be seen over long distances. **Recall** that radio signals take a long time to travel through the Solar System. **Compare** the resources needed by manned and unmanned spacecraft. **Describe** why unmanned spacecraft are sent into space.	**Recall** the relative nature and size of the features of the Universe. **Describe** a light-year. **Describe** the difficulties of manned space travel between planets. **Recall** that unmanned spacecraft can withstand conditions lethal to humans. **Compare** how information from space is returned to Earth from different distances.	**Recall** that circular motion requires a centripetal force. **Understand** that gravitational attraction provides the centripetal force for orbital motion. **Explain** why a light-year is a useful unit for measuring large distances. **Explain** the advantages and disadvantages of using unmanned spacecraft.	**P2f**
Understand the origins of the Moon. **Recall** that large asteroids have collided with Earth in the past. **Recall** that asteroids are rocks. **Describe** the consequences of a collision with a large asteroid. **Describe** the make-up of a comet. **Describe** a Near Earth Object (NEO). **Describe** how NEOs may be seen.	**Describe** how a collision between two planets can result in an Earth-Moon system. **Describe** the origin and orbit of asteroids. **Describe** evidence for past asteroid collisions. **Describe** the origin and orbit of comets. **Describe** how the speed of a comet changes as it approaches a star. **Describe** how observations of NEOs are used to determine their trajectories. **Explain** why it is difficult to observe NEOs.	**Discuss** evidence for the Earth-Moon system as the result of a collision between two planets. **Explain** the location of the asteroid belt. **Explain** why the speed of a comet changes as it approaches a star. **Suggest** and discuss possible actions to reduce the threat of NEOs.	**P2g**
Describe the Big Bang theory for the origin of the Universe. **Recall** the properties of stars. **Understand** that not even light can escape from black holes. **Recognise** change in the accepted models of the size and shape of the Universe over time. **Describe** and **recognise** the Ptolemaic and Copernican models and how they differ from each other and the modern day model of the Universe.	**Recall** the movement of galaxies away from Earth. **Recall** that microwave radiation is received from all parts of the Universe. **Describe** the end of the life cycle of a small star. **Describe** the end of the life cycle of a large star. **Describe** the evidence or observations behind Copernicus and Galileo's new models of the Universe. **Explain** how technological advances contributed to the new models.	**Explain** how the Big Bang theory accounts for red shift, and greater red shift in more distant galaxies. **Explain** how the Big Bang theory accounts for the age and starting point of the Universe. **Describe** the life history of a star. **Explain** the properties of a black hole. **Explain** why Copernicus and Galileo's new models were considered controversial.	**P2h**

Revising module P3

To help you start your revision, the specification for module P3 has been summarised in the checklist below. Work your way along each row and make sure that you are happy with all the statements for your target grade.

If you are not sure of any of the statements for your target grade, make a note of them as part of your revision plan. You can then work back through the relevant parts of pages 90–121 to fill gaps in your knowledge as a start to your revision.

	To aim for a grade G–E	To aim for a grade D–C	To aim for a grade B–A*
P3a	**Use** the average speed equation, to include change of units from km to m. **Understand** why one type of speed camera takes two different photographs. **Understand** how average speed cameras work. **Draw** and **interpret** qualitatively graphs of distance against time.	**Use** the average speed equation, including a change of subject. **Describe** and **interpret** the gradient (steepness) of a distance-time graph as speed.	**Draw** and **interpret** graphs of distance against time.
P3b	**Describe** trends in speed and time from a simple speed-time graph. **Recognise** that acceleration involves a change in speed. **Recall** that acceleration is measured in metres per second squared (m/s^2). **Use** the acceleration equation when given the change in speed. **Recognise** that direction is important when describing the motion of an object. **Understand** that the velocity of an object is its speed combined with its direction.	**Describe**, **draw** and **interpret** qualitatively simple graphs of speed against time for uniform acceleration. **Describe** acceleration as change in speed per unit time, with positive acceleration giving increase in speed and negative acceleration giving decrease in speed. **Use** the acceleration equation, including prior calculation of the change in speed. **Recognise** that for the velocities of two objects moving in opposite directions at the same speed will have identical magnitude but opposite signs. **Calculate** the relative velocity of objects moving in parallel.	**Explain** how acceleration can involve either a change in speed, in direction, or both. **Use** the acceleration equation, including a change of subject.
P3c	**Recognise** situations where forces cause things to speed up, slow down or stay at the same speed. **Use** the force equation, given mass and acceleration. **Describe** thinking, braking, and stopping distance. **Calculate** stopping distance given values for thinking and braking distance. **Explain** why thinking, braking, and stopping distances are significant for road safety.	**Describe** and **interpret** the relationship between force, mass, and acceleration in everyday examples. **Use** the force equation, including a change of subject. **Explain** how certain factors may increase thinking and braking distance. **Explain** the implications of stopping distances in road safety.	**Use** the force equation, including a change of subject and the need to previously calculate the accelerating force. **Explain** qualitatively everyday situations where braking distance is changed, including friction, mass, speed, and braking force. **Draw** and **interpret** the shapes of graphs for thinking and braking distance against speed. **Explain** the effects of increased speed on thinking distance and braking distance.
P3d	**Recall** everyday examples in which work is done and power is developed. **Describe** how energy is transferred when work is done. **Understand** that the amount of work done depends on the size of the force in newtons (N) and the distance travelled in metres. **Recall** that the joule is the unit for both work and energy. **Use** the equation to calculate work done.	**Use** the weight equation. **Use** the equation to calculate work done, including a change of subject. **Use** the power equation.	**Use** the weight equation, including a change of subject. **Use** the equation to calculate work done, then use the value for work done in the power equation. **Use** the power equation, including a change of subject, when work done has been calculated. **Use** and understand the derivation of the power equation in the form power = force × speed.

To aim for a grade G–E	To aim for a grade D–C	To aim for a grade B–A*	
Describe power as a measurement of how quickly work is being done. **Recall** that power is measured in watts (W). **Recognise** that cars have different power ratings and engine sizes, and that these relate to fuel consumption.			P3d
Understand that kinetic energy depends on the mass and speed of an object. **Recognise** and describe (derivatives of) fossil fuels as the main fuels in road transport. **Recall** that biofuels and solar energy are possible alternatives to fossil fuels. **Describe** how electricity can be used for road transport, and its effects on people and the environment. **Recognise** that the shape of moving objects can influence their top speeds and fuel consumption.	**Understand** that kinetic energy is greater for objects with higher speed and greater mass. **Describe** arguments for and against the use of battery powered cars. **Explain** why electrically powered cars do not pollute at the point of use, whereas fossil fuel cars do. **Recognise** that battery driven cars need to have the battery recharged. **Explain** why we may have to rely on biofuel and solar powered vehicles in the future.	**Use** and apply the kinetic energy equation. **Apply** the ideas of kinetic energy to braking distances and speed, and to situations involving moving objects. **Explain** how biofuel and solar powered vehicles both produce and reduce pollution. **Describe** how car fuel consumption figures depend on different factors.	P3e
Use the momentum equation. **Understand** that a sudden change in momentum results in a large force. **Describe** the typical modern car safety features that absorb energy when vehicles stop. **Recall** some typical car safety features intended to prevent accidents. **Recall** some typical car safety features intended to protect occupants in the event of an accident. **Explain** why seatbelts have to be replaced after a crash. **Recognise** the risks and benefits arising from the use of seatbelts.	**Use** the momentum equation, including a change of subject. **Describe** why the greater the mass and/or velocity of an object, the more momentum the object has in the direction of motion. **Use** the force equation. **Describe** why some injuries in vehicle collisions are due to a very rapid deceleration of parts of the body. **Explain**, using the ideas about momentum, the use of crumple zones, seatbelts, and airbags in cars. **Describe** how seatbelts, crumple zones, and airbags are useful in a crash. **Describe** how test data may be gathered and used to identify and develop safety features for cars.	**Use** and **apply** the force equation, including a change of subject. **Use** Newton's second law of motion. **Explain** how spreading the change in momentum over a longer time reduces the forces acting and reduces potential injury. **Explain** why forces can be reduced when stopping by increasing stopping or collision time, distance, or acceleration. **Evaluate** the effectiveness of given safety features in terms of saving lives and reducing injuries. **Describe** how ABS brakes help to keep control of a vehicle in hazardous situations. **Analyse** personal and social choices in terms of the risks and benefits of wearing seatbelts.	P3f
Recognise that frictional forces have an effect on movement and energy loss, and can be reduced. **Describe** how objects falling through the Earth's atmosphere reach a terminal speed. **Understand** that falling objects do not experience drag when there is no atmosphere.	**Describe**, in terms of balance of forces, the different speeds of moving objects. **Recognise** that acceleration due to gravity is the same for any object at a given point on the Earth's surface.	**Explain**, in terms of balance of forces, why objects reach a terminal speed. **Understand** that gravitational field strength or acceleration due to gravity is unaffected by atmospheric changes but varies at different points on the Earth's surface.	P3g
Recognise that objects have gravitational potential energy because of their mass and position in Earth's gravitational field. **Recognise** everyday examples in which objects use gravitational potential energy.	**Describe** everyday examples in which objects have gravitational potential energy. **Use** the gravitational potential energy equation. **Recognise** and **interpret** examples of energy transfer between gravitational potential energy and kinetic energy. **Describe** the effect of changing mass and speed on kinetic energy.	**Understand** that the kinetic energy of a body falling through the atmosphere at terminal speed does not increase, and that its gravitational potential energy is transferred to the surrounding air as heat. **Use** and **apply** the gravitational potential energy equation, including a change of subject. **Use** and **apply** the relationship $mgh = \frac{1}{2} mv^2$. **Show** that for a given object falling to Earth, this relationship can be expressed as $h = v^2 \div 2g$, and give an example of how this formula could be used.	P3h

Revising module P4

To help you start your revision, the specification for module P4 has been summarised in the checklist below. Work your way along each row and make sure that you are happy with all the statements for your target grade.

If you are not sure of any of the statements for your target grade, make a note of them as part of your revision plan. You can then work back through the relevant parts of pages 128–159 to fill gaps in your knowledge as a start to your revision.

To aim for a grade G–E	To aim for a grade D–C	To aim for a grade B–A*
P4a **Recognise** that when some materials are rubbed, they attract other objects. **Recognise** that insulating materials can become charged when rubbed with another insulating material. **State** that there are two kinds of charge. **Describe** how you can get an electrostatic shock from charged objects. **Describe** how you can get an electrostatic shock if you become charged and then become earthed.	**Recognise** that like charges repel and unlike charges attract. **Understand** that electrostatic phenomena are caused by the transfer of electrons that have a negative charge. **Explain** how static electricity can be dangerous. **Explain** how static electricity can be a nuisance.	**Describe** static electricity in terms of the movement of electrons. **Recognise** that atoms or molecules that have become charged are ions. **Explain** how the chance of receiving an electric shock can be reduced. **Explain** how anti-static sprays, liquids and cloths help reduce the problems of static electricity.
P4b **Recall** that electrostatics can be useful for electrostatic precipitators. **Recall** that electrostatics can be useful for spraying. **Understand** that electrostatics can be useful for restarting the heart when it has stopped. **Recall** that defibrillators work by discharging charge.	**Explain** how static electricity can be useful for electrostatic dust precipitators. **Explain** how static electricity can be useful for paint spraying. **Explain** how static electricity can be useful for restarting the heart when it has stopped.	**Explain** how static electricity is used in electrostatic dust precipitators. **Explain** how static electricity is used in paint spraying, in terms of paint and car gaining and losing electrons, and the resulting effects.
P4c **Explain** the behaviour of simple circuits in terms of the flow of electric charge. **Describe** and recognise how resistors can be used to change the current in a circuit. **Describe** how variable resistors can be used to change the current in a circuit. **Recall** that resistance is measured in ohms. **Recall** the colour coding for live, neutral, and earth wires. **State** that an earthed conductor cannot become live. **Describe** reasons for the use of fuses in circuit breakers. **Recognise** that double insulated appliances do not need earthing.	**Explain** how variable resistors can be used to change the current in a circuit. **Describe** the relationships between current, voltage, and resistance. **Use** the resistance equation. **Describe** the functions of the live, neutral, and earth wires. **Explain** how a wire fuse reduces the risk of fire if an appliance develops a fault. **Use** the equation power = voltage × current. **Explain** why double insulated appliances do not need earthing.	**Use** and apply the resistance equation, including a change of subject. **Explain** the reasons for the use of fuses and circuit breakers as resettable fuses. **Explain** how the combination of a wire fuse and earthing protects people. **Use** the equation power = voltage × current, including a change of subject, to select a suitable fuse for an appliance.
P4d **Recall** that ultrasound is a longitudinal wave. **Recognise** features of a longitudinal wave. **Recognise** that ultrasound can be used in medicine for diagnostic purposes.	**Describe** features of longitudinal waves. **Recall** and identify that the frequency of ultrasound is higher than the upper threshold of human hearing. **Recognise** that ultrasound can be used in medicine for non-invasive therapeutic purposes.	**Describe** and compare the motion and arrangement of particles in longitudinal and transverse physical waves. **Explain** how ultrasound is used in body scans and in breaking down accumulations in the body. **Explain** the reasons for using ultrasound rather than X-rays for certain scans.

To aim for a grade G–E	To aim for a grade D–C	To aim for a grade B–A*	
Recognise how the radioactivity or activity of an object is measured. **Understand** that radioactivity decreases with time. **Recall** that nuclear radiation ionises materials. **Recall** that radiation comes from the nucleus of the atom.	**Describe** radioactive substances as decaying naturally and giving out nuclear radiation. **Describe** radioactivity as coming from the nucleus of an atom that is unstable. **Recall** that an alpha particle is a helium nucleus. **Recall** that a beta particle is a fast moving electron. **Explain** ionisation in terms of removal and gain of electrons and particles.	**Explain** and use the concept of half-life. **Explain** why alpha particles are such good ionisers. **Describe** what happens to a nucleus when an alpha particle is emitted. **Describe** what happens to a nucleus when a beta particle is emitted. **Construct** and balance simple nuclear equations in terms of mass numbers and atomic numbers to represent alpha and beta decay.	P4e
Understand that background radiation can vary. **Recall** that background radiation comes mainly from rocks and cosmic rays. **Recall** that radioisotopes are used as tracers in industry and hospitals. **Recall** that alpha sources are used in some smoke detectors. **Recall** that radioactivity can be used to date rocks.	**Recall** that some background radiation comes from waste products and man-made sources. **Recall** examples of the use of tracers. **Explain** how a smoke detector with an alpha source works. **Explain** how the radioactive dating of rocks depends on the uranium/lead ratio. **Recall** that measurements from radioactive carbon can be used to find the age of old materials.	**Recall** the relative contribution of radiation from waste products and man-made sources to background radiation. **Describe** how tracers are used in industry. **Explain** how measurements of the activity of radioactive carbon can lead to an approximate age for different materials.	P4f
Recall that materials can be made radioactive by putting them into a nuclear reactor. **Recall** that nuclear radiation is used in medicine. **Recall** that X-rays and gamma rays are electromagnetic waves. **Recall** that nuclear radiation can damage cells. **Recognise** that gamma rays are used to treat cancer. **Recall** that nuclear radiation is used to sterilise hospital equipment. **Recall** that the person in hospitals who takes X-rays and uses radiation is a radiographer.	**Describe** how materials become radioactive when they absorb extra neutrons. **Recall** that only beta and gamma radiation can pass through skin. **Describe** some similarities and differences between X-rays and gamma rays. **Describe** why gamma (and sometimes beta) emitters can be used as tracers in the body. **Recall** that gamma (and sometimes beta) rays can penetrate tissues, whereas alpha rays cannot. **Understand** why medical tracers should not remain active in the body for long periods.	**Explain** how gamma rays come from radioactive materials, how X-rays are made, and that X-rays are easier to control than gamma rays. **Explain** how radioactive sources are used in medicine to treat cancer, and as a tracer.	P4g
Recognise that nuclear power stations use uranium as a fuel. **Describe** the main stages in the production of electricity. **Describe** the process that gives out energy in a nuclear reactor as nuclear fission. **State** that nuclear fission produces radioactive waste. **Describe** the simple difference between fission and fusion. **Recall** that one group of scientists have claimed to have successfully achieved cold fusion. **Explain** why the claims are disputed because other scientists could not repeat their findings.	**Describe** how domestic electricity is generated at a nuclear power station. **Understand** how the decay of uranium starts a chain reaction. **Describe** a nuclear bomb as a chain reaction that has gone out of control. **Describe** how nuclear fusion releases energy. **Describe** why fusion for power generation is difficult. **Understand** that fusion power research is carried out as an international joint venture. **Explain** why the cold fusion experiments and data have been shared between scientists.	**Describe** what happens to allow uranium to release energy. **Explain** what is meant by a chain reaction. **Explain** how scientists stop nuclear reactions going out of control. **Explain** how different isotopes of hydrogen can undergo fusion to form helium. **Understand** how fusion happens in stars and bombs, and understand what is needed for power generation and any potential practical challenges. **Explain** why cold fusion is still not accepted as a realistic method of energy production.	P4h

Revising module P5

To help you start your revision, the specification for module P5 has been summarised in the checklist below. Work your way along each row and make sure that you are happy with all the statements for your target grade.

If you are not sure of any of the statements for your target grade, make a note of them as part of your revision plan. You can then work back through the relevant parts of pages 166–199 to fill gaps in your knowledge as a start to your revision.

To aim for a grade G–E	To aim for a grade D–C	To aim for a grade B–A*
P5a **Recall** what gravity is. **Recognise** that a satellite is an object that orbits a larger object in space. **Describe** the difference between artificial and natural satellites. **Describe** how height above the Earth affects the orbit of an artificial satellite. **Recall** how the height of orbit of an artificial satellite determines its use. **Recall** some uses of artificial satellites.	**Explain** why the Moon remains in orbit around the Earth, and the Earth and other planets in orbit around the Sun. **Describe** the orbit of a geostationary satellite. **Understand** that circular motion requires a centripetal force. **Explain** why different satellite applications require different orbits.	**Describe** the variation of gravitational force with distance (inverse square law). **Explain** the variation in speed of a periodic comet during its orbit around the Sun. **Explain** how the orbital period of a planet depends upon its distance from the Sun. **Understand** that artificial satellites are continually accelerating towards the Earth but they maintain an approximately circular orbit. **Explain** why artificial satellites in lower orbits travel faster than those in higher orbits.
P5b **Recall** that direction is important when describing the motion of an object. **Understand** that the relative speed of two objects is lower if moving in the same direction and higher if moving in opposite directions. **Recall** that speed is a scalar quantity. **Recognise** that distance travelled = average speed × time. **Use** the equation $v = u + at$.	**Describe** the difference between scalar and vector quantities. **Calculate** the vector sum from vector diagrams of parallel vectors. **Use** the equation $v = u + at$ to calculate v or u. **Use** the equation $s = \frac{(u + v)}{2 \times t}$, including a change of subject.	**Calculate** the resultant of two vectors that are at right angles to each other. **Use** the equation $v^2 = u^2 + 2as$, including a change of subject. **Use** the equation $s = ut + \frac{1}{2}at^2$, including a change of subject.
P5c **Recall** and **identify** that the path of an object projected horizontally in the Earth's gravitational field is curved. **Recall** that the path of a projectile is called the trajectory. **Recognise** examples of projectile motion in a range of contexts. **Recall** that the range of a ball struck in sport depends on the launch angle, with an optimum angle of 45 °C.	**Describe** the trajectory of an object projected in the Earth's gravitational field as parabolic. **Recall** that the horizontal and vertical velocities of a projectile are vectors. **Understand** that an object projected horizontally in the Earth's gravitational field has a steadily increasing vertical velocity. **Understand** that, other than air resistance, the only force acting on a ball in flight is gravity. **Understand** that projectiles have a downward acceleration.	**Understand** that the resultant velocity of a projectile is the vector sum of the horizontal and vertical velocities. **Use** the equations of motion for an object projected horizontally above the Earth's surface where the gravitational field is still uniform. **Explain** how the horizontal velocity of an object projected horizontally is unaffected by gravity. **Explain** how gravity causes the vertical velocity of an object projected horizontally to change. **Understand** that for a projectile there is no acceleration in the horizontal direction.
P5d **Describe** and **recognise** that every action has an equal and opposite reaction. **Describe** and **recognise** the opposite reactions in a simple collision. **Recall** everyday examples of collisions. **Explain**, using a particle model, how a gas exerts a pressure on the walls of its container. **Recall** that in a rocket, the force pushing the particles backwards equals the force pushing the rocket forwards.	**Describe** the opposite reactions in a number of static situations, including examples involving gravity. **Understand** that the equal but opposite forces act in a collision, and use this to **explain** the change in motion of the objects. **Explain**, using a particle model, how a change in volume or temperature produces a change in pressure. **Explain**, using simple kinetic theory, rocket propulsion in terms of fast moving particles colliding with rocket walls, creating a force.	**Understand** that when objects collide or interact, they exert an equal and opposite force on each other. **Understand** that momentum is always conserved, and use this to **explain** explosions, recoil, and rocket propulsion. **Apply** the principle of conservation of momentum to collisions when the colliding objects coalesce. **Explain** pressure in terms of the rate of change of momentum of the particles and the frequency of collisions. **Explain** how sufficient force is created in large rockets used to lift satellites into orbit.

To aim for a grade G–E	To aim for a grade D–C	To aim for a grade B–A*	
Recall that different frequencies are used for low orbit and geostationary satellites. **Recall** that some radio waves are reflected by part of the Earth's upper atmosphere. **Recall** that some radio waves and microwaves pass through the Earth's atmosphere. **Recall** that radio waves have a very long wavelength. **Recognise** that radio waves can spread around large objects. **Describe** a practical example of waves spreading out from a gap.	**Describe** how information can be transmitted to orbiting artificial satellites and then retransmitted to Earth or to other satellites. **Explain** why satellite communication uses digital signals. **Describe** how electromagnetic waves with different frequencies behave in the atmosphere. **Recall** the wave patterns produced by a plane wave passing through different sized gaps. **Explain** why long radio waves have a very long range.	**Describe** how the amount of diffraction depends upon the size of the gap and the wavelength of the wave, including the conditions for maximum diffraction.	**P5e**
Describe interference as an effect resulting from two overlapping waves. **Recognise** that when waves overlap there are areas where the waves add together or subtract. **Describe** the effect of interference on sound, light, and water waves. **Recall** that light travels in straight lines. **Recognise** that under certain circumstances light can bend. **Recall** that all electromagnetic waves are transverse. **Recall** that explanations of the nature of light have changed over time. **Describe** reflection of light.	**Describe** the interference of two waves in terms of reinforcement and cancellation. **Apply** understanding of interference to describe practical examples of interference effects. **Recall** that coherent wave sources are needed to produce a stable interference pattern. **Understand** that for light the coherent sources are monochromatic light. **Describe** diffraction of light for a single slit or double slits. **Understand** that electromagnetic waves are transverse waves so can be plane polarised. **Explain** why the particle theory of light is not universally accepted.	**Explain** interference patterns in terms of constructive and destructive interference. **Explain** that the number of half wavelengths in the path difference for two waves from the same source is odd for destructive and even for constructive interference. **Describe** the properties of coherent wave sources. **Explain** a diffraction pattern for light in terms of the size of the gap being in the order of the wavelength of light. **Explain** how polarisation is used. **Explain** how the wave theory of light has supplanted the particle theory over time.	**P5f**
Describe and **recognise** that refraction involves a change in direction of a wave as it passes from one medium into another. **Explain** why a ray of light travelling from air into glass usually has an angle of incidence greater than the angle of refraction. **Describe** and **recognise** that dispersion happens when light is refracted. **Recall** the order of the spectral colours and relate to orders of the wavelengths. **Describe** and **recognise** that some or all of a light ray can be reflected when travelling from glass or water to air. **Recall** the many uses of Total Internal Reflection.	**Explain** why refraction occurs at the boundary between two media. **Describe** refractive index as a measure of the amount of bending after a boundary. **Use** the refractive index equation. **Recall** that the amount of bending increases with greater change of wave speed and refractive index. **Explain** dispersion. **Describe** what happens to light incident on a glass/air surface when the angle of incidence is less than, equal to, or above the critical angle. **Describe** the optical path in devices using Total Internal Reflection. **Recognise** that different media have different critical angles.	**Use** the refractive index equation, including a change of subject. **Explain** dispersion in terms of spectral colours having a different speed in glass and different refractive indices (blue light has a greater refractive index than red). **Explain** the conditions under which Total Internal Reflection can occur. **Explain** that the higher the refractive index of a medium, the lower its critical angle.	**P5g**
Recall and **identify** the shape of a convex or converging lens. **Describe** what happens to light incident on a convex lens parallel to the axis. **Describe** the focal length of a convex lens. **Recognise** and **recall** that fat lenses have short focal lengths and thin lenses have long focal lengths. **Recognise** and **recall** that convex lenses produce real images on a screen. **Recall** uses of convex lenses.	**Describe** the effect of a convex lens on a diverging and a parallel beam of light. **Recall** and **recognise** the principal axis, focal length, focal point, and optical centre for a convex lens. **Describe** how a convex lens produces a real image on film and on screen. **Describe** the use of a convex lens as a magnifying glass in a camera and projector. **Explain** how the images produced by cameras and projectors are focussed. **Use** the magnification equation.	**Explain** the refraction by a convex lens of rays approaching at different angles. **Explain** how to find the position and size of the real image formed by a convex lens by drawing suitable ray diagrams. **Describe** the properties of real and virtual images. **Use** the magnification equation, including a change of subject.	**P5h**

Revising module P6

To help you start your revision, the specification for module P6 has been summarised in the checklist below. Work your way along each row and make sure that you are happy with all the statements for your target grade.

If you are not sure of any of the statements for your target grade, make a note of them as part of your revision plan. You can then work back through the relevant parts of pages 206–235 to fill gaps in your knowledge as a start to your revision.

To aim for a grade G–E	To aim for a grade D–C	To aim for a grade B–A*
P6a **Recognise** and draw circuit symbols. **Describe** and **recognise** that a variable resistor can be used to vary the brightness of a lamp. **Recall** the units of voltage, current, and resistance. **Use** the equation resistance = voltage/current. **Recall** and **identify** that for a given ohmic conductor the current increases as the voltage decreases. **Understand** that the current in a wire is a flow of charge carriers called electrons. **Use** models of electronic structure to explain electrical resistance in a metal conductor. **Recall** and **identify** how the resistance changes as a wire becomes hot.	**Explain** the effect of a variable resistor in a circuit. **Use** the equation resistance = voltage/current, including a change of subject. **Use** a voltage-current graph qualitatively to compare the resistances of ohmic conductors. **Use** kinetic theory to explain that for metallic conductors the collision of electrons with atoms makes the atoms vibrate more, increasing collisions and resistance, and increasing the temperature of the conductor. **Describe** and **recognise** how a voltage-current graph shows the changing resistance of a non-ohmic device, such as a bulb.	**Explain** that resistance is varied by changing the length of the resistance wire in a variable conductor. **Calculate** the resistance of an ohmic conductor from a voltage–current graph. **Explain** the shape of a voltage-current graph for a non-ohmic conductor (such as the filament in a lamp) in terms of increasing resistance and temperature.
P6b **Recall** that a potential divider is used to produce a required voltage in a circuit. **Understand** that two or more resistors in series increase the resistance of the circuit. **Calculate** the total resistance for resistors in series. **Recognise** and **draw** the symbol for an LDR and a thermistor. **Recall** and **identify** that an LDR responds to a change in light level and a thermistor responds to changes in temperature.	**Explain** how two fixed resistors can be used as a potential divider. **Understand** that the output voltage depends on the relative values of the resistors R_1 and R_2. **Explain** how one fixed resistor and one variable resistor in a potential divider allow variation of the output voltage. **Describe** how the resistance of an LDR varies with light level and the resistance of a thermistor varies with temperature. **Recall** that resistors in parallel can reduce the total resistance of the circuit.	**Calculate** the value of V_{out} when R_1 and R_2 are in a simple ratio. **Understand** that when R_2 is very much greater than R_1, the value of V_{out} is approximately V_{in}. **Understand** that when R_2 is very much less than R_1, the value of V_{out} is approximately zero. **Explain** how two variable resistors can provide an output voltage with an adjustable threshold. **Explain** why an LDR or a thermistor can be used to provide an output signal dependent on light or temperature conditions. **Calculate** the total resistance for resistors in parallel.
P6c **Understand** that the transistor is an electronic switch. **Recognise** and **draw** the symbol for an npn transistor and label its terminals. **Recall** that transistors can be connected together to make logic gates. **Recall** the input signals for a logic gate. **Describe** the truth table for a NOT logic gate.	**Describe** the benefits and drawbacks of increasing miniaturisation. **Describe** how a small base current is needed to switch a greater current flowing through the collector and emitter. **Use** the equation $I_e = I_b + I_c$. **Recall** that other logic gates can be made from a combination of two transistors. **Describe** truth tables for AND and OR logic gates.	**Explain** how society has to make choices about acceptable uses of new technologies. **Complete** a labelled circuit diagram to show how an npn transistor can be used as a switch. **Explain** why a high resistor is placed in the base circuit. **Complete** a labelled diagram to show how two transistors are connected to make an AND gate. **Describe** truth tables for NAND and NOR logic gates.
P6d **Recall** and **identify** the input and output signals in an electronic system with a combination of logic gates. **Recognise** that the output current from a logic gate is able to light an LED.	**Complete** a truth table for a logic system with up to three inputs made from logic gates. **Describe** how to use switches, LDRs, and thermistors in series with fixed resistors to provide input signals for logic gates.	**Complete** a truth table for a logic system with up to four inputs made from logic gates. **Explain** how a thermistor or an LDR can be used to generate a signal for a logic gate that depends on temperature or light conditions.

To aim for a grade G–E	To aim for a grade D–C	To aim for a grade B–A*	
Recognise and **draw** the symbols for an LED and a relay. **Recall** that a relay can be used as a switch.	**Explain** how an LED and series resistor can be used to indicate the output of a logic gate. **Describe** how a relay uses a small current to switch on a circuit in which a larger current flows.	**Explain** that a thermistor or an LDR can be used to provide a signal with an adjustable threshold voltage for a logic gate. **Explain** why a relay is needed for a logic gate to switch a current in a mains circuit.	P6d
Recall that a current-carrying wire has a circular magnetic field around it. **Describe** and **recognise** that this field is made up of concentric circles. **Explain** why a current-carrying wire placed in a magnetic field can move. **Recall** that motors are found in a variety of everyday applications. **Recall** that electric motors transfer energy to the load (as useful work) and to the surroundings (as waste heat).	**Describe** the shape of magnetic fields. **Understand** that a current-carrying wire at right angles to a magnetic field experiences a force. **Describe** the effect of reversing the current and/or the direction of the magnetic field. **Explain** how the forces on a current-carrying coil in a magnetic field are used in a simple DC electric motor. **Describe** factors influencing the strength of the magnetic field.	**Explain** how Fleming's left-hand rule is used to predict the direction of the force on a current-carrying wire. **Explain** how the direction of the force on the coil in a DC electric motor is maintained. **Describe** how this is achieved using a split-ring commutator in a DC electric motor. **Explain** why practical motors have a radial field produced by curved pole pieces.	P6e
Describe and **recognise** the dynamo effect. **Label** a diagram of an AC generator to show the coil, the magnets, slip rings, and bushes. **Describe** a generator as a motor working in reverse. **Explain** why electricity is useful (enabling long-distance energy transmission and energy storage). **Recall** that in the UK, mains electricity is supplied at 50 Hz.	**Understand** that a voltage is induced across a wire when the wire moves relative to a magnetic field. **Understand** that a voltage is induced across a coil when the magnetic field within it changes. **Describe** the effect of reversing the direction of the changing magnetic field. **Understand** that an alternating current is generated when a magnet rotates inside a coil. **Describe** factors influencing the voltage generated.	**Explain** how the size of the induced voltage depends on the rate at which the magnetic field changes. **Explain** how an AC generator works, including the action of the slip-rings and brushes.	P6f
Understand that transformers are devices that reduce or increase voltage. **Recall** that step-down transformers are used in a variety of everyday applications. **Recognise** and **draw** the symbol for a transformer. **Recall** that an isolating transformer is used in a bathroom shaver socket. **Recall** that step-up transformers are used to increase the voltage to supply the National Grid. **Recall** that step-down transformers are used in sub-stations to reduce the voltage for domestic and commercial use.	**Describe** the construction of a transformer as two coils of wire wound on an iron core. **Describe** the difference in construction of a step-up and a step-down transformer and how this construction changes the size of the output. **Explain** why an isolating transformer is used in some mains circuits. **Recall** and **identify** that some power is lost through heat in the transmission of electrical power in cables and transformers.	**Explain** why the use of transformers requires the use of alternating current. **Describe** how the changing field in the primary coil of a transformer induces an output voltage in the secondary coil. **Explain** how isolating transformers improve safety in some mains circuits. **Understand** that power loss in transmission is related to the square of the current flowing in the transmission lines. **Use** and **manipulate** the equation power loss = current² × resistance. **Explain** why power is transmitted at high voltages.	P6g
Recognise and **draw** the symbol for a diode. **Recall** that a diode only allows a current to pass in one direction (shown by diode symbol). **Recognise** half-wave rectification and full-wave rectification from a voltage–time graph. **Recognise** and **draw** the capacitor symbol. **Understand** that a capacitor stores charge. **Recall** and **identify** that a capacitor will produce a more constant (smoothed) output. **Explain** why many devices need a more constant voltage supply.	**Recognise** the current–voltage characteristics for a silicon diode. **Explain** that a diode only allows current to flow in one direction. **Recall** and **identify** that a single diode produces half-wave rectification. **Recall** that four diodes in a bridge circuit obtain full-wave rectification. **Understand** that charge is stored and the voltage across the capacitor increases. **Describe** how the flow of current changes with time when a conductor is connected across a capacitor.	**Explain** the current–voltage graph for a silicon diode. **Describe** the action of a silicon diode in terms of the movement of holes and electrons. **Explain** how four diodes in a bridge circuit can produce full-wave rectification. **Describe** the flow of current and reduction in voltage across a capacitor when a conductor is connected across it. **Explain** the action of a capacitor in a simple smoothing circuit.	P6h

Glossary

ABS brakes Means of stopping a car without skidding by rapidly turning the brakes on and off.

acceleration Speeding up, slowing down or changing direction. Change in velocity per second, measured in m/s^2.

acceleration due to gravity Rate of change of velocity due to the force of gravity.

action Force that acts on an object.

active device Safety feature of a car that is activated when danger is detected.

activity Number of radioactive decays per second.

aerial Piece of metal that absorbs radio waves to produce an alternating electrical current.

alpha particle Very ionising, but not very penetrating form of ionising radiation. Made up of 2 protons and 2 neutrons (a helium nucleus).

alternating current Electrical current that continually changes direction. It goes in each direction for only half of the time.

amplitude The maximum displacement of a wave or oscillation (the maximum height of a wave from the crest to the middle).

analogue Describes a signal that can have an unlimited number of values.

AND gate Logic gate whose output is high when both inputs are high.

artificial satellite Man-made object in orbit around the Earth or other planets.

asteroid belt Region of the solar system between Mars and Jupiter that contains a large number of asteroids.

asteroids Lumps of rock in orbit around the Sun that are too small to be planets.

atmosphere Thin layer of gases between the solid surface of the Earth and empty space.

attract Pull towards.

average speed Total distance travelled ÷ the time taken.

background radiation Radiation around us all of the time from a variety of natural and man-made sources.

base One of the terminals of a transistor.

battery Scientific name for two or more cells connected together.

beta particle Ionising form of radiation. It is a fast electron from the nucleus.

Big Bang Supposed origin of the Universe, when all matter and energy emerged from one place.

bio-fuel Liquid fuel similar to diesel, made from plants.

biomass Plant matter that can be used as a fuel.

black hole Region of space that contains enough matter to prevent the escape of light (or anything else) from its gravity.

braking distance Distance moved by a vehicle when it slows down and stops after the brakes have been applied.

bridge circuit Full-wave rectifier made from four diodes.

capacitor Component that stores charge, usually on a pair of parallel plates separated by an insulator.

carbon neutral An energy transfer which does not result in an overall change in the amount of carbon dioxide in the atmosphere.

cell A device that transfers chemical energy into electrical energy.

centripetal force Force acting on an object that allows it to follow a circular path. The force must act towards the centre of the circle.

chain reaction One reaction going on to create another, which creates another, and so on, such as a nuclear fission chain reaction inside a nuclear reactor.

change of state Changing from one physical state to another, eg from a solid to a liquid or a liquid to a gas.

charge Property of some objects (like electrons and protons). There are two types of charge, negative and positive.

circuit breaker Device that detects an electrical fault and breaks the circuit.

climate change Change in long-term weather patterns.

coalesce Join together.

coherent Describes different waves that have the same frequency and velocity.

cold fusion Attempt to fuse hydrogen nuclei together at room temperature.

collector One of the terminals of a transistor.

comet Ball of rock and ice in a very elliptical orbit around the Sun.

compression Pushing together of particles caused by the passing of a sound wave.

conduction One way of transferring energy by vibrations being passed on from one particle to another.

constructive interference Where overlapping waves are in step and make a wave with a bigger amplitude.

control rods Metal rods lowered into nuclear reactors to absorb neutrons and so control the reaction.

convection How thermal energy is transferred by the movement of particles in fluids.

convection current The movement of particles by convection when heat energy is transferred.

converging Describes a lens that changes the direction of parallel rays of light so that they meet at a focus once they have passed through the lens.

convex Describes a lens whose thickness decreases with increasing distance from its centre.

cosmic microwave background radiation Microwaves received from all directions of space.

cost-effective Describes when the cost of making a change is low in relation to the resultant savings in energy bills.

crest The top part of a wave where its displacement is at a maximum.

critical angle Smallest angle of incidence for which Total Internal Reflection takes place.

current Movement of charged particles (usually electrons) through a material.

DAB radio Radio broadcasts that transmit information as a digital signal.

deceleration An acceleration which involves the slowing down of an object.

decommissioning Dismantling of a power station at the end of its useful life.

defibrillator Device for providing a short flow of charge through the heart of a patient to set it beating again.

destructive interference Where overlapping waves are out of step and cancel each other out to leave no wave at all.

diffraction Spreading out of waves when they pass through a gap or around an obstacle.

digital Describes a signal that can have only have one of two values; on (1), or off (0).

diode Component that only allows charge to flow through it in one direction.

direct current Electrical current that flows in one direction only.

direction Where a vector quantity points to.

dispersion The splitting of white light into its component colours (ROYGBIV).

distance-time graph Graph showing distance on the y-axis and time on the x-axis. It shows the distance travelled from a certain point at a particular moment.

double-insulated Describes an appliance in which all the live components are sealed away from the case, so the case cannot become live.

dynamo effect Where changes of magnetic field around conductors result in the generation of electricity.

earth Pin/wire that carries energy safely away from an appliance if there is a fault.

Earth-centred model Ancient model of the Universe, with the Earth at its centre.

efficiency Percentage of energy transferred by a device that is useful.

electric motor Device with a rotating shaft powered by electric current interacting with a magnet.

electromagnetic spectrum All the different types of electromagnetic wave: radio waves, microwaves, infrared, visible, ultraviolet, X-rays, and gamma rays.

electromagnetic wave Wave that has oscillating electric and magnetic fields at right angles to its direction of motion.

electrostatic charge Charge from electrons that have been moved to or from an insulator.

electrostatic dust precipitator Apparatus for removing smoke from flue gases by means of electricity.

electrostatic shock Effect on a person who rapidly conducts charge from a charged object.

emit To give out.

emitter One of the terminals of a transistor.

endoscope A medical instrument which uses optical fibres to produce an image of the inside of a patient.

evidence Scientific observations that can be used to disprove a scientific hypothesis.

Fleming's left-hand rule Uses thumb and first two fingers of left hand to show directions of force, current, and magnetic field in a motor.

fluid A liquid or a gas.

focal length Distance from the centre of a lens to the principal focus.

focus To aim something at one point, or the single point to which rays of light are focussed by a lens.

fossil fuel Fuel that was formed by the decay of the remains of creatures that lived millions of years ago. Coal, oil, and natural gas are all fossil fuels.

fossil fuels Non-renewable fuels buried in the ground that are based on the decomposed remains of plants and animals that lived millions of years ago.

free electrons Electrons that are free to move through a substance.

frequency The number of oscillations per second for a vibration.

fuel consumption Measure of the efficiency of an engine that burns fuel. A more efficient vehicle has lower fuel consumption and so travels a greater distance using the same amount of fuel.

full-wave rectification Process of using both positive and negative parts of alternating current to make direct current.

fuse Thin piece of wire that melts (and breaks the circuit) if too much current flows through it.

fusion Melting (not to be confused with nuclear fusion).

galaxy Large collection of stars and dust clustered together at a point in space.

gamma knife Device that focuses many separate beams of gamma rays onto a brain tumour, giving it a much larger dose than the surrounding tissue.

gamma ray Very penetrating, but not very ionising form of ionising radiation. It is a high frequency electromagnetic wave.

generator Machine that rotates to generate electricity.

geostationary orbit An orbit where the satellite orbits at the same speed that the planet rotates.

global warming Increase in the temperature of the Earth's surface due to changes in its atmosphere. Mainly caused by increases in carbon dioxide and methane in the atmosphere from human activity.

gradient Slope of a graph.

gravitational attraction The force pulling two objects together because of their mass.

gravitational potential energy Energy an object has when it is above the ground.

gravity A force that pulls one object towards another, depending on their mass and seapration.

greenhouse effect Process where greenhouse gases absorb the longer wavelength radiation emitted by the Earth, warming the atmosphere.

greenhouse gas Gas in the atmosphere that reduces the amount of heat lost to space by the Earth.

half-life Time taken for half of the nuclei in the atoms of a radioactive substance to decay, or the time taken for the activity from a substance to halve.

half-wave rectification Process of allowing only the positive parts of alternating current to pass through.

heat Form of energy, or a flow of energy from hotter objects to colder ones.

hydrogen bombs Explosive device based on the fusion of hydrogen to form helium.

induce To produce a current by means of the dynamo effect.

infrared radiation Form of electromagnetic radiation that you can feel as heat. It has a shorter wavelength than microwaves but a longer wavelength than visible light.

insulating material Does not allow electrons to move easily through it.

intensity Measure of the energy received by an area each second.

interference What happens when waves overlap and reinforce or cancel each other out.

intermolecular bond Bond between particles of a substance.

inverse square law Any relationship where if one variable increases by a factor of x the other falls by x^2. For example, if one doubles the other falls by 4 (2 squared).

ionisation When electrons are either added to or removed from atoms, giving them an overall charge.

ionising radiation High energy particles or waves that ionise matter as they pass through it.

ionosphere Layer of ionised particles in the upper atmosphere, on the edge of space.

iron core Central part of a transformer around which the primary and secondary coils are wrapped.

isolating transformer Transformer with the same number of turns on the primary and secondary coils.

joule Unit of energy or work done.

kilwatt hour The amount of energy transferred by a device using 1 kW in 1 hour.

kinetic energy Energy any object has when it is moving.

laser Source of high intensity light with a single frequency and direction.

law of conservation of momentum Law that states that momentum is conserved in collisions. Total momentum of a system before a collision or explosion is the same as the total momentum of the system after a collision or explosion.

light-dependent resistor Special type of resistor whose resistance decreases when the intensity of light falling on it increases.

light-emitting diode Diode that emits light when an electric current flows through it.

line of sight Straight line path followed by light from an object to an observer.

live Pin/wire that transfers electrical energy to an appliance.

logic gate Circuit that has two levels of input and output, low and high. The output depends on the input(s).

longitudinal wave Wave whose vibrations and energy flow are in the same direction.

magnetic field Region of space around a magnet where magnetic forces act on objects.

magnification How much larger the image is than the object.

mains supply The electricity supply available in most homes.

mass Amount of matter in an object. It is measured in kilograms.

medical tracer Radioactive material emitting gamma rays that is either injected or ingested into the body. As the rays leave the body they are detected by special cameras producing a picture of the inside of the body.

medium Any substance that a wave passes through, eg air, water, metal.

microwave Wave that fits between radio waves and infrared in the electromagnetic spectrum.

modulation Process of attaching information to a radio wave or other electrical signal.

momentum Mass of an object × velocity.

monochromatic Describes a wave that has just one value for its wavelength. Monochromatic light waves contain only one colour.

Morse code Digital code that uses long and short bursts of sound or light to represent letters of the alphabet.

motor effect The push on an electric current placed in a magnetic field.

multiplexing A technique used to transmit several digital signals at once.

NAND gate Logic gate that is the reverse of an AND gate.

National Grid UK electricity distribution system that transfers electrical energy from power stations to consumers.

natural satellite A satellite that is there because of natural causes, eg the Moon.

near-Earth object Asteroid or comet that passes close to the Earth at some point on its way around the solar system.

nebula Cloud of dust and gas in outer space.

negative gradient Line on a graph whose y-value decreases as the x-value increases.

neutron star Small high density star left behind after a supernova. Often spins very rapidly.

noise Random signal with no meaning.

non-ohmic conductor Conductor that produces a current-voltage graph that is not a straight line.

non-renewable Energy resource that can only be used once.

NOR gate Logic gate that is the reverse of an OR gate.

NOT gate Logic gate with one input that reverses it.

nuclear fission Splitting of a large nucleus when it absorbs a neutron, into two or more smaller nuclei.

nuclear fusion The collision of two nuclei to make one larger nucleus, often with a large transfer of energy from mass to radiation.

nuclear reactor Part of a power station fuelled by uranium that transfers nuclear energy to heat energy.

number of turns Number of times a wire is wrapped around in a transformer to make a coil.

optical centre Point where the principal axis passes through the plane of a lens.

optical fibre A fine glass tube designed so light can travel through it by Total Internal Reflection.

optimum angle Describes the launch angle that gives a projectile maximum range.

orbit Path followed by a planet or satellite around a more massive object due to a gravitational attraction.

OR gate Logic gate whose output is high when either or both inputs are high.

oscillation Back-and-forth motion that repeats over and over again.

ozone layer Layer of ozone gas high up in the atmosphere. It is a strong absorber of ultraviolet light from the Sun.

paddle controls Set of levers and buttons that allow the driver of a car to turn devices on and off without taking hands off the wheel.

parabolic Describes the shape of the path followed by a projectile.

parallel Describes circuit components connected side by side so that there is more than one route around the circuit.

passive device Safety feature of a car that does not need activation to operate in dangerous situations.

passive solar heating When light energy from the Sun goes through a window and is absorbed by materials inside a building.

path difference Extra distance travelled by one wave compared to another from the same source before they overlap at the detector.

payback time Time taken to recover the amount of money paid out in making a change from the resultant savings in energy bills.

phase Waves that are in step with each other. Their crests line up with other crests.

photocell Device that transfers light energy into electricity. Also known as a solar cell.

planet Object in the solar system that orbits the Sun and is large enough for its own gravity to make it spherical.

polar orbit An orbit that goes over the north and south poles of a planet.

polarisation Limiting the vibrations of a transverse wave to one plane only (side-to-side, or up and down).

Polaroid filter Sheet of plastic that only transmits light with a particular polarisation.

positive gradient Line on a graph whose y-value increases as the x-value increases.

positive hole Point in a semiconductor where an electron has been freed.

potential divider Circuit that can be used to produce an output voltage that is less than the input voltage.

power Work done (or energy transferred) in a given time. Measured in watts.

power rating Indicates the amount of energy a device uses each second. Can be found by multiplying the voltage and current.

power supply Source of electrical energy.

primary coil Coil in a transformer where the input is applied.

principal axis Line through the centre of a lens, at right angles to its plane.

prism Block of glass with triangular cross-section.

projectile Object that travels horizontally or at an angle to the Earth's surface.

proto-star Ball of gas in outer space that is collapsing under its own gravity until it gets hot enough to start nuclear fusion and become a star.

Ptolemaic model Variation on the Earth-centred model of the Universe, put forward by Ptolemy in 100 AD.

P-wave Seismic wave whose oscillations are in the same direction as the direction of travel. Sometimes called pressure, primary, or push waves.

radial field Magnetic field whose lines of force appear to come from a single point.

radioactive dating Process used to date materials depending on the proportional of radioactive material they contain.

radioactive decay Change in an atom's nucleus that results in the emission of an ionising radiation.

radioactive waste By-product of nuclear reactors that contains a high concentration of radioactive atoms.

radioisotope Radioactive substance whose nucleus contains a specific number of protons and neutrons.

range How far a projectile will travel when it is in the air.

rarefaction Pulling apart of particles caused by the passing of a sound wave.

reaction Force that acts against an action.

reaction time Time taken from seeing a hazard to starting to press the brake pedal.

real image Image that can be displayed on a screen.

recoil Backward movement induced by a force exerted on an object.

rectification Process of converting alternating current into direct current.

red giant Star that is large enough to fuse helium nuclei to make carbon.

red shift Increase in wavelength of light emitted from an object that is moving away from the observer.

red supergiant Very large red giant star.

reflection Occurs when waves bounce off objects.

refraction Change of speed and direction of a wave when it passes from one medium to another.

refractive index Sine of the angle of incidence of light divided by the sine of the angle of refraction; a measure of the speed of light in a transparent material.

relative velocity How fast one object is moving as measured from another object.

relay Switch that uses a small current flowing through an electromagnet to turn on a larger current.

renewable Energy resource that does not run out.

repel Push away.

resistance How much a component is able to slow down the flow of electrons through it.

resistor Circuit component that reduces the current flowing in a circuit.

resultant Describes the sum of two or more quantities.

resultant force Single force that would have the same overall effect of all the forces combined.

rheostat Type of variable resistor.

rocket Vehicle used to place objects in orbit, usually propelled by ejecting high speed gas.

Sankey diagram Diagram that shows all the energy transfers taking place in a device.

satellite An object that orbits a planet.

scalar Quantity where direction is not relevant.

secondary coil Coil in a transformer from where the output is taken.

seismic waves Waves in the Earth's crust caused by sudden changes in the arrangement of the rocks.

seismometer Device that records seismic waves, often as a displacement-time graph on a sheet of paper.

series Describes circuit components connected end-to-end – there is only one way around the circuit.

size How much space something occupies.

slip rings These rotate with the coil of a motor or generator, pushing against the brushes, allowing current in and out of the coil.

solar flare Jet of hot gas flung out of the Sun at high speed.

solar stove Cooker that focuses light energy from the Sun onto a cooking pot.

solar system The Sun and the objects, such as planets, which are in orbit around it.

specific heat capacity Amount of energy needed to increase the temperature of 1 kg of a material by 1°C.

specific latent heat Amount of energy needed to change the state of 1 kg of a substance.

speed Distance moved ÷ time taken. How fast something is moving.

speed camera Camera used to find the speed of a vehicle.

speed-time graph Graph with speed on the y-axis and time on the x-axis. It shows the speed of an object at a particular moment.

split-ring commutator Rotary switch in an electric motor that reverses current in the coil every half revolution.

static electricity Build up of charge from electrons that have been moved to or from an insulator.

stationary Not moving, at rest.

step-down transformer Device that reduces the voltage of an electricity supply.

step-up transformer Device that increases the voltage of an electricity supply.

sterilisation Use of ionising radiation (usually gamma rays) to kill microorganisms on medical equipment.

stopping distance Sum of the thinking distance and braking distance.

substation Place that contains one or more transformers.

sun protection factor Measure of how much longer a sun cream allows you to sunbathe safely.

Sun-centred model Model of the Solar System where the Sun (rather than the Earth) is at its centre. Championed by Copernicus and Galileo.

supernova Explosion of a massive star when its iron core suddenly collapses under its own weight.

S-wave Seismic wave whose oscillations are at right angles to the direction of travel. Sometimes called secondary, shear, or shake waves.

switch Circuit component that can be used to switch the circuit on or off by creating a gap in the circuit.

temperature Measure of how hot or cold an object is.

terminal speed Maximum speed of an object when the forces on it are balanced. Usually applied to objects falling under gravity.

thermal conductor Material that conducts heat well.

thermal insulator Material that does not conduct heat well.

thermal power station A power station that uses a fuel to heat water to turn it into steam.

thermistor Special type of resistor whose resistance decreases as temperature increases.

thermogram Image taken by an infrared camera that shows how much infrared radiation is being emitted by a body.

thinking distance Distance travelled by a vehicle in the reaction time.

time period TIme taken to complete one full cycle. For example, one orbit or one full oscillation.

Total Internal Reflection When a wave travelling inside a denser medium reflects off the boundary with another medium, and so stays inside the original material.

traction control Means of preventing cars skidding by controlling the power delivered to each wheel.

trajectory Path followed by a projectile due to gravity.

transistor Electronic device that can act as a switch.

transverse wave Wave whose vibrations are at right angles to the direction of wave motion.

trough The bottom part of a wave where its displacement is at a maximum.

truth table Table summarising all the possible outputs from all the different combinations of inputs to a system of logic gates.

turbine Machine that is turned by something moving through it, eg air or water.

ultrasound Sound waves with a very high frequency, above human hearing (20 000 Hz).

ultrasound body scan Using ultrasound waves to produce an image of a part of the body. Most commonly used in pre-natal scans.

ultraviolet Part of the electromagnetic spectrum between X-rays and visible light.

unit (of electricity) A unit for measuring the amount of energy transferred. It is the same as a kilowatt-hour.

vacuum Region that contains no atoms or other particles. Not possible to create in practice, but outer space gets close.

vaporisation Boiling and evaporating into a gas.

variable resistor Resistor whose resistance can be changed.

vector Quantity that includes direction.

velocity How fast something is moving in a certain direction.

virtual image Image that cannot be displayed on a screen.

visible spectrum Range of colours present in light.

voltage Measure of the energy given to charge by a power supply.

watt Unit of power.

wave equation The speed of a wave equals its frequency multiplied by its wavelength.

wavelength Distance from one crest of a wave to the next crest.

weight Force on an object due to the force of gravity on a planet.

white dwarf Remains of a small star which has run out of hydrogen to fuse into helium.

wind turbine Turbine that generates electricity from the kinetic energy in the wind.

wireless communication Use of electromagnetic waves (usually radio waves) to carry information from one place to another.

work done Energy transferred, measured in joules. Work is done whenever a force moves a distance. Work done = force applied × distance moved in the direction of the force.

X-ray A high frequency, very penetrating electromagnetic wave.

Index

Reference material

Fundamental physical quantities	
Physical quantity	Unit(s)
length	metre (m) kilometre (km) centimetre (cm) millimetre (mm)
mass	kilogram (kg) gram (g) milligram (mg)
time	second (s) millisecond (ms)
temperature	degree Celsius (°C) kelvin (K)
current	ampere (A) milliampere (mA)
voltage	volt (V) millivolt (mV)

Derived quantities and units	
Physical quantity	Unit(s)
area	cm^2; m^2
volume	cm^3; dm^3; m^3; litre (l); millilitre (ml)
density	kg/m^3; g/cm^3
force	newton (N)
speed	m/s; km/h
energy	joule (J); kilojoule (kJ); megajoule (MJ)
power	watt (W); kilowatt (kW); megawatt (MW)
frequency	hertz (Hz); kilohertz (kHz)
gravitational field strength	N/kg
radioactivity	becquerel (Bq)
acceleration	m/s^2; km/h^2
specific heat capacity	J/kg°C
specific latent heat	J/kg

Electrical symbols

junction of conductors		ammeter	(A)	diode		capacitor	
switch		voltmeter	(V)	electrolytic capacitor		relay	NO COM NC
primary or secondary cell		indicator or light source		LDR		LED	
battery of cells	or			thermistor		NOT gate	NOT
power supply		motor	(M)	AND gate	AND	OR gate	OR
fuse		generator	G	NOR gate	NOR	NAND gate	NAND
fixed resistor		variable resistor					

Acknowledgements

The publisher and authors would like to thank the following for their permission to reproduce photographs and other copyright material:

p13 James Brittain/VIEW/Corbis; **p14R** Jacob Wackerhausen/Istockphoto; **p14L** Tony McConnell/SPL; **p15L** Reinhold Tscherwitschke/Istockphoto; **p15R** Robert Hardholt/Istockphoto; **p16** Raul Souza/Shutterstock; **p17TR** Dave King/Dorling Kindersley/Getty Images; **p17TL** Trevor Clifford Photography/SPL; **p17B** Peter Mukherjee/Istockphoto; **p18** Sandsun/Istockphoto; **p20** Ashley Cooper, Visuals Unlimited/SPL; **p21** Anton Saykov/Istockphoto; **p22** T-Service/SPL; **p22** Victor De Schwanberg/SPL; **p23** Lillisphotography/Istockphoto; **p24** Tony Mcconnell/SPL; **p26** Jiri Hera/Shutterstock; **p28** Sally Woods; **p29** Amra Pasic/Shutterstock; **p33R** Tek Image/SPL; **p33L** Belmonte/SPL; **p34L** Navy.mil; **p34R** Mauro Fermariello/SPL; **p35** Power and Syred/SPL; **p36R** Chris Rose/Alamy; **p36L** Vidux/Shutterstock; **p37** Gudella/Dreamstime; **p38** Richard Hutchings/SPL; **p39** Cordelia Molloy/SPL; **p41B** Peter Kirillov/Shutterstock; **p41T** Tobi Jenkins/Daily Mail/Rex Features; **p42B** Matt Henry Gunther/Taxi/Getty Images; **p42T** Juice Images/Fotolia; **p44** Yai/Shutterstock; **p46R** Pascal Goetgheluck/SPL; **p46TL** Mangostock/Fotolia; **p46BL** DH Webster/Photolibrary; **p47** NASA; **p53** Lidacheng/Dreamstime; **p54L** Zoran Simin/Istockphoto; **p54R** Ruslan Dashinsky/Istockphoto; **p55L** Nikada/Istockphoto; **p55R** NASA; **p56** kshishtof/Istockphoto; **p57T** Julio Etchart/Photolibrary; **p57B** Irina Belousa/Istockphoto; **p59T** U.S. Nuclear Regulatory Commission; **p59B** Pedalite; **p60** Alexandru Romanciuc/Istockphoto; **p62L** dgmata/Shutterstock; **p62R** Zhuda/Shutterstock; **p63** Martin Bond/SPL; **p64** Ria Novosti/SPL; **p65** Steve Allen/SPL; **p66** SPL; **p70T** PPS/SPL; **p70B** SPL; **p71** Patrick Landmann/SPL; **p73** Prof. J. Leveille/SPL; **p74** Nasa/Esa/Stsci/R.Beebe, New Mexico State U./SPL; **p76** Detlev Van Ravenswaay/SPL; **p77** Joao Virissimo/Shutterstock; **p78R** NASA/JPL-Caltech/ESA/Harvard-Smithsonian CfA; **p78L** Vakhrushev Pavel/Shutterstock; **p79** Goddard Space Flight Center/NASA; **p80** NASA; **p81** NASA; **p83T** Sheila Terry/SPL; **p83B** Nasa/SPL; **p83M** Nasa/SPL; **p89** Nürburgring Automotive GmbH/Fotoagentur Urner; **p90** Andrew Wong/Getty Images Sport/Getty Images; **p91** Cordelia Molloy/SPL; **p94** Alan & Sandy Carey/SPL; **p98** Akihiro Sugimoto/Photolibrary; **p100** Barry Phillips/Evening Standard/Rex Features; **p101** Ken McKay/Rex Features; **p102** Orange Line Media/Shutterstock; **p103L** Stephen Hird/Reuters; **p103R** Andrew Lambert Photography/SPL; **p104R** Jeff Gilbert/Rex Features; **p104L** Bryn Lennon/Getty Images Sport/Getty Images; **p105** Kondrashov MIkhail Evgenevich/Shutterstock; **p106** John Gichigi/Getty Images Sport/Getty Images; **p108TL** Philippe Hays/Photolibrary; **p108BL** Vladimir Bikhovskiy/Fotolia; **p108R** Image reproduced courtesy of Stagecoach Group; **p109** Peter Menzel/SPL; **p110** Joshua Hodge Photography/Istockphoto; **p112** Andrew Lambert Photography/SPL; **p118** Henrique Daniel Araujo/Shutterstock; **p119** 2happy/Shutterstock; **p120** Laurel Scherer/Photolibrary; **p127** Keith Kent/SPL; **p128** Martyn F. Chillmaid/SPL; **p129** Leslie Banks/Istockphoto; **p130L** Andrew Howe/Istockphoto; **p130R** Denis Lazarenko/Shutterstock; **p131R** Jim Newall; **p131L** Skyhobo/Istockphoto; **p133R** Charles D. Winters/SPL; **p133L** microgen/Istockphoto; **p134B** Trevor Clifford Photography/SPL; **p134T** Trevor Clifford Photography/SPL; **p135** John shepherd/Istockphoto; **p136** oksana2010/Shutterstock; **p137** David J. Green/Alamy; **p138** Sciencephotos/Alamy; **p139** Bob Crook/Photographers Direct; **p140** Zephyr/SPL; **p141T** AJ Photo/Hop Americain/SPL; **p141B** Dr. Gladden Willis, Visuals Unlimited/SPL; **p143** CERN; **p145** Steve Allen/SPL; **p146** Picture Contact BV/Alamy; **p149** Art Media/Photolibrary; **p150L** SPL; **p150R** Doncaster And Bassetlaw Hospials/SPL; **p152R** Andy Crump/SPL; **p152L** dra_schwartz/Istockphoto; **p153** doc-stock/Alamy; **p154L** Catherine Pouedras/SPL; **p154R** James W. Olive/U.S. Navy; **p156** US Navy/SPL; **p157** Vaughan Melzer/JVZ/SPL; **p158** Roger Harris/SPL; **p159** EFDA-JET/SPL; **p165** NASA/SPL; **p166** NASA/SPL; **p172** Marcus Lindstrom/Istockphoto; **p173** Bjorn Kindler/Istockphoto; **p174T** Technotr/Istockphoto; **p174B** Albo/Dreamstime; **p177** Drbueller/Istockphoto; **p178B** Lisa Davis/Istockphoto; **p178T** 1 design/Istockphoto; **p179** NASA/SPL; **p180** [TO COME]; **p182** David J. Green/Alamy; **p185** James Scott/Dreamstime; **p186** Andres Rodriguez/Bigstock; **p187R** Mehmet Fatih Kocyildir/Dreamstime; **p187L** Andrew Lambert Photography/SPL; **p188TL** American Institute Of Physics/SPL; **p188TR** SPL; **p188B** Laurent Laveder/SPL; **p189** Giphotostock/SPL; **p190** Erich Schrempp/SPL; **p192R** Stewyphoto/Shutterstock; **p192L** Lawrence Lawry/SPL; **p194** Giphotostock/SPL; **p195** Mark Bourdillon/Alamy; **p196R** Jeffrey L. Rotman/Photolibrary; **p196L** Phil Degginger/Alamy; **p198** Imagemore Co., Ltd./Alamy; **p199** Diego Cervo/Shutterstock; **p205** Dr Jeremy Burgess/SPL; **p206T1** Andrew Lambert Photography/SPL; **p206T2** Paul Reid/Shutterstock; **p206T3** Chris Hutchison/Istockphoto; **p206T4** Andrew Lambert Photography/SPL; **p206T5** Trevor Clifford Photography/SPL; **p206T6** Doug Martin/SPL; **p206T7** Trevor Clifford Photography/SPL; **p209** Pali Rao/Istockphoto; **p212B** Andrew Lambert Photography/SPL; **p212T** Martyn F. Chillmaid/SPL; **p214** Alexander Khromtsov/Istockphoto; **p224L** Zcw/Shutterstock; **p224R** Lisa F. Young/Istockphoto; **p225L** Sciencephotos/Alamy; **p226R** U.S. Nuclear Regulatory Commission; **p226L** Awe Inspiring Images/Shutterstock; **p227** Vydrin/Shutterstock; **p228** Jeronimo Create/Istockphoto; **p230TL** Sheila Terry/SPL; **p230BL** Sheila Terry/SPL; **p230TMR** Edhar/Shutterstock; **p230TML** Mark Goble/Alamy; **p230TR** Judith Collins/Alamy; **p234** Vydrin/Shutterstock.

Illustrations by Wearset Ltd, HL Studios, Peter Bull Studios, Mike Hall.

Although we have made every effort to trace and contact all copyright holders before publication this has not been possible in all cases. If notified, the publisher will rectify any errors or omissions at the earliest opportunity.

OXFORD
UNIVERSITY PRESS

Great Clarendon Street, Oxford OX2 6DP

Oxford University Press is a department of the University of Oxford.
It furthers the University's objective of excellence in research,
scholarship, and education by publishing worldwide in

Oxford   New York

Auckland   Cape Town   Dar es Salaam   Hong Kong   Karachi
Kuala Lumpur   Madrid   Melbourne   Mexico City   Nairobi
New Delhi   Shanghai   Taipei   Toronto

With offices in
Argentina   Austria   Brazil   Chile   Czech Republic   France   Greece
Guatemala   Hungary   Italy   Japan   Poland   Portugal   Singapore
South Korea   Switzerland   Thailand   Turkey   Ukraine   Vietnam

Oxford is a registered trade mark of Oxford University Press
in the UK and in certain other countries

© Oxford University Press 2011

British Library Cataloguing in Publication Data

Data available

ISBN 978-0-19-913578-3

10 9 8 7 6 5

Printed in China by Printplus

Paper used in the production of this book is a natural, recyclable product
made from wood grown in sustainable forests. The manufacturing process
conforms to the environmental regulations of the country of origin.